TP
594
M4

Date Due

22			

POLYHYDRIC ALCOHOLS

I. General Characteristics of Polyhydric Alcohols
II. Dihydric Alcohols: Glycols
Ethylene Glycol
Propylene Glycol
1,3-Propanediol
The Butanediol
1,3-Butanediol
1,2-Butanediol
2,3-Butanediol
1,4-Butanediol
2-Butyne-1,4-Diol
2-Butene-1,4-Diol
1,5-Pentanediol
2,2-Dimethyl-1,3-Propanediol
2,4-Pentanediol
2,5-Hexanediol
1,6-Hexanediol
2-Methyl-2,4-Pentanediol
Pinacol
2,2-Diethyl-1,3-Propanediol
2-Ethyl-1,3-Hexanediol
2,5-Dimethyl-3-Hexyne-2,5-Diol
3,6-Dimethyl-4-Octyne-3,6-Diol
p-Xylylene Glycol
"Kromfax" Solvent
2-Ethyl-2-Butyl-1,3-Propanediol
III. Trihydric Alcohols
Glycerol
1,2,4-Butanetriol
1,2,6-Hexanetriol
Trimethylolpropane
IV. Other Polyhydric Alcohols
Erythritol and *d*-Arabitol
Pentaerythritol
Sorbitol

RAMAKER LIBRARY
Northwestern College
Orange City, Iowa

POLYHYDRIC ALCOHOLS

BY IBERT MELLAN

Director of Research, Polychrome Corporation

SPARTAN BOOKS

6411 CHILLUM PLACE, N. W. • WASHINGTON 12, D. C.

18529

Library of Congress Catalog Card No. 62-19193

Copyright © 1962 by Ibert Mellon. Printed in the United States of America. All rights reserved. This book or parts thereof, may not be reproduced in any form without permission of the publishers.

Manufactured by McGregor & Werner, Inc.
Washington 12, D. C.

CONTENTS

Page

Polyhydric alcohols 1

Characteristics 1
Nomenclature 2
Physical characteristics 2
Structure 2
Production 12

Dihydric alcohols 18

Glycols 18
Ethylene glycol 24
Propylene glycol (1,2-Propanediol) 46
1,3-Propanediol 71
Butanediols 76
1,3-Butyene glycol 80
1,2-Butanediol 85
2,3-Butanediol 86
1,4-Butanediol 119
2-Butyne-1,4-Diol 122
2-Butene-1,4-Diol 123
1,5-Pentanediol 124
2,2-Dimethyl-1,3-Propanediol 126
2,4-Pentanediol 126
2,5-Hexanediol 127
1,6-Hexanediol 127
2-Methyl-2,4-Pentanediol 127
Pinacol 137
2,2-Diethyl-1,3-Propanediol 137
2-Ethyl-1,3-Hexanediol 138
2,5-Dimethyl-3-Hexyne-2,5-Diol 139
p-Xylyene glycol 140
"Kromfax" Solvent 140
2-Ethyl-2-butyl-1,3-propanediol 143
2,2,4-Trimethyl-1,3-pentanediol 143

Page

Trihydric alcohols 144

Glycerol 144
1,2,4-Butanetriol 179
1,2,6-Hexanetriol 180
Trimethylolpropane 181

Other Polyhydric Alcohols 184

Erythritol and Arabitol 184
Pentaerythritol 184
Sorbitol 185

Hydrates of Polyhydric Alcohols 190

References 205

Tables - 55

Figures - 108

POLYHYDRIC ALCOHOLS

1. GENERAL CHARACTERISTICS OF POLYHYDRIC ALCOHOLS

The polyhydric alcohols have only recently come to occupy a prominent place among industrial solvents and chemicals. Until about fifty years ago, glycerol, the only major type, supplied the limited demand for such products. But as the need increased steadily to free industry from its complete dependence upon glycerol, with its price fluctuations and uncertain availability, during national emergencies, substitutes were eagerly sought to replace this trihydric alcohol. Also, as the textile, alkyd resin, lacquer, and automotive industries expanded and increased in complexity, polyhydric alcohols assumed a new significance and their special properties were explored with intensity. Consequently, within a short time, polyhydric alcohols acquired such importance that they were regarded as an index of development in these industries. For example, the glycols are absorbed chiefly in the antifreeze market, but these and other polyhydric alcohols are essential in the preparation of alkyd resins, new synthetic fibers, a synthetic polyester rubber, and so on.

The polyhydric alcohols are defined as derivatives of aliphatic hydrocarbons, either saturated or unsaturated, formed by the replacement of two or more hydrogen atoms by two or more monovalent hydroxyl groups, each being attached to a different carbon atom. The dihydric alcohols, with two hydroxyl groups in their molecular structure, are known as glycols; the trihydric alcohols, with three hydroxyls, include glycerol and 1,2,6-hexanetriol; the tetrahydric alcohols, with four hydroxyls, are represented by erythritol and pentaerythritol; the pentahydric alcohols contain five hydroxyls and the best-known examples are arabitol, xylitol, and adonitol; finally, the hexahydric alcohols, with six hydroxyls, bear a kinship to the simple class of sugars known as hexoses, from which the alcohols may be obtained by reduction. Examples of these alcohols are mannitol, dulcitol, and sorbitol.

Nomenclature

The simplest of the polyhydric alcohols, the glycols, form a homologous series to which the general formula $C_nH_{2n}(OH)_2$ is given. The term "glycols" stems from the name of its simplest member ethylene glycol, also known simply as glycol. An early system for distinguishing the glycols lay in indicating the relationships of the hydroxyl groups to one another. Thus α-, β-, or γ- glycol indicates the 1:2, 1:3, or 1:4 positions, respectively, of the hydroxyl groups. Ethylene glycol, for example, with its two hydroxyl groups on adjacent carbon atoms, is also known as α-glycol. [61] The Geneva method of nomenclature is more widely accepted for the purpose of indicating the positions of the hydroxyl groups. By this system ethylene glycol is designated 1,2-ethanediol.

Physical Characteristics

The glycols of lower molecular weight are colorless, oily liquids, with boiling points ranging above 190° C. The boiling points of glycols are considerably higher than those of the monohydric alcohols with similar carbon chains. The water solubility of glycols is influenced by molecular weight. The lower molecular weight glycols are freely soluble in water; solubility decreases as the molecular weight increases, however.

The trihydric alcohols are characterized by the three hydroxyl groups in their composition. Glycerol, the first trihydric alcohol of industrial interest, contains one secondary and two primary hydroxyl groups which determine its chemical behavior.

The higher polyhydric alcohols are generally sweet, crystalline compounds, soluble in water and with an evident relationship to the sugars.

Relationship of Structure to Properties

The presence of the hydroxyl group in a compound permits such reactions as esterification, etherification, oxidation, halogenation, and the formation of alcoholates to take place. Such reactions may take place with one, two, or more hydroxyl groups present in a polyhydric alcohol. The fundamental characteristics of each group are maintained, and the behavior of these groups is the same as that of the single hydroxyl group in monohydric alcohols.

The hydroxyl groups (OH) which characterize these compounds, are therefore the central core of the chemistry of polyhydric alcohols. Some of these reactions are observed in the following processes.

1. By means of dehydration, water is split off:

(a) One molecule of water from one molecule of ethylene glycol results in

$$\begin{array}{l} CH_2-OH \\ | \\ CH_2-OH \end{array} \longrightarrow CH_3-CHO + H_2O$$

Ethylene glycol ⟶ Acetaldehyde + Water

(b) One molecule of water from two molecules of glycol results in

$$2\begin{array}{l}CH_2-OH\\ |\\ CH_2-OH\end{array} \longrightarrow O\begin{array}{l}\diagup CH_2-CH_2-OH\\ \diagdown CH_2-CH_2-OH\end{array} + H_2O$$

Ethylene glycol ⟶ Diethylene glycol + Water

(c) Two molecules of water from two molecules of ethylene glycol results in

$$2\begin{array}{l}CH_2-OH\\ |\\ CH_2-OH\end{array} \longrightarrow \begin{array}{c}O\\ \diagup \quad \diagdown\\ CH_2 \quad CH_2\\ | \qquad |\\ CH_2 \quad CH_2\\ \diagdown \quad \diagup\\ O\end{array} + 2H_2O$$

Ethylene glycol ⟶ Dioxane + Water

2. With organic acids the polyhydric alcohols react to form mono-, di-, and polyesters.

(a)

$$\begin{array}{l}CH_2-OH\\ |\\ CH_2-OH\end{array} + CH_3COOH \longrightarrow \begin{array}{l}CH_2OOCR\\ |\\ CH_2OH\end{array} + H_2O$$

Ethylene glycol + Acetic acid ⟶ Glycol monoacetate + Water

(b)

$$\begin{array}{l}CH_2-OH\\ |\\ CH_2-OH\end{array} + 2CH_3COOH \longrightarrow \begin{array}{l}CH_2OOCR\\ |\\ CH_2OOCR\end{array} + 2H_2O$$

Ethylene glycol + Acetic acid ⟶ Glycol diacetate + Water

(c)

$$\begin{array}{l}CH_2-OH\\ |\\ CH_2-OH\end{array} + 2ROCOCl \longrightarrow \begin{array}{l}CH_2OOCOR\\ |\\ CH_2OOCOR\end{array} + 2HCl$$

Ethylene glycol + Chlorocarbonic acid ester ⟶ Carbonate ester + Hydrochloric acid

(d)

$$\begin{array}{l}CH_2OH\\ |\\ CH_2OH\end{array} + H_3BO_3 \longrightarrow \begin{array}{l}CH_2-O\diagdown\\ | \qquad\qquad B-OH\\ CH_2-O\diagup\end{array} + H_2O$$

Ethylene glycol + Boric acid ⟶ Glycol borate + Water

(e)

$$\begin{matrix} CH_2-OH \\ | \\ CH_2-OH \end{matrix} + 2HNO_3 \xrightarrow{H_2SO_4} \begin{matrix} CH_2ONO_2 \\ | \\ CH_2ONO_2 \end{matrix} + H_2O$$

Ethylene glycol + Nitric acid ⟶ Ethylene glycol dinitrate + Water

3. With hydrochloric acid, one or more of the hydroxyl groups can be replaced with chlorine.

(a)

$$\begin{matrix} CH_2-OH \\ | \\ CH_2-OH \end{matrix} + HCl \longrightarrow \begin{matrix} CH_2Cl \\ | \\ CH_2OH \end{matrix} + H_2O$$

Ethylene glycol + Hydrogen chloride ⟶ Ethylene chlorohydrin + Water

(b)

$$\begin{matrix} CH_2-OH \\ | \\ CH_2-OH \end{matrix} + 2HCl \longrightarrow \begin{matrix} CH_2-Cl \\ | \\ CH_2-Cl \end{matrix} + 2H_2O$$

Ethylene glycol Hydrogen chloride ⟶ Ethylene dichloride + Water

4. Polyesters are formed when polyhydric alcohols (polyhydroxy alcohols) are reacted with polybasic acids (polycarboxylic acids). Many types of polyesters have been synthesized and innumerable variations can be made in their composition. The important factors which determine their basic properties are the kind and amount of polybasic acids and polyhydric alcohols used in their formation, the kind and amount of cross-linking which takes place, and the average molecular weight of the final product. Some of the commercial acids used in the formation of polyesters are adipic, azelaric, citraconic, chloromaleic, fumaric, glutaric, hexahydrophthalic, isophthalic, itaconic, phthalic, succinic, tetrahydrophthalic, and so forth. The polyhydric alcohols which are used for making these products are ethylene, propylene, butylene, amylene, and hexalyene glycols.

$$HO\text{-}R - R - OH + OH - \overset{\overset{O}{\parallel}}{R} - \overset{\overset{O}{\parallel}}{R} - OH \longrightarrow$$

Dihydric alcohol   Dibasic acid

$$HO - CH_2CH_2 - OH + HO - \overset{\overset{O}{\parallel}}{C} - (CH_2)_4 - \overset{\overset{O}{\parallel}}{C} - OH \longrightarrow$$

Ethylene glycol   Adipic acid

$$HO\text{-}CH_2CH_2O\overset{O}{\overset{\|}{C}}(CH_2)_4\overset{O}{\overset{\|}{C}}OCH_2CH_2O\overset{O}{\overset{\|}{C}}(CH_2)_4\overset{O}{\overset{\|}{C}}O\text{-}$$

5. The mono-, di-, or polyethers are another group of compounds that can be formed through the reaction of the hydroxyl group in polyhydric alcohols.

(a)

$$\begin{matrix} CH_2 - OH \\ | \\ CH_2 - OH \end{matrix} + R_2SO_4 \longrightarrow ROCH_2CH_2OH + NaRSO_4 + H_2O$$

Ethylene glycol + Dialkyl sulfate ⟶ Ethylene glycol monoether

(b)

$$\begin{matrix} CH_2 - OH \\ | \\ CH_2 - OR \end{matrix} + R_2SO_4 + NaOH \longrightarrow ROCH_2CH_2OR + NaRSO_4 + H_2O$$

Ethylene glycol monoether + Dialkyl sulfate ⟶ Ethylene glycol diether

(c)

$$\begin{matrix} CH_2 - OH \\ | \\ CH_2 - OR \end{matrix} + RCOOH \longrightarrow \begin{matrix} CH_2OOCR^1 \\ | \\ CH_2OR \end{matrix} + H_2O$$

Ethylene glycol monoether + acid ⟶ Ether-ester

6. The reaction between ethylene glycol and aldehydes is observed in the following example:

$$\begin{matrix} CH_2 - OH \\ | \\ CH_2 - OH \end{matrix} + RCHO \longrightarrow \begin{matrix} CH_2 - O \\ | \\ CH_2 - O \end{matrix} \!\!> C <\!\! \begin{matrix} R \\ \\ H \end{matrix} + H_2O$$

Ethylene glycol → Substituted 1,3-Dioxolane

7. An example of the reaction between ethylene glycol and ketones is as follows:

$$\begin{matrix} CH_2 - OH \\ | \\ CH_2 - OH \end{matrix} + R_2CO \longrightarrow \begin{matrix} CH_2 - O \\ | \\ CH_2 - O \end{matrix} \!\!> C <\!\! \begin{matrix} R \\ \\ R \end{matrix} + H_2O$$

Ethylene glycol → Substituted 1,3-Dioxolane

8. Replacement of hydrogen in the hydroxyl groups is observed in the following examples:

(a)

$$\begin{array}{l} CH_2 - OH \\ | \\ CH_2 - OH \end{array} + 2Na \longrightarrow \begin{array}{l} CH_2 - ONa \\ | \\ CH_2 - OH \end{array} + H_2$$

Ethylene glycol + Sodium ⟶ Monosodium derivative of Ethylene glycol + Hydrogen

(b)

$$\begin{array}{l} CH_2 - OH \\ | \\ CH_2 - OH \end{array} + NaOH \longrightarrow \begin{array}{l} CH_2 - ONa \\ | \\ CH_2 - OH \end{array} + H_2O$$

Ethylene glycol + Sodium hydroxide ⟶ Monosodium derivative of Ethylene glycol + Water

When oxidation takes place, the polyhydric alcohols are converted into aldehydes, ketones, and polybasic acids. Also, these alcohols are able to assume a double chemical character, with the replacement of one or more of the hydroxyl groups by the functional groups of other classes of compounds, thereby acquiring the properties of these compounds. For example, a hydroxy aldehyde is both an alcohol and an aldehyde. Others are hydroxy ketones, hydroxy acids, and the like. Other characteristics of polyhydric alcohols are the increases in boiling point, melting point, viscosity, specific gravity, and physiological activity, concurrent with increase in molecular weight.

As in the case of the monohydric alcohols, a polyhydric compound may be a primary, secondary, or tertiary alcohol, or it may be a mixture of these. The behavior of ethylene glycol, a primary alcohol, is characteristic of that type, whereas glycerol, with one secondary and two primary hydroxyl groups in its molecule, shows a difference in degree of reactivity. This is due to the fact that a primary hydroxyl is more reactive than a secondary hydroxyl group. As the number of hydroxyl groups in polyhydric alcohols increase, a corresponding increase in acidity takes place.

In common with monohydric alcohols, the polyhydric compounds are also subject to isomerism, denoted by a difference in water solubility, boiling points, and melting points of the isomers. Clendenning *et al.* [1] confirmed this observation and proved that the physical properties of glycols are influenced by position isomerism. The lengthening of the distance between the hydroxyl substituents increases the specific gravity, refractivity, boiling point, and viscosity, and it also reduces thermal expansion and isothermal contraction when the compound is mixed with water (Table 1). These investigators also found that the glycol concentration at which maximum specific gravity is attained increases with increasing distance

Table 1. Refractive Index, Specific Gravity, and Boiling Point Measurements on Propanediols, Butanediols, and Pentanediols*

Compound	Refractive Index	Specific Gravity, d_4^t	Boiling Point, °C., 760 mm.
1,2-Propanediol	25°C. 1.4316 (17)	23°C. 1.0354 (17)	187 (17)
	1.4313†		
	20°C. 1.4331 (14)	20°C. 1.0364 (14)	186†
	1.4324†	1.0361†	
1,3-Propanediol	25°C. 1.4385 (17)	20°C. 1.0538 (17)	215 (17)
	1.4380†	1.0529†	
	21°C. 1.4394 (17)		213.5†
	20°C. 1.4389†		
1,2-Butanediol	20°C. 1.4378†	20°C. 1.0024†	190.5†
1,3-Butanediol	25°C. 1.4410 (17)	20°C. 1.0053 (17)	207.5 (17)
	1.4391 (12)	1.0035 (12)	208 (2)
	1.4388†	1.002 (2)	207†
	20°C. 1.4404 (2)	1.0037†	
	1.4398†		
1,4-Butanediol	20°C. 1.4467 (10)	20°C. 1.0171 (10)	230 (2)
	1.4459 (2)	1.0160 (2)	
	1.4460†	1.0185†	228†
1,2-Pentanediol	24°C. 1.4390 (16)	24°C. 0.9691 (16)	210 (16)
	25°C. 1.4380†		
	20°C. 1.4390†	20°C. 0.9723†	206†
1,5-Pentanediol	26°C. 1.4480 (16)	26°C. 0.9890	239 (16)
	25°C. 1.4484†		
	20°C. 1.4500†	20°C. 0.9914†	238†

*Courtesy of Can. J. Research.
†Authors' observations.
§As cited in the fifth and earlier editions of Getman and Daniels' Outlines of Physical Chemistry, John Wiley and Sons Inc., New York, 1931.

between the hydroxyl constituents. Aqueous solutions of all these glycols show pronounced specific gravity maxima. The glycols used in this investigation were 1,2-propanediol, 1,3-propanediol, 1,2-butanediol, 1,3-butanediol, 1,4-butanediol, 1,2-pentanediol, and 1,5-pentanediol, in the pure state and in aqueous solution. These glycols were found to exhibit a decrease in effectiveness as freezing point depressants on a weight basis, and in the following order: 1,2-propanediol, levo-2,3-butanediol, 1,3-propanediol, 1,3-butanediol, 1,4-butanediol, 1,2-butanediol, 1,5-pentanediol, [62] and 1,2-pentanediol.

Table 2. Isothermal Contraction in Volume on Mixing Glycols with Water at 20° and 40° C. (ml. contraction per 100 ml. initial volume)*

Glycol, %	1,2-Propanediol		1,3-Propanediol		1,2-Butanediol		1,3-Butanediol		1,4-Butanediol		1,2-Pentanediol		1,5-Pentanediol	
	20° C.	40° C.	20° C.	40° C.	20° C.	40° C.	20° C.	40° C.	20° C.	40° C.	20° C.	40° C.	20° C.	40° C.
20	0.83	0.86	0.37	0.29	1.12	1.01	0.69	0.65	0.70	0.58	1.125	0.95	0.52	0.43
40	1.84	1.58	0.90	0.81	1.96	1.67	1.58	1.36	1.10	0.86	1.49	1.22	1.04	0.80
60	2.08	1.79	1.19	1.07	1.92	1.65	1.94	1.64	0.98	0.76	1.38	1.06	1.23	0.98
80	1.47	1.30	1.01	0.89	1.27	1.10	1.50	1.29	0.59	0.46	0.97	0.735	1.01	0.88

*Courtesy of Can. J. Research.

Table 3. Thermal Expansion of Aqueous Glycol Solutions Between 20° and 40° C. (a x 10^3)*

Glycol, %	1,2-Propanediol	1,3-Propanediol	1,2-Butanediol	1,3-Butanediol	1,4-Butanediol	1,2-Pentanediol	1,5-Pentanediol
20	0.40	0.39	0.454	0.390	0.375	0.50	0.415
40	0.61	0.47	0.645	0.557	0.50	0.61	0.57
60	0.695	0.55	0.726	0.675	0.645	0.72	0.64
80	0.67	0.60	0.765	0.702	0.645	0.75	0.65
100	0.71	0.61	0.775	0.666	0.646	0.72	0.65

*Courtesy of Can J. Research

Table 4. Refractive Indices of Aqueous Propanediol Solutions at 20°, 30°, and 40° C*

1, 2-Propanediol				1, 3-Propanediol			
Glycol, %	n_D^{20}	n_D^{30}	n_D^{40}	Glycol, %	n_D^{20}	n_D^{30}	n_D^{40}
9.94	1.3435	1.3422	1.3411	10.98	1.3433	1.3430	1.3410
20.03	1.3552	1.3540	1.3522	19.96	1.3540	1.3528	1.3511
30.23	1.3670	1.3650	1.3630	30.21	1.3654	1.3640	1.3623
40.01	1.3780	1.3758	1.3732	40.34	1.3770	1.3755	1.3735
49.41	1.3887	1.3863	1.3833	49.94	1.3880	1.3861	1.3839
60.04	1.3995	1.3970	1.3940	60.32	1.3997	1.3975	1.3951
69.50	1.4082	1.4055	1.4028	70.24	1.4103	1.4080	1.4065
79.43	1.4174	1.4144	1.4111	79.87	1.4205	1.4183	1.4155
89.74	1.4252	1.4221	1.4190	89.68	1.4300	1.4276	1.4250
100	1.4324	1.4295	1.4255	100	1.4389	1.4364	1.4332

*Courtesy of Can. J. Research.

The lower glycols are selective solvents for dyes; synthetic resins such as phenolic, acrolein, and glyceryl phthalate types; essential oils; and certain natural gums and resins. The glycols are solvents for pyroxylin lacquers, and for flavoring extracts and drugs. As the molecular weight increases, the solubility of polyhydric alcohols in water, as well as in organic compounds, decreases. Glycerol and the glycols are more soluble in acetone and ethyl alcohol than are the sugar alcohols, and they will form azeotropes with turpentine, cyclohexane, chloroform, and other materials.

The characteristic of polyhydric alcohols—notably ethylene glycol—of lowering the freezing point of solutions is of great value in some applications, such as antifreeze. Ross, [2] in his study of mono- and polyhydric alcohols as freezing point depressants, comes to certain general conclusions about alkyl hydroxy compounds containing only hydroxyl groups. Since all water-soluble alkyl hydroxide compounds tend to associate with water to form hydrates, solutions of these compounds have lower than normal freezing points, provided the ratio of carbon atoms to hydroxyl groups is no greater than 2 to 1. He found that the lower the dipole moment, the more readily will the association between solvent and solute occur, and this association takes place at a lower temperature. When the ratio of carbon atoms to hydroxyls in the alkyl hydroxy compound is above 2 to 1, the alcohol compound associates with itself at temperatures below T_c,* and freezing points result which are found to be higher

*T_c is a constant critical temperature in °K above which complete hydration occurs in the liquid phase.

Table 5. Refractive Indices of Aqueous Butanediol Solutions at 20°, 30°, and 40° C*

1,2-Butanediol				1,3-Butanediol				1,4-Butanediol			
Glycol, %	n_D^{20}	n_D^{30}	n_D^{40}	Glycol, %	n_D^{20}	n_D^{30}	n_D^{40}	Glycol, %	n_D^{20}	n_D^{30}	n_D^{40}
10.13	1.3452	1.3436	1.3420	9.51	1.3442	1.3430	1.3417	10.51	1.3444	1.3432	1.3420
19.69	1.3572	1.3553	1.3534	19.18	1.3552	1.3548	1.3520	20.01	1.3563	1.3550	1.3532
29.72	1.3693	1.3672	1.3650	30.20	1.3688	1.3670	1.3649	30.02	1.3682	1.3671	1.3659
39.79	1.3813	1.3788	1.3760	39.94	1.3800	1.3778	1.3755	39.86	1.3802	1.3790	1.3768
49.68	1.3920	1.3892	1.3865	49.45	1.3920	1.3895	1.3870	49.70	1.3935	1.3918	1.3898
59.88	1.4027	1.4000	1.3966	60.02	1.4040	1.4012	1.3983	59.95	1.4052	1.4042	1.4020
69.37	1.4120	1.4090	1.4058	70.10	1.4145	1.4118	1.4090	70.15	1.4183	1.4167	1.4140
79.73	1.4212	1.4185	1.4165	80.20	1.4242	1.4215	1.4185	79.85	1.4283	1.4258	1.4236
89.40	1.4297	1.4265	1.4230	89.67	1.4323	1.4295	1.4264	90.10	1.4370	1.4349	1.4318
100	1.4375	1.4347	1.4310	100	1.4398	1.4370	1.4331	100	1.4451	1.4425	1.4395

*Courtesy of Can. J. Research.

Table 6. Refractive Indices of Aqueous Pentanediol Solutions at 20° and 40° C*

1,2-Pentanediol			1,5-Pentanediol		
Glycol, %	n_D^{20}	n_D^{40}	Glycol, %	n_D^{20}	n_D^{40}
10.36	1.3452	1.3430	10.17	1.3444	1.3420
19.97	1.3585		20.29		1.3543
20.64		1.3500	20.59	1.3572	
30.94	1.3705	1.3682	30.42	1.3700	1.3682
41.26	1.3830	1.3800	40.43	1.3833	1.3800
51.05	1.3930	1.3895	50.45	1.3960	1.3910
61.28	1.4050	1.3990	60.51	1.4080	1.4033
70.00	1.4120	1.4068	70.73	1.4198	1.4159
80.04	1.4223	1.4182	80.08	1.4304	1.4260
90.05	1.4320	1.4254	90.15	1.4417	1.4367
100	1.4390	1.4326	100	1.4500	1.4448

*Courtesy of Can. J. Research.

than usual. Also, alkyl hydroxy compounds having a carbon to hydroxyl ratio of more than 4 to 1 were found not to be miscible in all proportions at lower temperatures. Ross's final conclusion concerning the efficiency of an alkyl hydroxy compound as a freezing point depressant for water was that the most efficient substance would have the lowest molecular weight, lowest ratio of carbon atoms to hydroxyls, and lowest dipole moment.

Table 11 presents the results of Bernstein's investigation, [3] the purpose of which was to determine whether nonbonded interactions will account for the additive properties in the straight-chain and branched alkane diols, in which there is considerable bonding. To distinguish between the isomeric diols, he considered interactions which are 2 and 3 bonds apart. The hydroxyl group was designated as X, and the contribution to the additive property from interaction between a carbon atom and X, which are ② and ③ bonds apart, was defined as P_cX_2 and P_cX_3, respectively; and the contribution from interaction between ② carbon atoms which are ② and ③ bonds apart, as Pcc_2 and Pcc_3, respectively; and that due to X with X, ③ bonds apart, as Pxx_3.

Production

The polyhydric alcohols are produced commercially by synthetic manufacture. Some are also obtained by fermentation, examples of which are propylene glycol, 2,3-butylene glycol, glycerol, and mannitol. Others can be prepared by means of hydrogenolysis of sugar, examples of which are sorbitol, glycols, and glycerol. [63-67]

Table 7. Kinematic Viscosity of Aqueous Butanediol Solutions at 20° and 40° C (data are expressed in centistokes)*

1, 2-Butanediol			1, 3-Butanediol			1, 4-Butanediol		
Glycol, %	Viscosity		Glycol, %	Viscosity		Glycol, %	Viscosity	
	20°C	40°C		20°C	40°C		20°C	40°C
10.125	1.520	0.910	9.505	1.51	0.91	10.51	1.446	0.89
19.69	2.187	1.243	19.175	2.295	1.291	20.01	2.109	1.218
29.72	3.310	1.690	30.20	3.529	1.818	30.02	2.867	1.6602
39.79	4.802	2.311	39.94	5.419	2.593	39.86	4.258	2.382
49.685	6.739	3.088	49.45	8.313	3.695	49.70	6.57	3.202
59.88	9.72	4.227	60.02	13.44	5.600	59.95	10.20	4.707
69.37	13.82	5.744	70.1	21.57	8.413	70.15	18.48	7.982
79.73	21.37	8.372	80.20	35.36	12.88	79.85	30.63	12.62
89.40	35.54	12.57	89.67	63.43	21.21	90.1	54.35	21.40
100	68.0	21.25	100	129.8	39.70	100	87.62	33.8

*Courtesy of Can. J. Research.

Table 8. Kinematic Viscosity of Aqueous Pentanediol Solutions at 20° and 40° C (data are expressed in centistokes)*

1,2-Pentanediol			1,5-Pentanediol		
Glycol, %	Viscosity		Glycol, %	Viscosity	
	20° C	40° C		20° C	40° C
10.36	1.5475	0.9275	10.17	1.516	0.9210
19.97	2.264	1.258	20.09	2.246	1.277
30.18	2.88	1.538	30.42	3.300	1.795
40.13	4.06	2.08	39.82	4.735	2.331
50.02	5.73	2.82	50.04	7.08	3.350
59.96	8.02	3.742	60.12	11.30	5.250
69.97	13.03	5.725	70.45	20.9	8.842
79.85	19.85	8.138	80.20	36.22	14.46
90.05	38.20	13.62	89.75	66.25	25.70
100	68.55	20.82	100	115.65	43.58

*Courtesy of Can. J. Research.

Table 9. Freezing Points of Aqueous Propanediol, Butanediol, and Pentanediol Solutions, °C*

Glycol, %	1,2-Propanediol	1,3-Propanediol	1,2-Butanediol	1,3-Butanediol	levo-2,3-Butanediol	1,4-Butanediol	1,2-Pentanediol	1,5-Pentanediol
10	-3.12	-2.86	-2.60	-2.34	-3.1	-2.30	-2.3	-2.3
20	-7.6	-6.5	-6.0	-5.2	-7.1	-5.48	-4.8	-4.9
30	-14.0	-11.8	-11.0	-10.5	-12.4	-10.0	-6.8	-8.4
40	-22.7	-18.8	-16.5	-16.8	-19.4	-14.8	-8.4	-11.3
50	-34.5	-27.7	-22.4	-25.2	-29.6	-22.0	-10.2	-15.3
60	-48.2	-40.0	-29.0	-35.3	-40.4	-31.3	-12.6	-21.0

*Courtesy of Can. J. Research.

Table 10. Observed and Computed Freezing Points of Hydroxy Compounds, Percentage of Hydroxy Compound by Weight*

Hydroxy Compound	0	10	20	30	40	50	60	64	66.7	68	70
	Freezing Points, °C										
Methanol											
Obsd.	0	-6.5	-15.0	-26.0	-39.7	-55.4	-75.0	-84.6	---	---	---
Comp.	0	-6.5	-14.8	-26.0	-40.2	-55.6	-75.7	-83.4	---	---	---
Ethanol											
Obsd.	0	-4.5	-10.3	-18.8	-29.3	-36.5	-44.5	---	---	---	-53.5
Comp.	0	-4.5	-10.3	-17.8	-28.0	-36.8	-45.0	---	---	---	-53.5
1-Propanol											
Obsd.	0	-3.4	-7.8	-10.1	-10.8	-10.9	-11.8	---	---	---	-13.7
Comp.	0	-3.4	-7.8	-9.6	-10.5	-11.3	-12.2	---	---	---	-13.5
2-Propanol											
Obsd.	0	-3.4	-8.0	-14.8	-19.4	-21.4	-23.3	---	---	---	-27.2
Comp.	0	-3.4	-7.8	-14.0	-19.6	-21.4	-22.7	---	---	---	-27.2
Ethylene glycol											
Obsd.	0	-3.5	-7.8	-13.7	-23.2	-36.8	-53.5	---	---	---	---
Comp.	0	-3.5	-7.7	-13.9	-23.2	-36.8	-61.2	---	---	---	---
Propylene glycol (1, 2)											
Obsd.	0	-2.8	-6.5	-11.4	-20.0	-33.6	-51.0	---	---	-66.0	---
Comp.	0	-2.8	-6.6	-11.9	-19.9	-33.6	-51.2	---	---	-67.5	---
Propylene glycol (1, 3)											
Obsd.	0	-2.7	-6.0	-10.4	-16.2	-24.2	-36.8	---	---	---	-53.0
Comp.	0	-2.7	-6.0	-10.5	-16.4	-24.7	-36.6	---	---	---	-50.5
Hexylene glycol†											
Obsd.	0	-1.8	-4.0	-7.4	-11.0	-13.6	-15.8	---	---	---	-18.5
Comp.	0	-2.0	-4.1	-7.3	-11.2	-13.7	-15.5	---	---	---	-17.0
Glycerol											
Obsd.	0	-2.4	-5.2	-9.3	-15.0	-23.4	-35.6	---	-48.5	---	---
Comp.	0	-2.4	-5.2	-9.3	-15.2	-24.0	-36.0	---	-46.4	---	---
Hexanetriol (1, 2, 6)											
Obsd.	0	-1.6	-3.5	-6.1	-9.7	-14.5	-21.9	---	---	---	---
Comp.	0	-1.6	-3.5	-6.1	-9.6	-14.2	-20.0	---	---	---	---

*Courtesy of Ind. Eng. Chem.
†2-Methyl-2, 4-pentanediol.

Table 11. The Boiling Points of the Alkane Diols Calculated with $A = 252$, $p_{cx_2} = 19$, $p_{cx_3} = -1$, $p_{cc_2} = 5$, $p_{cc_3} = 6$ and $p_{xx_3} = -16$*

Diols	Coefficients of the interactions					B.p., °C	
	cx_2	cx_3	cc_2	cc_3	xx_3	Calcd.	Obsd.
1,2-Propane	3	1	1	0	1	183	186†
1,3-Propane	2	2	1	0	0	217	214†
1,2-Butane	3	2	2	1	1	193	191†
1,3-Butane	3	2	2	1	0	209	207†
1,4-Butane	2	2	2	1	0	228	228†
2,3-Butane	4	2	2	1	0	190	184‡
2-Me-1,2-propane	4	3	3	0	1	172	
2-Me-1,3-propane	2	4	3	0	0	225	
1,2-Pentane	3	2	3	2	1	204	206†
1,3-Pentane	3	3	3	2	0	219	
1,4-Pentane	3	2	3	2	0	220	
1,5-Pentane	2	2	3	2	0	239	238†
2,3-Pentane	4	3	3	2	1	184	187‡
2,4-Pentane	4	2	3	2	0	201	199†
2-Me-1,2-butane	3	3	4	2	1	208	206‡
2-Me-1,3-butane	4	2	4	2	0	206	204‡
2-Me-1,4-butane	2	3	4	2	0	243	
2-Me-2,3-butane	5	3	4	2	1	170	177‡
1,2-Hexane	3	2	4	3	1	215	
1,3-Hexane	3	3	4	3	0	230	
1,4-Hexane	3	3	4	3	0	230	
1,5-Hexane	3	2	4	3	0	231	
1,6-Hexane	2	2	4	3	0	250	250‡
2,3-Hexane	4	3	4	3	1	195	207‡
2,4-Hexane	4	3	4	3	0	211	
2,5-Hexane	4	2	4	3	0	212	221
3,4-Hexane	4	4	4	3	1	194	
2-Me-1,2-pentanediol	4	3	5	3	1	200	
2-Me-1,3-pentanediol	3	5	5	3	0	233	
2-Me-1,4-pentanediol	3	3	5	3	0	235	
2-Me-1,5-pentanediol	2	3	5	3	0	254	
2-Me-2,3-pentanediol	5	4	5	3	1	180	
2-Me-2,4-pentanediol	5	2	5	3	0	198	197‡
2-Me-3,4-pentanediol	4	3	5	3	1	200	
3-Me-1,2-pentanediol	3	3	5	4	1	225	
3-Me-1,3-pentanediol	4	3	5	4	0	222	
3-Me-1,4-pentanediol	3	3	5	4	0	241	
3-Me-1,5-pentanediol	2	2	5	4	0	263	
3-Me-2,3-pentanediol	5	4	5	4	1	186	

*Courtesy of J. Am. Chem. Soc.

†K. A. Clendening, F. J. Macdonald and D. E. Wright, Can. J. Research, B28, 608 (1950).

‡Handbook of Chemistry and Physics, Chemical Rubber Publishing Co., Cleveland, Ohio.

Higher Diols, Carbide and Carbon Chemicals, Ltd., N. Y., 1951.

Table 11—Continued

Diols	Coefficients of the interactions					B.p., °C	
	cx_2	cx_3	cc_2	cc_3	xx_3	Calcd.	Obsd.
3-Me-2, 4-pentanediol	4	4	5	4	0	221	
2, 3-diMe-1, 2-butanediol	4	4	6	3	1	204	
2, 3-diMe-1, 3-butanediol	4	4	6	3	0	220	
2, 3-diMe-1, 4-butanediol	2	4	6	3	0	258	
2, 3-diMe-2, 3-butanediol	6	4	6	3	1	170	173‡
Miscellaneous diols							
1, 7-Heptanediol	2	2	5	4	0	261	259‡
3-Et-1, 3-hexanediol	4	4	7	7	0	249	244‡
3, 4-diEt-3, 4-hexanediol	6	8	12	12	1	236	230‡

‡Handbook of Chemistry and Physics, Chemical Rubber Publishing Co., Cleveland, Ohio.

2. Dihydric Alcohols: Glycols

The glycols, like the monohydric alcohols, form a homologous series, beginning with the simplest member, ethylene glycol. The series comprises ethylene glycol, propylene glycol, butylene glycol, pentylene glycol, hexylene glycol, heptylene glycol, octylene glycol, and so on. However, only two of these, namely, ethylene glycol and propylene glycol, have received attention as major chemicals, having undergone intensive development in manufacture and for other uses. The field continues to grow rapidly, and other glycols are now being prepared in commercial quantities. These include the butanediols, pentanediols, and hexanediols.

The glycols are derivatives of saturated hydrocarbons in which two hydrogens have been replaced by hydroxyl groups, each of which is attached to a separate carbon atom. The chemical and physical behavior of the glycols resemble that of monohydric alcohols. They range from colorless liquids to solid crystalline compounds with practically no odor. They are heavier and more viscous than water at any given temperature, with much higher boiling points than either the corresponding monohydric alcohols or water. The glycols are di-primary alcohols when the two groups $CH_2 \cdot OH$ are present, as in ethylene glycol; primary-secondary when they contain the groups $-CH_2 \cdot OH$ and $-CH \cdot OH$, as in propylene glycol; others are either di-secondary, primary-tertiary, secondary-tertiary, or di-tertiary. Being alcohols, these diols give rise to every class of alcoholic derivative, but they behave as monohydric alcohols if only one hydroxyl group has been replaced in forming a derivative. Also, as alcohols they are readily oxidized and can be recognized by their oxidation products.

The names assigned to the glycols arose either from the process of manufacture or from trade names arbitrarily chosen. With the growing complexity of structure in the higher glycols, which have long chain molecules, the more exact Geneva system of nomenclature is found to be far more satisfactory. Starting with the corresponding saturated hydrocarbon, the suffix diol is added, indicating ② hydroxyl groups; the position of these groups is indicated by numbers—for example, propylene glycol is correctly written as 1,2-propanediol.

Although the glycols have been known since about 1860, when the French chemist Charles Wurtz first prepared several of the series, they excited no industrial interest, because of the lack of an economically feasible method of production. Such applications as they suggested were satisfactorily supplied by glycerol. This picture changed rapidly with the shortage of glycerol caused by the unprecedented demand during World War I. Attention was turned to the creation of substitutes, and with the phenomenal development of the petrochemical industry during the postwar period, cheap sources of hydrocarbons were made available as raw materials for the manufacture of such substitutes. With the availability of ethylene and propylene from the cracked gases of petroleum oil, ethylene glycol and propylene glycol, and derivatives of these hydrocarbons, soon appeared in commercial quantities, and new applications for them were explored. The more recent developments in polyester resins, synthetic fibers, and rubbers created new uses which augmented earlier ones, such as for antifreezes, solvents, humectants, lubricants, and explosives. The choice of a particular glycol is based on its characteristic physical behavior—solubility, hygroscopicity, viscosity, freezing point, and so on—as well as on price.

Of the total amount of ethylene glycol produced in the United States, 90 per cent is made from ethylene oxide, either by the chlorohydrin method or by direct oxidation. Hydrolysis takes place either at atmospheric pressure in the presence of a catalyst or at high pressure without the aid of a catalyst. Ethylene glycol is also manufactured from formaldehyde, methyl alcohol, and carbon monoxide at high pressure and temperature. [94]

Owing to their hygroscopicity, the glycols pick up and retain moisture in an atmosphere containing water vapor. Since the presence of water modifies the properties of glycols, the use of glycol-water solutions must take into consideration those differences between anhydrous glycols and their aqueous solutions. The physical properties of glycol-water solutions generally fall between those of anhydrous glycols and water. Humidity and temperature variations are also factors which influence the relative humectant value of glycols.

Diefenbach [4] has developed a unique key hygroscopicity curve providing a convenient method for calculating, with reasonable accuracy, the amount of water absorbed by a glycol for system equilibrium under various atmospheric conditions. Since his calculated results agree closely with data now available in the literature, his key hygroscopicity curves and method of calculation provide a simple and convenient means of deriving such data.

In the use of glycols for dehydrating gases, the dew point is an important means by which a measure of the amount of water vapor present in the gas can be made. The dew point is the temperature at which water will condense from a gas. The glycol solutions draw out the moisture until a state of equilibrium is attained.

The low molecular weight glycols possess the common property of being freely soluble in water. At the same time, the mutually soluble glycols make it possible, by means of their coupling action, to carry many water-immiscible materials into clear solutions.

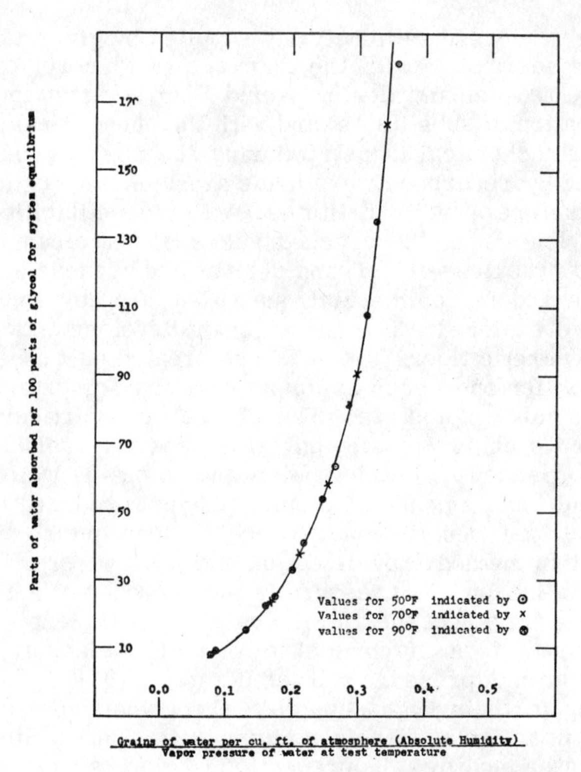

Courtesy of Am. Ink Maker.

Figure 1. Key hygroscopicity curve for ethylene glycol showing influence of vapor pressure of water at test temperature on amounts of moisture absorbed by ethylene glycol for system equilibrium at various temperatures and various absolute humidities.

Since the water solubility decreases as the molecular weight of the glycol increases, propylene glycol is found to be a better solvent for oils and organic chemicals than ethylene glycol. Saturated hydrocarbon oils are practically insoluble in the lower molecular weight glycols. These alcohols will dissolve, in varying degree, the ester or acid type of oils and gums. Generally, such glycols can dissolve aromatic compounds to some extent, and readily dissolve such alcohols and aromatic hydroxy compounds as phenols and resorcinol. Natural and synthetic rubbers are practically insoluble in the low molecular weight glycols.

The glycols are high-boiling liquids, which explains their low vapor pressure as compared to that of water at any given temperature. For example, water at 68° F has a vapor pressure over 100 times as great as that of propylene glycol, although the latter is the

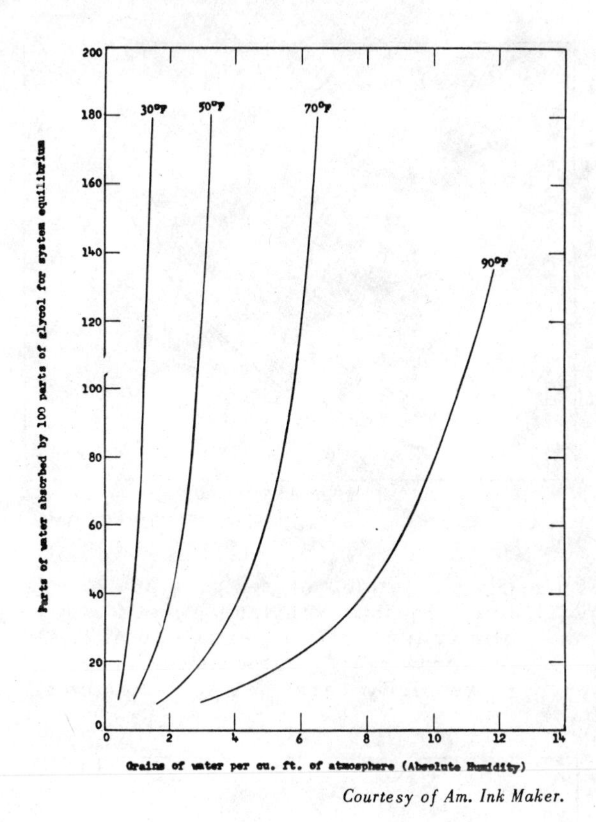

Courtesy of Am. Ink Maker.

Figure 2. The effect of temperature on the moisture absorption of ethylene glycol for system equilibrium of various absolute humidities. Values plotted were from experimentally obtained data.

most volatile of the low-boiling glycols. The boiling point of a glycol-water solution is lower than that of anhydrous glycol, and the boiling point decreases as the concentration of glycol is decreased.

Viscosity is defined as a measure of the internal friction of a liquid. The viscosities of the glycols vary inversely with temperature. Hot glycols will flow freely, but as they cool their viscosities will increase, until they finally cease to flow and become set. Therefore the pour point becomes of interest, since it is the lowest temperature at which a liquid will flow. Ethylene glycol will freeze above its pour point when agitated or seeded.

Specific heat is an important property where the glycols are used as heat-transfer media. As defined, specific heat is the amount of heat required to raise a unit weight of a substance one degree in temperature. This is expressed either as calories per gram per

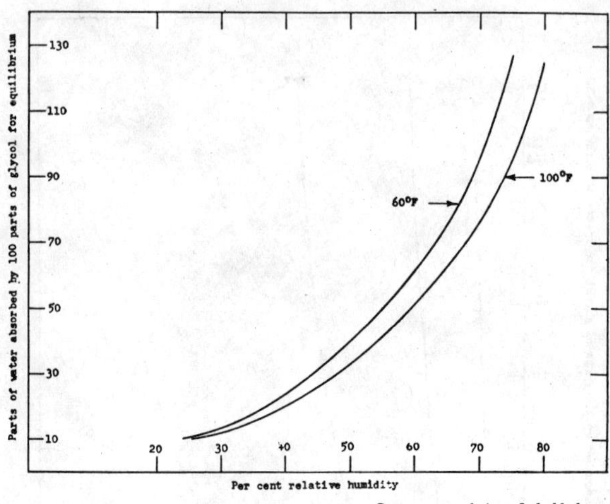

Courtesy of Am. Ink Maker.

Figure 3. The effect of temperature on the moisture absorption of ethylene glycol for system equilibrium at various relative humidities. Values plotted were calculated from those of the key hygroscopicity curve for ethylene glycol.

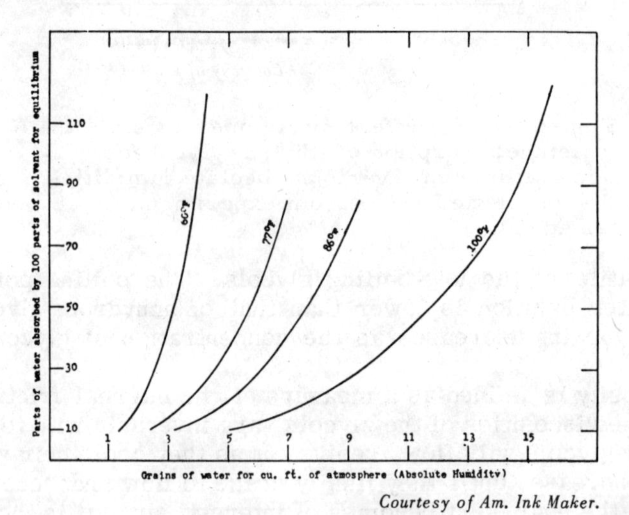

Courtesy of Am. Ink Maker.

Figure 4. The effect of temperature on the moisture absorption of ethylene glycol for system equilibrium at various absolute humidities. Values used were calculated from those in key hydroscopicity curve for ethylene glycol.

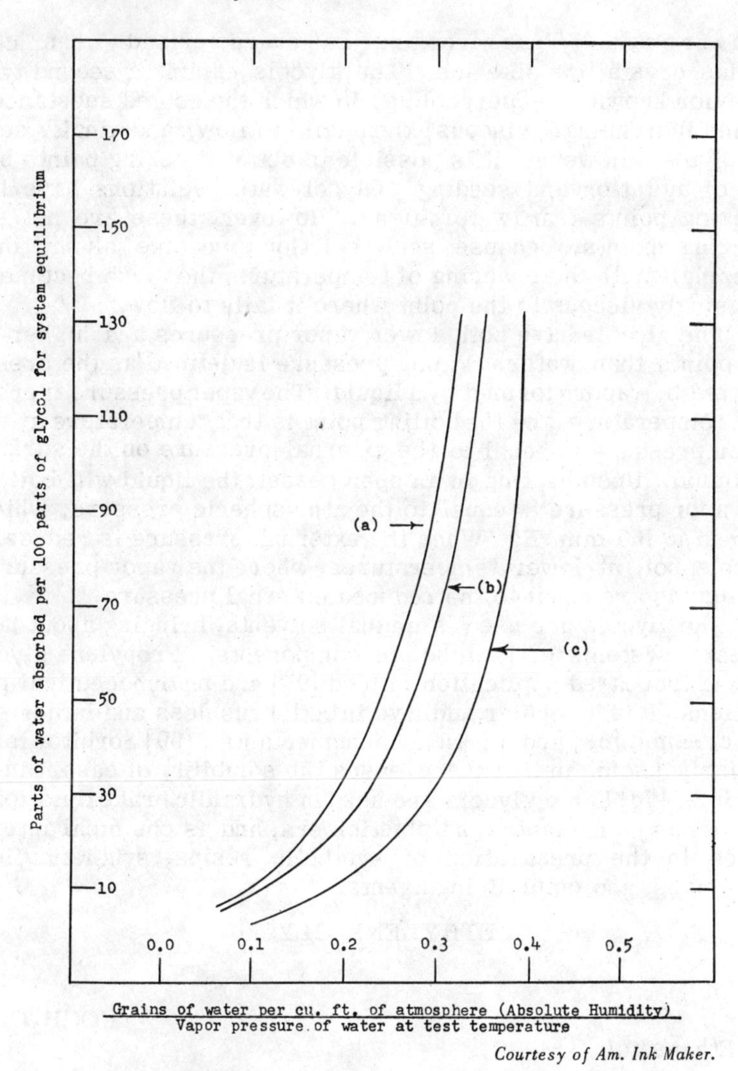

Courtesy of Am. Ink Maker.

Figure 5. Key hygroscopicity curves for the various glycols: (a) ethylene glycol; (b) diethylene glycol; and (c) dipropylene glycol.

degree centigrade, or as Btu per pound per degree Fahrenheit, and these expressions are numerically equal. A liquid having a high specific heat is capable of doing more workper unit weight than one having a low one, provided that all other factors are equal. By the addition of water to a glycol, the specific heat is increased.

The glycols do not possess sharp freezing points. This is due to the fact that under normal conditions glycols will supercool rather than freeze. True freezing is characterized when cooled liquids crystallize like ice. The glycols exhibit a second type of behavior known as supercooling, in which the cooled substance becomes increasingly viscous, then fails to flow, and finally sets up like glass. However, it is possible to obtain freezing points by the use of agitation and seeding. Glycol-water solutions have lower freezing points than water alone. However, these are not sharp freezing points, because such solutions become slushy during freezing. With the lowering of temperature, the slush becomes increasingly viscous to the point where it fails to flow.

The glycols have both lower vapor pressures and higher boiling points than water. Vapor pressure is defined as the pressure exerted by vapors formed by a liquid. The vapor pressure increases with temperature, and the boiling point is that temperature at which vapor pressure is equal to the external pressure on the surface of the liquid. Upon heating in an open vessel, the liquid will boil when its vapor pressure is equal to the atmospheric pressure, which is defined at 760 mm. Hg. When the external pressure is reduced, the glycols boil at lower temperatures, where the vapor pressures of the liquids are equal to the reduced external pressure.

The glycols are used as mutual solvents, bringing about homogeneous systems of immiscible components. Propylene glycol is finding increased application in food [94] and pharmaceutical preparations. It is a popular additive in both brushless and lather shaving creams, [68] and in tobacco humectants. [69] Sorbitol is particularly useful in that it increases the solubility of casein in milk powder. [70] Some glycols are used in hydraulic brake fluid formulations, as humectants, and plasticizers, and as chemical intermediates in the preparation of synthetic resins, synthetic fibers, explosives, and emulsifying agents.

ETHYLENE GLYCOL

Glycol

$HOCH_2CH_2OH$

1,2 Ethanediol

The first synthetic polyhydric alcohol to be made in commercial quantities was ethylene glycol, which owes its industrial origin and phenomenal growth to its unique properties. Early interest in this glycol extended only so far as it's ability to substitute for glycerol. This situation changed rapidly when it was found not only to be frequently adequate for this purpose but possessed of superior characteristics for other applications.

History and Development

In 1859 Charles Wurtz prepared ethylene glycol by converting ethylene into its iodide and mixing with silver acetate. Some time later he formed ethylene glycol by reacting ethylene oxide with water, these being heated in a sealed tube. The reaction foreshadowed the modern hydration process by which ethylene glycol is prepared from ethylene oxide. Ethylene glycol remained a comparatively rare organic chemical until World War I when, with the scarcity of glycerol, Germany produced a limited supply as a replacement. Following the war, it was again regarded as a raw material "for scientific preparation." [5]

Meanwhile, ethylene glycol had attracted attention in the form of its dinitrate. Intensive studies were made, exploring the glycols as freezing-point depressants for nitroglycerin, to be used in dynamite. The first patent to be issued covering this use was German patent 179,789, issued in 1904. British patent 12,770, also claiming ethylene glycol dinitrate as an additive to prevent nitroglycerin explosives from freezing, appeared in 1912. During World War I, Germany turned to ethylene glycol dinitrate as a substitute for the scarce nitroglycerin, and conducted extended investigations in a keen search for economical methods of production. That country succeeded in synthesizing this glycol from alcohol by way of ethylene and the hydrolysis of ethylene dichloride. The dinitrate of ethylene glycol was used not only in mixtures with nitroglycerin but proved to be a completely effective substitute in addition. In the United States a similar interest in the use of ethylene glycol in its nitrated form occupied the attention of investigators. The work of McElroy resulted in a number of patents on ethylene glycol manufacture, and in 1917, based on his methods in which ethylene chlorohydrin was used, ethylene glycol was produced on a semicommercial scale by the Commercial Research Company. This company operated only until 1920.

The earliest commercial process for manufacturing ethylene glycol is the chlorohydrin process in which ethylene is treated with hypochlorous acid to produce ethylene chlorohydrin, which is then converted to ethylene glycol by the action of a weak alkali, such as calcium hydroxide or sodium bicarbonate. The pressing need for an adequate and cheap source of ethylene as the basic raw material in this synthesis was finally obtained through the work of Curme [6] and his associates. Curme discovered a means of separating and concentrating ethylene from the mixed gases produced in cracking petroleum. This new source of ethylene spurred the further commercial development of ethylene glycol, and as a consequence, Carbide and Carbon Chemicals,* in August 1922, emerged as the first volume producer of this glycol. Beginning on a semicommercial scale, the volume was increased to full production by 1925. A further improvement in its manufacture was made by the direct oxidation of ethylene to ethylene oxide. This relieved the dependence

*Now Union Carbide Chemicals Company.

on a chlorine supply as required by the chlorohydrin method. About 1937, Dow Chemical Company also started manufacturing ethylene glycol by the chlorohydrin process. In 1948, a plant started operation at Sarnia, Ontario, in which Dow attempted to meet the large Canadian demand for ethylene glycol as an automotive antifreeze. Owing to its cold winters, Canada consumes the highest quantity per capita of antifreeze products in the world.

As the supply of ethylene became readily available—and with it, efficient processes developed for the synthesis of ethylene glycol—other companies joined the ranks of manufacturers of this glycol and related products. In 1940, E. I. du Pont de Nemours & Company entered the field with the manufacture of ethylene glycol by a process unique among those in operation. It is said to be based on the hydrogenation of methyl glycolate, which in turn had been formed by the reaction of formaldehyde and methanol. U.S. Industrial Chemicals also appeared as a producer, but discontinued operations about 1943. In 1948, Jefferson Chemical Company, and Wyandotte Chemicals Corporation* also made their appearances, manufacturing ethylene glycol and related products by means of the chlorohydrin process. In 1951, Mathieson Chemical Corporation and Allied Chemical Corporation entered the field, also using the chlorohydrin process.

Methods of Production

There are several practical methods by which ethylene glycol can be manufactured, but one is of major importance in the United States. This is basically the hydrolysis of ethylene oxide. There are two methods of preparing the ethylene oxide.

Chlorohydrin Process. Ethylene, a 5 per cent solution of hypochlorous acid solution, and an aqueous solution of chlorine are reacted at about 118° F to form ethylene chlorohydrin. This compound is dehydrochlorinated to ethylene oxide by the reaction a 10 per cent solution of milk of lime and steam at pH 8 and at about 215° F. To insure maximum yield—which is about 95 per cent—the ethylene oxide is removed as quickly as it is produced. It is then purified by fractionation and the ethylene dichloride and dichloroethyl ether by-products are recovered. To reduce the formation of the ethylene dichloride and 2,2'-dichloroethyl ether by-products, and to a large extent to prevent the formation of the gas-phase chlorine-olefin reaction, the water is saturated with chlorine, and the ethylene is introduced to the aqueous solution of hypochlorous acid held in a separate container.

*The Wyandotte process yields a mixed ethylene glycol-propylene glycol product.

Oxidation Process. This more recent process is based on the discovery by T. S. Lefort in 1931 that oxygen could be added directly to the ethylene bond. Since then, considerable research has been directed toward the development and refinements of this process.

With this method ethylene oxide is made by reacting ethylene and air, which are fed to the converter over a silver catalyst, at temperatures slightly over 200° C and at pressures up to 200 lb./in. [2] The temperature is carefully controlled, and the large amount of heat liberated by the reaction, mostly from the formation of carbon dioxide, is quickly removed. The resulting ethylene oxide is then separated either by absorption on activated carbon or by absorption in water, methanol, or other solvent.

In both the chlorohydrin and oxidation processes, propylene glycol is finally prepared by the hydrolysis of ethylene oxide with sulfuric acid as a catalyst. To remove the sulfuric acid, the solution of glycols is traversed over an ion-exchange bed. After evaporation to concentrate the ethylene glycol, the latter is separated and purified by fractionation. When ethylene oxide is hydrated without a catalyst, a mixture of ethylene glycol and polyglycols is formed. The relative proportions of these compounds can be determined by the ratio of the oxide to water. The formation of polyglycols can be controlled and restricted to a large extent by using a large excess of water.

Characteristics and Uses

Ethylene glycol is a slightly viscous, clear and practically colorless and odorless liquid with a sweetish taste. It is stable, has a very low vapor pressure, excellent heat-transfer properties, and is very hygroscopic, being about one and a half times as hygroscopic as glycerol. Its physical properties are intermediate between those of ethyl alcohol and glycerol. The vapor pressure of ethylene glycol is much lower than ethyl alcohol, and its boiling point is more than 100° C higher. Ethylene glycol oxidizes to glycolic acid and then to oxalic acid.

Ethylene glycol is miscible with water, the lower aliphatic alcohols, glycerol, acetone and similar ketones, aldehydes, furfural, phenol, acetic and glacial acetic acids, mono- and diethanolamine, pine oil, and pyridine and similar coal tar bases. It is slightly soluble in ethyl ether, petroleum ether, benzene, toluene, xylene, turpentine, carbon tetrachloride, carbon disulfide, chloroform, chlorinated hydrocarbons, hydrocarbons, heptanes, raw linseed oil, and esters. It will dissolve casein, gelatin, low-viscosity silicones, some phenol-formaldehyde resins, dyes, and zein. It is not a solvent for cellulose esters and ethers, ester gum, waxes, vegetable oils, rubber and rubber chloride, and vinyl resins. It is partly soluble in dammar, kauri, rosin, shellac, dextrin, and animal glue.

It is used as a solvent in paints and plastics, in the formulation of lacquers, printing inks, stamp pad inks, and inks for ballpoint pens. It is a solvent and conducting medium for boric acid and borates in electrolytic condensers used in the radio and television industries. It is a mutual solvent or coupling agent for inks, soluble oils, hydraulic fluids, and textile processing compounds. As a mutual solvent with methanol, it dissolves dyes used in quick-drying wood stains, producing stains that are fast to daylight, dry rapidly, possess brilliancy, do not bleed, and prevent raising of grain. The hygroscopic and solvent properties of ethylene glycol are utilized in dye pastes, in printing, in glue mixtures, and in dyeing of leather. [7]

The largest consumption of ethylene glycol is as a nonevaporating, permanent-type antifreeze for automobile engine-cooling systems, where the low freezing points of its aqueous solutions make it particularly suitable for protecting the engine in the coldest weather. It behaves as a solvent for inhibitors in some hydraulic fluids and has a tendency to inhibit rubber swelling which may result from other ingredients present. It is used in chemical and oil-type fire extinguishers as an antifreeze and foam stabilizer. It is also a component of deicing fluids used on aircraft, railroads, and refrigerator plants to prevent the formation of ice at critical points. Its hygroscopic and plasticizing properties are utilized in cellophane, paper, gelatin and glue preparations. It adds strength, softness, and pliability when added to leather and fibers.

The second largest outlet for ethylene glycol is in the preparation of explosives. In the form of ethylene glycol dinitrate, it is the basic ingredient of low-freezing gelatin dynamites. Ethylene glycol is also a valuable intermediate in the preparation of certain polyester fibers, polyester rubber, alkyd resins, and esters used as solvents, plasticizers, and so forth. Because of its toxicity, ethylene glycol should not be used in pharmaceutical and food preparations.

Other uses for ethylene glycol are in adhesive formulations, in air sterilization, as a conditioning agent, in the dehydration of gases, as a lubricant, a softening agent, as a high-temperature coolant, and in formulations used in textile processing.

Physical Properties and Specifications of Ethylene Glycol

Acidity as acetic acid	0.01% by wt., max.
Ash	0.005 g./100 ml., max.
Boiling point at 760 mm. Hg	197.2-197.6° C
Coefficient of expansion at 20° C	0.00062/°C 0.0006375/°C
Color, APHA	10-15 max.
Density (true) at 20° C	1.1134 g./ml.

Dielectric constant, 20° C	38.66 esu
Distillation at 760 mm. Hg	193° C, min.
Ibp	
5 ml.	194° C, min.
95 ml.	200° C, min.
Dp	205-208° C
Electric conductivity at 25° C	1.07 x 10^6 recip. ohms (mhos) cm.
Fire point, Cleveland, tag	250° F
ASTM, open cup	245° F
Flash point (open cup)	245° F
ASTM, open cup	240° F
Free energy of formation at 25° C	-80.2 kcal./mole
Heat of combustion (const. pressure) at 20° C	-283.3 kcal./mole
Heat of dilution [$C_2H_4(OH)_2$ x 2 H_2O]	0.06 cal./g.
Heat of formation at 20° C	-108.1 kcal./mole
Heat of fusion	44.7 cal./g.
Heat of vaporization at 760 mm. Hg	191 cal./g. 344 Btu/lb.
Inorganic chlorides, as Cl	0.1 ppm, max.
Iron	0.15 ppm, max.
Molecular weight	62.07
Odor	Mild
Pour point	-75° F
Refractive index n_D 25° C	1.4306
n_D 20° C	1.4316
Specific gravity (apparent), 25/25° C	1.1133
20/20° C	1.1155
Specific heat at 20° C	0.561
at 0° C	0.544
Spontaneous ignition temperature	398.9° C 412.8° C

Sulfates	Not detectable
Surface tension at 20° C	48.4 dynes/cm.
Suspended matter	Substantially free
Vapor at 20° C (68° F)	0.06 mm. Hg
25° C (77° F)	0.12 mm. Hg
93° C (200° F)	11.0 mm. Hg
132.2° C (270° F)	75.0 mm. Hg
Viscosity at 10° C (50° F)	33.6 cp.
25° C (77° F)	17.4 cp.
35° C (95° F)	12.3 cp.
60° C (140° F)	5.2 cp.
Water content	0.3% by wt., max.
Weight per gallon at 20° C	9.28 lb.

Ethylene Glycol*

Glycol % by Wt.	% by Vol.	Flash Point °F Cleveland, Tag	Fire Point °F Cleveland
100	100	245	250
95	94.7	260	270
90	89.4	270	280

*From "Properties of Ethylene Glycol and Its Aqueous Solutions," prepared by C. S. Cragoe, Senior Physicist, National Bureau of Standards.

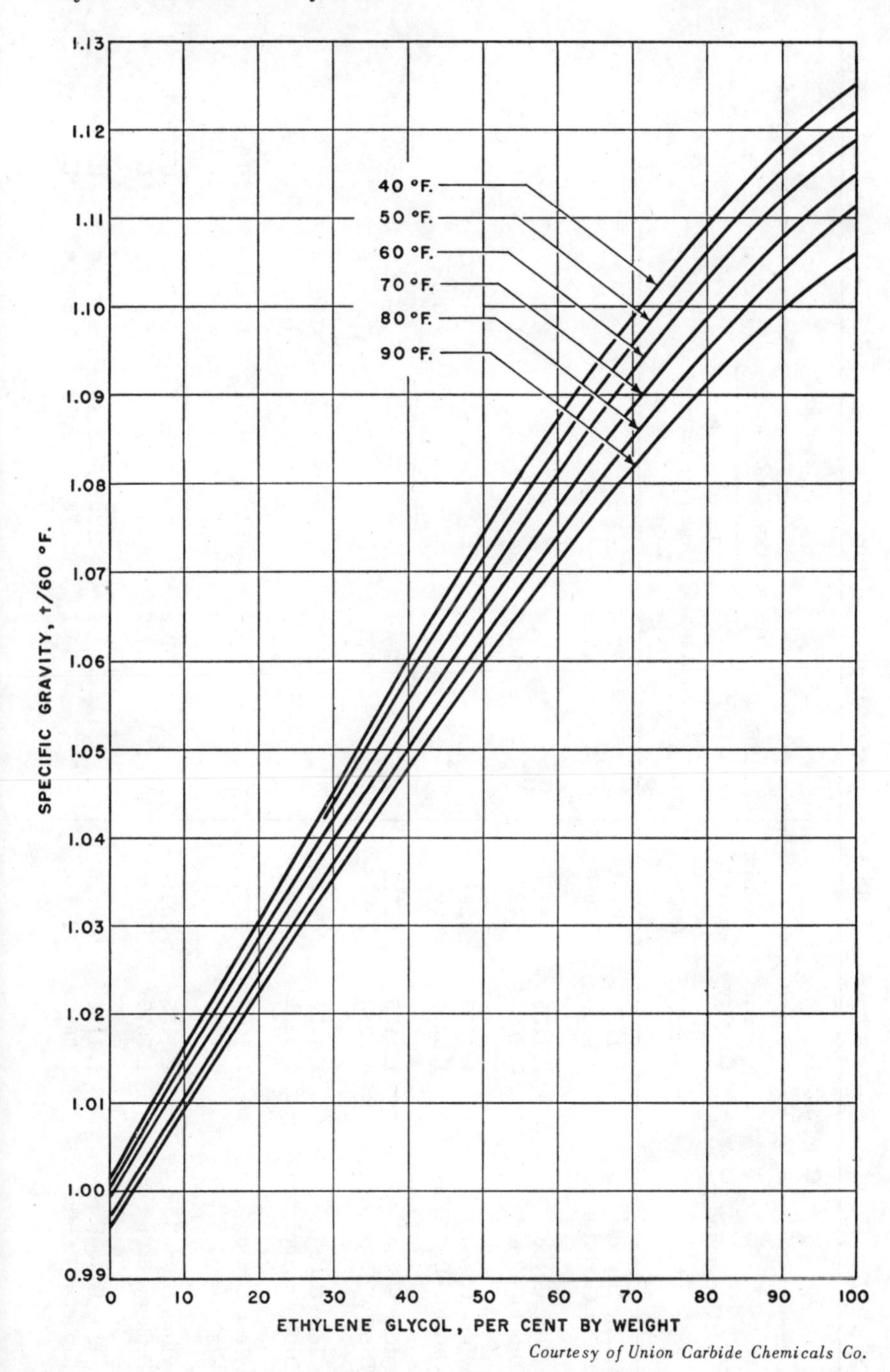

Courtesy of Union Carbide Chemicals Co.

Figure 6. Specific Gravity of Ethylene Glycol Water Solutions vs. Composition, at t/60° Fahrenheit.

Table 12. Constant Boiling Mixtures*

Components			Azeotrope					
Compound	Specific Gravity at 20/20° C	Boiling Point, °C at 760 mm.	Boiling Point, °C at 760 mm.	Composition, % by wt. In Azeo-trope	In Upper Layer	In Lower Layer	Relative Volume of Layers at 20° C	Sp. Gr. 20/20° C of Azeotrope or Layers
Ethylene Blycol Butyl Carbitol	1.1155 0.9536	197.5 230.6	196.2	72.5 27.5				1.074
Ethylene Glycol Dibutyl Ether	1.1155 0.7694	197.5 142.1	139.5	6.4 93.6	2 98	99 1	U 95 L 5	U 0.777 L 1.114
Ethylene Glycol Dichlorethyl Ether	1.1155 1.2220	123† 96†	92.7†				U 9.9 L 90.1	
Ethylene Glycol Diethyl Carbitol	1.1155 0.9082	197.5 188.4	178.0	26.1 73.9				0.959
Ethylene Glycol Di(2-ethylhexyl) Ether)	1.1155 0.8121	91‡ 135‡	87‡				U 50 L 50	
Ethylene Glycol Di-N-hexyl Ether	1.1155 0.7942	123† 137†	112.8†	35.6 64.4	0.1 99.9	99.9 0.1	U 71.8 L 28.2	U 0.795 L 1.115
Ethylene Glycol Diphenyl Ether	1.1155 1.0677#	123† 161†	120.4†	62.3 37.7	0.2 99.8	98.5 1.5	U 37.6 L 62.4	U 1.076 L 1.114
Ethylene Glycol Diphenyl Ether	1.1155 1.0677#	197.5 257.4	192.3	64.5 35.5	0.22 99.78	98.28 1.72	U 35.3● L 64.7●	U 1.068# L 1.108#

Ethylene Glycol	1.1155	197.5	192	45.5	1.050
Exthoxydiglycol	0.9898	208.8		54.5	
Ethylene Glycol	1.1155	123†	114	4	1.025
Methyl Carbitol	1.0211	115†		96	
Ethylene Glycol	1.1155	157.1▲	149▲	12	1.033
Methyl Carbitol	1.0211	151.2▲		88	
Ethylene Glycol	1.1155	197.5	192	30	1.051
Methyl Carbitol	1.0211	193.6		70	

*Courtesy of Union Carbide Chemicals Co.
†At 50 mm. Hg
‡At 10 mm. Hg
Heterogeneous at 20° C
#At 30/20° C
●At 30° C
▲At 200 mm. Hg

Table 13. Boiling Point of Aqueous Solutions at Atmospheric Pressure*

Glycol, % by Wt.	% by Vol.	Boiling Point °F	Glycol, % by Wt.	% by Vol.	Boiling Point °F
0	0.0	212	80	78.9	252
10	9.1	214	81	79.9	254
20	18.4	216	82	81.0	256
25	23.2	217	83	82.0	258
30	28.0	218	84	83.1	260
35	32.8	219	85	84.1	262
40	37.8	221	86	85.2	265
45	42.8	223	87	86.2	268
50	47.8	225	88	87.3	271
55	52.9	227	89	88.4	275
60	58.0	230	90	89.4	279
62	60.1	232	91	90.5	284
64	62.2	233	92	91.5	289
66	64.2	235	93	92.6	294
68	66.3	236	94	93.6	301
70	68.4	238	95	94.7	309
72	70.5	240	96	95.8	319
74	72.6	243	97	96.8	330
76	74.7	245	98	97.9	345
78	76.8	248	99	98.9	363
80	78.9	252	100	100	388

*From "Properties of Ethylene Glycol and Its Aqueous Solutions," prepared by C. S. Cragoe, Senior Physicist, National Bureau of Standards.

Table 14. Freezing Points of Ethylene Glycol Aqueous Solutions*

Ethylene Glycol		Freezing Point		Ethylene Glycol		Freezing Point	
Wt. %	Vol. %	°C	°F	Wt. %	Vol. %	°C	°F
0	0.0	0.0	32.0	40	37.8	-24	-11
2	1.8	-0.6	30.9	42	39.8	-26	-15
4	3.6	-1.3	29.7	44	41.8	-28	-18
6	5.4	-2.0	28.4	46	43.8	-31	-23
8	7.2	-2.7	27.0	48	45.8	-33	-27
10	9.1	-3.5	25.6	50	47.8	-36	-32
12	10.9	-4.4	24.0	52	49.8	-38	-37
14	12.8	-5.3	22.4	54	51.9	-41	-42
16	14.6	-6.3	20.6	56	53.9	-44	-48
18	16.5	-7.3	18.8	58	56.0	-48	-54
20	18.4	-8	17	80	78.9	-47	-52
22	20.3	-9	15	82	81.0	-43	-46
24	22.2	-11	12	84	83.1	-40	-40
26	24.1	-12	10	86	85.2	-36	-33
28	26.0	-13	8	88	87.3	-33	-27
30	28.0	-15	5	90	89.4	-29	-21
32	29.9	-17	2	92	91.5	-26	-15
34	31.9	-18	-1	94	93.6	-23	-9
36	33.8	-20	-4	96	95.8	-19	-3
38	35.8	-22	-7	98	97.9	-16	+3
				100	100.0	-13	+9

*Courtesy of E. I. duPont de Nemours Co.

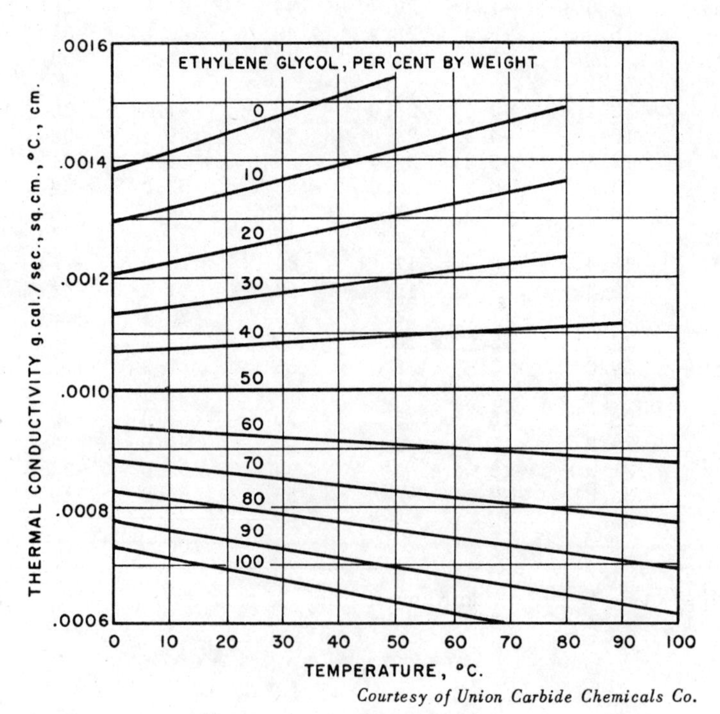

Courtesy of Union Carbide Chemicals Co.

Figure 7. Thermal Conductivity of Aqueous Ethylene Glycol Solutions at Various Temperatures.

Table 15. Vapor Pressure of Aqueous Ethylene Glycol Solutions*

	Ethylene Glycol Percentage							
By Wt.	70	75	80	85	90	95	97	100
By Vol.	68.4	73.6	78.9	84.1	89.4	94.7	96.8	100
Temp. °F	Absolute Pressure in psi							
150	2.2	2.0	1.7	1.4	1.1	0.6	0.4	0.04
160	2.9	2.6	2.2	1.8	1.4	0.8	.5	.06
170	3.6	3.2	2.8	2.3	1.7	1.0	.7	.08
180	4.5	4.1	3.5	2.9	2.2	1.3	.8	.12
190	5.6	5.1	4.4	3.6	2.7	1.6	1.0	.16
200	7.0	6.3	5.5	4.5	3.4	2.0	1.3	0.2
210	8.5	7.7	6.7	5.5	4.1	2.4	1.6	.3
220	10.4	9.4	8.2	6.7	5.0	3.0	2.0	.4
230	12.6	11.4	9.9	8.2	6.1	3.6	2.5	.5
240	15.2	13.7	11.9	9.9	7.4	4.4	3.0	.7
250	18.1	16.4	14.3	11.8	8.9	5.3	3.7	0.9
260	21.6	19.5	17.0	14.1	10.6	6.4	4.4	1.1
270	25.5	23.0	20.1	16.7	12.6	7.6	5.3	1.4
280	30.1	27.1	23.7	19.7	14.9	9.1	6.4	1.8
290	35.2	31.8	27.9	23.2	17.6	10.8	7.6	2.3
300	41.1	37.1	32.5	27.1	20.6	12.7	9.0	2.8
310	47.7	43.1	37.8	31.5	24.0	14.9	10.6	3.5
320	55.2	49.9	43.8	36.6	27.9	17.4	12.5	4.3
330	63.5	57.5	50.5	42.2	32.3	20.2	14.6	5.2
340	72.9	66.0	58.0	48.5	37.2	23.5	17.1	6.3
350	83.3	75.5	66.4	55.6	42.7	27.1	19.8	7.6

*From "Properties of Ethylene Glycol and Its Aqueous Solutions," prepared by C. S. Cragoe, Senior Physicist, National Bureau of Standards.

Table 16. Ethylene Glycol, Specific Heat of Aqueous Solutions*

	Ethylene Glycol Percentage										
By Wt.	0	10	20	30	40	50	60	70	80	90	100
By Vol.	0	9.1	18.4	28.0	37.8	47.8	58.0	68.4	78.9	89.4	100
Temp. °F	Specific Heat in Btu/lb. °F										
60	0.9996	0.968	0.928	0.882	0.835	0.785	0.734	0.687	0.642	0.599	0.556
70	0.9987	0.968	0.930	0.887	0.841	0.792	0.742	0.695	0.650	0.606	0.563
80	0.9982	0.969	0.933	0.892	0.847	0.799	0.750	0.703	0.658	0.613	0.570
90	0.9980	0.970	0.935	0.896	0.852	0.822	0.758	0.711	0.665	0.620	0.575
100	0.9980	0.971	0.938	0.900	0.858	0.813	0.766	0.719	0.672	0.627	0.581
110	0.9982	0.972	0.940	0.904	0.863	0.819	0.773	0.727	0.680	0.634	0.588
120	0.9985	0.973	0.942	0.907	0.868	0.825	0.780	0.734	0.687	0.640	0.594
130	0.9989	0.974	0.944	0.910	0.872	0.851	0.787	0.740	0.694	0.647	0.600
140	0.9994	0.975	0.947	0.914	0.877	0.837	0.794	0.747	0.700	0.653	0.606
150	1.0001	0.977	0.949	0.917	0.881	0.842	0.800	0.753	0.707	0.659	0.612
160	1.0008	0.978	0.951	0.921	0.886	0.847	0.805	0.759	0.713	0.666	0.619
170	1.0017	0.980	0.954	0.924	0.890	0.852	0.810	0.765	0.720	0.673	0.625
180	1.0027	0.981	0.956	0.927	0.894	0.857	0.816	0.771	0.726	0.679	0.631
190	1.0039	0.983	0.959	0.931	0.898	0.861	0.821	0.777	0.733	0.686	0.637
200	1.0052	0.985	0.961	0.934	0.902	0.866	0.826	0.783	0.739	0.692	0.644
210	1.0067	0.987	0.964	0.937	0.905	0.870	0.831	0.789	0.745	0.698	0.650
220	1.008	0.989	0.966	0.940	0.909	0.875	0.836	0.794	0.750	0.704	0.656
230	1.010	0.992	0.969	0.943	0.913	0.879	0.841	0.799	0.756	0.710	0.662
240	1.013	0.994	0.972	0.947	0.917	0.884	0.846	0.805	0.762	0.716	0.668

250	1.015	0.997	0.976	0.951	0.922	0.889	0.852	0.811	0.768	0.723	0.675
260	1.018	1.000	0.979	0.954	0.926	0.893	0.857	0.817	0.774	0.729	0.681
270	1.021	1.003	0.983	0.958	0.930	0.898	0.862	0.822	0.780	0.735	0.687
280	1.024	1.006	0.986	0.962	0.935	0.903	0.867	0.828	0.786	0.741	0.693
290	1.027	1.010	0.990	0.966	0.939	0.908	0.873	0.834	0.792	0.747	0.700
300	1.030	1.014	0.994	0.970	0.943	0.913	0.878	0.840	0.798	0.754	0.706
310	1.034	1.018	0.998	0.975	0.948	0.918	0.883	0.845	0.804	0.760	0.712
320	1.039	1.023	1.003	0.980	0.953	0.923	0.889	0.851	0.810	0.766	0.718
330	1.044	1.028	1.008	0.985	0.958	0.928	0.894	0.857	0.816	0.772	0.724
340	1.050	1.033	1.013	0.990	0.963	0.933	0.900	0.863	0.822	0.778	0.731
350	1.056	1.038	1.018	0.995	0.968	0.939	0.906	0.869	0.828	0.784	0.737

*From "Properties of Ethylene Glycol and Its Aqueous Solutions," prepared by C. S. Cragoe, Senior Physicist, National Bureau of Standards.

Table 17. Ethylene Glycol, Density*

	Ethylene Glycol Percentage										
By Wt.	0	10	20	30	40	50	60	70	80	90	100
By Vol.	0	9.1	18.4	28.0	37.8	47.8	58.0	68.4	78.9	89.4	100
Temp. °F	Density in g./ml.										
-50							1.110	1.125	1.137		
-40							1.108	1.122	1.134		
-30						1.087	1.105	1.120	1.131		
-20						1.086	1.103	1.117	1.128	1.138	
-10					1.068	1.084	1.100	1.114	1.125	1.135	
0					1.066	1.082	1.097	1.111	1.122	1.131	
10				1.048	1.064	1.080	1.095	1.107	1.118	1.128	1.136
20			1.031	1.147	1.063	1.077	1.092	1.104	1.115	1.124	1.132
30		1.015	1.030	1.045	1.061	1.075	1.089	1.101	1.111	1.121	1.128
40	1.000	1.014	1.029	1.044	1.059	1.073	1.086	1.098	1.108	1.117	1.124
50	1.000	1.013	1.027	1.042	1.056	1.070	1.083	1.094	1.105	1.113	1.120
60	0.999	1.012	1.026	1.040	1.054	1.067	1.080	1.091	1.101	1.109	1.116
70	0.998	1.011	1.024	1.038	1.051	1.064	1.076	1.087	1.097	1.105	1.113
80	0.997	1.009	1.022	1.035	1.049	1.061	1.073	1.084	1.093	1.101	1.109
90	0.995	1.007	1.020	1.033	1.046	1.058	1.069	1.080	1.088	1.097	1.105
100	0.993	1.005	1.018	1.030	1.043	1.054	1.066	1.076	1.085	1.094	1.101
110	0.991	1.003	1.015	1.027	1.039	1.051	1.062	1.072	1.882	1.090	1.097
120	0.989	1.000	1.012	1.024	1.036	1.047	1.058	1.068	1.078	1.186	1.093
130	0.986	0.997	1.009	1.021	1.033	1.044	1.055	1.064	1.074	1.082	1.089
140	0.983	0.994	1.006	1.018	1.029	1.040	1.051	1.060	1.069	1.078	1.085

150	0.980	0.991	1.003	1.014	1.026	1.036	1.047	1.056	1.065	1.074	1.081
160	0.977	0.988	0.999	1.011	1.022	1.032	1.043	1.052	1.061	1.069	1.077
170	0.974	0.985	0.996	1.007	1.018	1.028	1.039	1.048	1.057	1.065	1.073
180	0.970	0.981	0.992	1.003	1.014	1.024	1.034	1.044	1.053	1.061	1.068
190	0.967	0.977	0.988	0.999	1.009	1.020	1.030	1.040	1.048	1.057	1.064
200	0.963	0.974	0.984	0.995	1.006	1.016	1.026	1.035	1.044	1.052	1.060
210	0.959	0.970	0.980	0.991	1.001	1.011	1.021	1.031	1.040	1.048	1.056
220	0.995	0.965	0.976	0.987	0.997	1.007	1.017	1.026	1.035	1.044	1.051
230	0.951	0.961	0.972	0.982	0.992	1.003	1.012	1.022	1.031	1.039	1.047
240	0.947	0.957	0.967	0.978	0.988	0.998	1.008	1.017	1.026	1.034	1.042
250	0.942	0.952	0.963	0.973	0.983	0.993	1.003	1.012	1.021	1.030	1.038
260	0.938	0.948	0.958	0.968	0.978	0.988	0.998	1.008	1.017	1.025	1.033
270	0.933	0.943	0.953	0.963	0.973	0.983	0.993	1.003	1.012	1.020	1.029
280	0.928	0.938	0.948	0.958	0.968	0.978	0.988	0.998	1.007	1.016	1.024
290	0.923	0.933	0.943	0.953	0.963	0.973	0.983	0.993	1.002	1.011	1.019
300	0.918	0.928	0.938	0.948	0.958	0.968	0.978	0.988	0.977	1.006	1.014
310	0.913	0.923	0.933	0.943	0.953	0.963	0.973	0.983	0.992	1.001	1.010
320	0.907	0.917	0.928	0.938	0.948	0.958	0.968	0.977	0.987	0.996	1.005
330	0.902	0.912	0.922	0.932	0.942	0.952	0.962	0.972	0.982	0.991	1.000
340	0.896	0.906	0.917	0.927	0.937	0.947	0.957	0.967	0.976	0.985	0.994
350	0.890	0.900	0.911	0.921	0.931	0.941	0.951	0.961	0.971	0.980	0.989

*From "Properties of Ethylene Glycol and Its Aqueous Solutions," prepared by C. S. Cragoe, Senior Physicist, National Bureau of Standards.

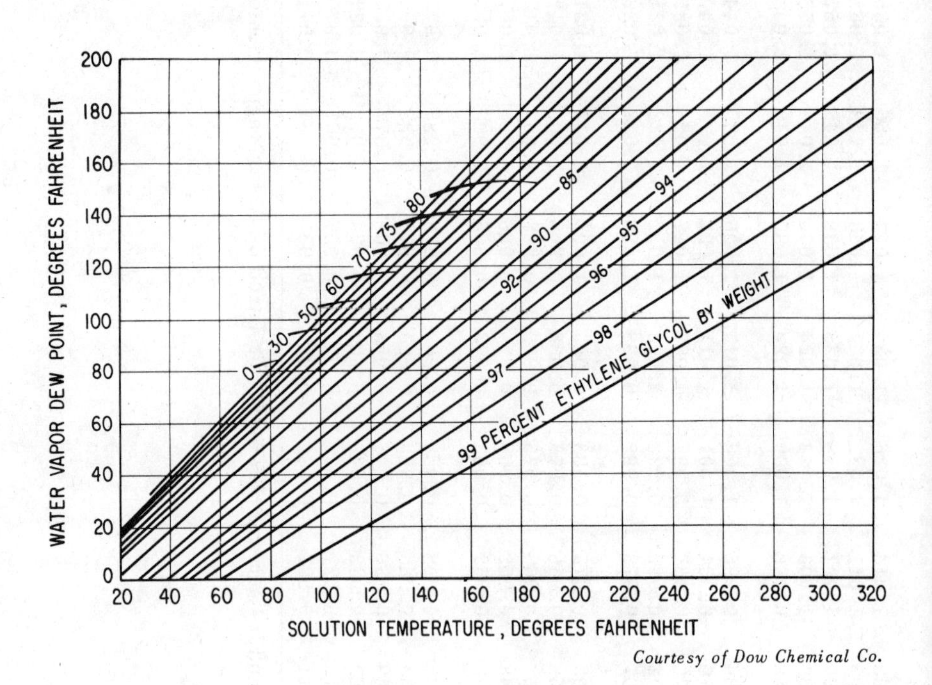

Courtesy of Dow Chemical Co.

Figure 8. Water Vapor Dew Points Over Aqueous Ethylene Glycol Solutions.

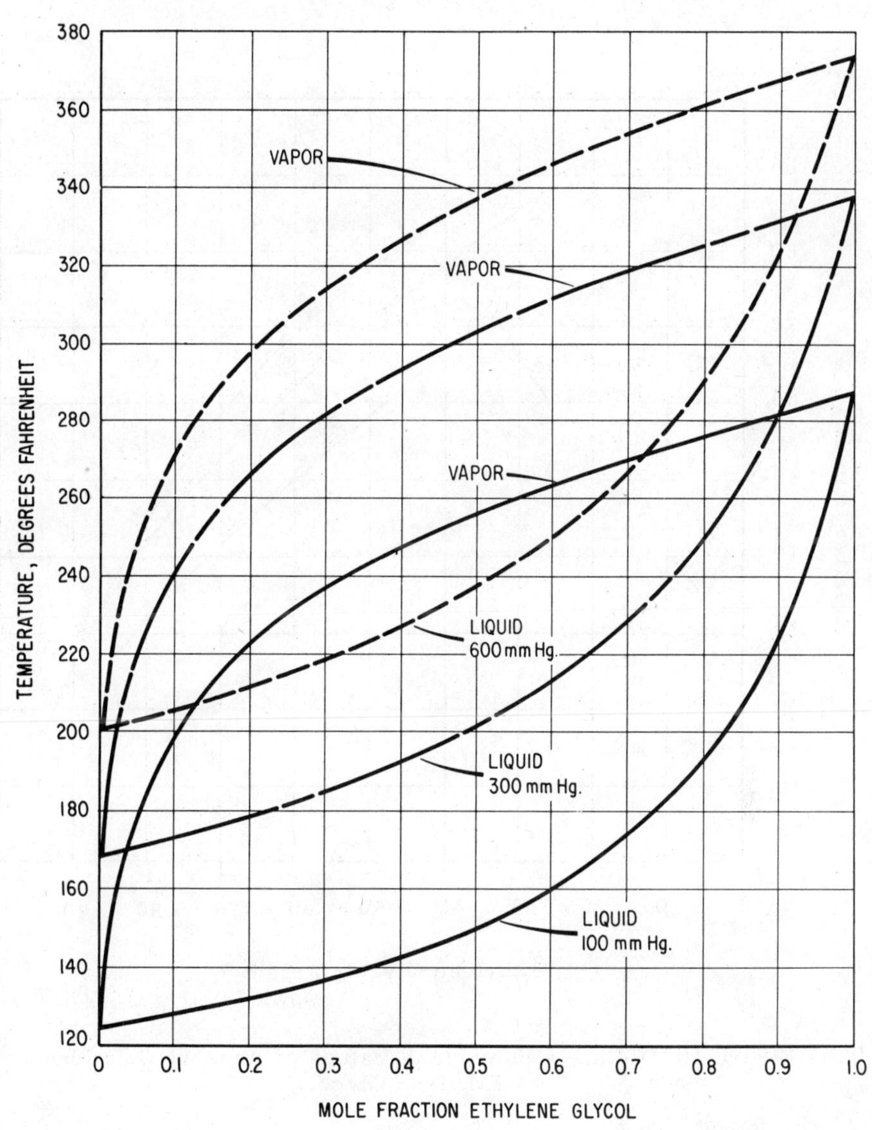

Courtesy of Dow Chemical Co.

Figure 9. Vapor-Liquid Composition Curves For Aqueous Ethylene Glycol Solutions.

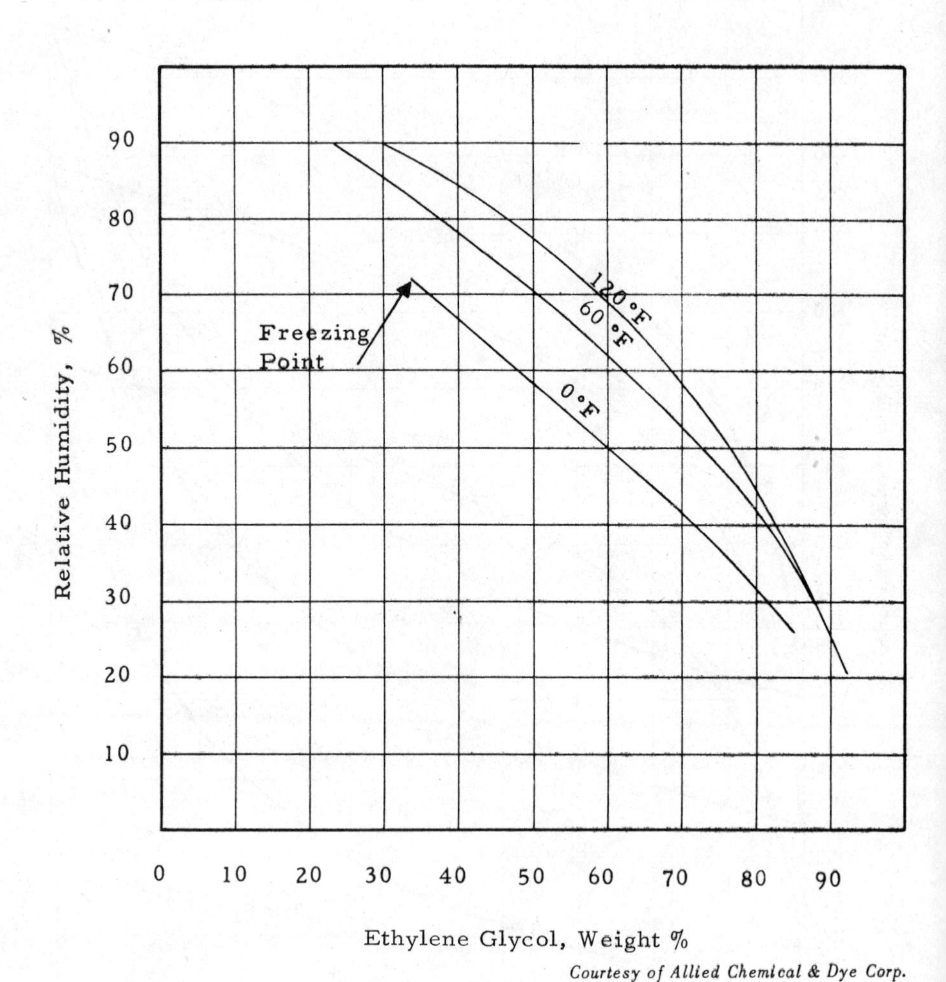

Courtesy of Allied Chemical & Dye Corp.

Figure 10. Relative Humectant Values of Aqueous Solutions of Ethylene Glycol.

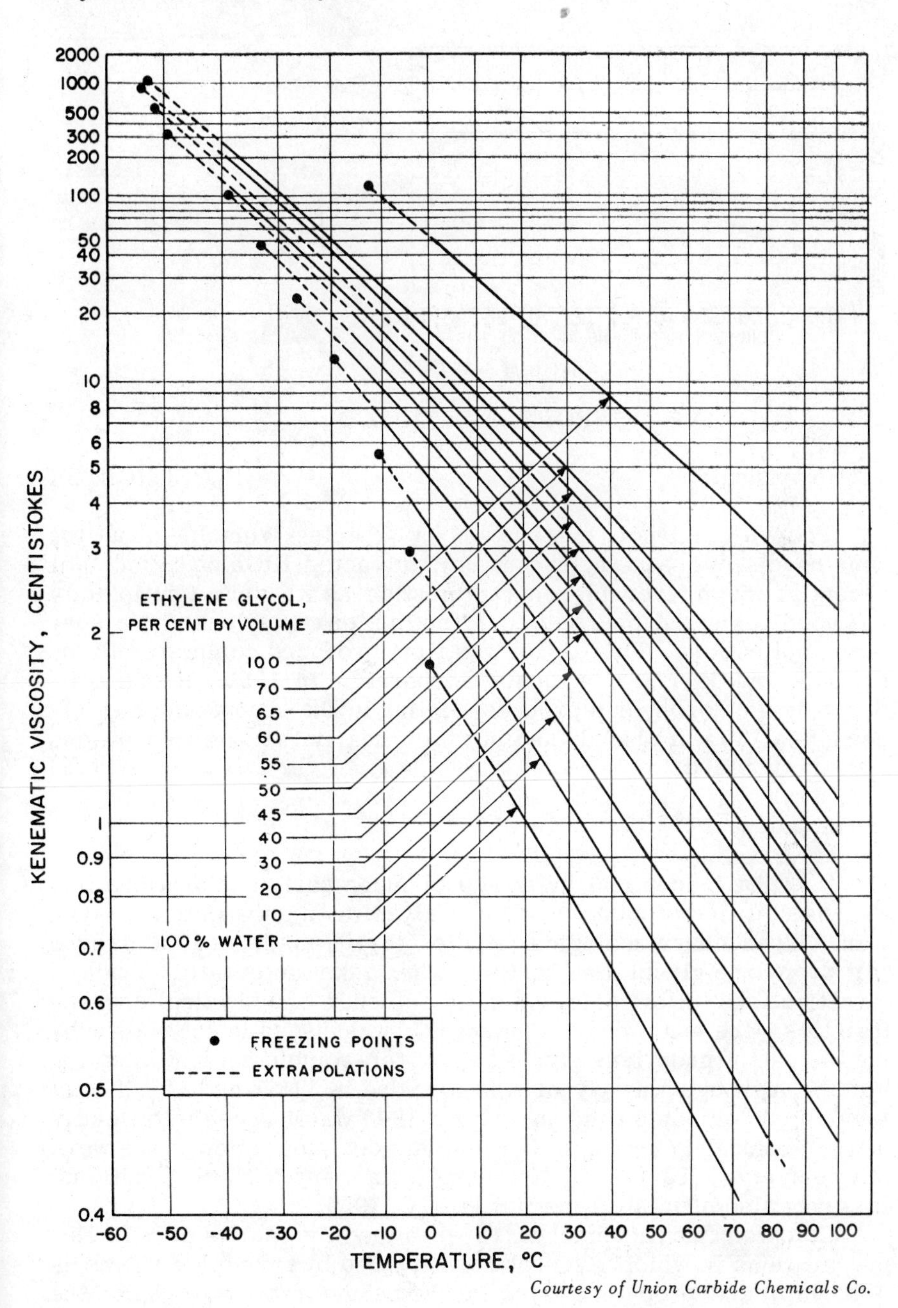

Courtesy of Union Carbide Chemicals Co.

Figure 11. Viscosity of Aqueous Ethylene Glycol Solutions.

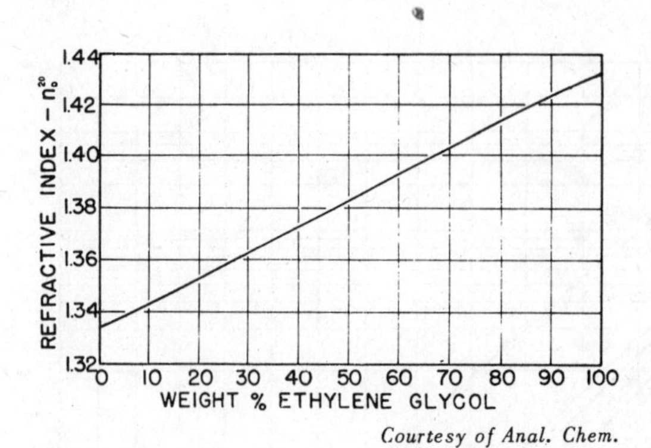

Courtesy of Anal. Chem.

Figure 12. Refractive Index--Composition Data, Ethylene Glycol-Water Solution.

PROPYLENE GLYCOL

1,2-Propanediol $CH_3CHOHCH_2OH$

Propylene glycol, synthesized by Charles Wurtz at about the time he discovered ethylene glycol, attracted little attention until recently. Such favorable characteristics as its very low toxicity and good solvent properties could not be long overlooked for specific applications. This glycol was first produced commercially by Carbide and Carbon Chemicals Corporation in 1931. It was produced by a chlorohydrin process similar to the one by which ethylene glycol was produced, and in which nearly the same conditions were maintained.

Development

The pharmaceutical industry had made early explorations into the possibilities of using propylene glycol as a substitute for glycerol. When pharmacological studies [8-10] made in 1932 proved that propylene glycol was nontoxic when taken internally, a tide of investigations followed in which its solvency and physical characteristics were examined. A patent [11] was issued in 1936 describing the use of propylene glycol as a water-soluble solvent for vitamin D. Although this glycol was included in "New and Nonofficial Remedies" for some time, not before 1943 was it accepted officially by the National Formulary (N.F.). This decision followed the work of Green *et al.* [12] on its effectiveness in many N.F. preparations. It is now also official in the U.S.P. XIV, 1950.

Goldstein and Biermacher [13] examined the merits of N.F. XIV preparations in which glycerol was replaced by sorbitol or mixtures of sorbitol and propylene glycol. The behavior of mixtures in the proportion of 1 to 1 of 70 per cent sorbitol solution and propylene glycol was found to compare with the official solutions. A difference in flavor was evident, however, and this difference was more marked with the use of propylene glycol alone. It was their opinion that such substitutions for glycerol should be considered only as an emergency measure.

Other industries soon joined in the mounting interest in propylene glycol. It was found to be an excellent solvent for flavors, essential oils, drugs, and some fruits and culinary herbs. The antifreeze market claims a considerable share of the available propylene glycol.

Preparation

To meet the increased demand during World War II, Dow, in 1942, began manufacturing propylene glycol in commercial quantities. Induced by the stortage of glycerol and ethylene glycol as a consequence of the greater demand for antifreeze, Wyandotte Chemicals Corporation [19] entered this field in 1948, by manufacturing a product of mixed ethylene glycol-propylene glycol. E. I. du Pont de Nemours Co., before 1949, also manufactured some propylene glycol, which appeared as a by-product among higher alcohols made by the high-pressure catalytic hydrogenolysis of coconut oil glycerides. Celanese Corporation of America also became a producer of propylene glycol in 1950, employing a process of its own which involves the direct oxidation of hydrocarbon gases. In this, propylene oxide is formed by the vapor-phase partial oxidation of such aliphatic hydrocarbons as propane and butane, and then is hydrolyzed to propylene glycol.

The hydrogenolysis of pentose and hexose sugars as a means of preparing lower polyhydric alcohols has engaged the interest of researchers since 1912. The mixtures of polyhydric alcohols resulting from this process have been found to vary with reaction conditions. [14-17, 72, 73] When copper-chromium catalysts are used, the mixture contains little or no glycerol; 60 to 90 per cent of propylene glycol; and small amounts of ethylene glycol, ethanol, methanol, and anhydrohexitols. The use of nickel catalysts increased the glycerol yield from 30 to 40 per cent. An investigation of the hydrogenolysis process using wood sugars [18] was undertaken to provide another means of producing polyhydric alcohols in times of national emergency. Levorotatory propylene glycol has been prepared from hydroxyacetone by yeast reduction. [20]

Properties and Uses

Although the physical properties of propylene glycol resemble those of ethylene glycol, the former differs chemically in that it is a secondary, as well as a primary, alcohol. This glycol occurs in two isomeric forms: 1.3-propanediol, $H_2OCH_2 \cdot CH_2 \cdot CH_2OH$, also known as β-propylene glycol and trimethylene glycol; and 1,2-propanediol, $CH_3CH(OH) \cdot CH_2OH$, and referred to as α-propylene glycol. The former isomer will be discussed in the next section of this chapter.

Propylene glycol is a stable, colorless, odorless and hygroscopic liquid with a sweetish, but slightly acrid, taste. Compared with ethylene glycol, it is slightly more volatile and about three times as viscous at room temperature. Besides the industrial grades of propylene glycol, a U.S.P. grade is available for use in pharmaceuticals and foodstuffs.

Physical Properties and Specifications of Propylene Glycol

Boiling point at 10 mm. Hg	85° C
50 mm. Hg	116° C
760 mm. Hg	187.4° C
ΔBoiling point/Δpressure	0.042° C/mm.Hg
Coefficient of expansion to 20° C	0.695×10^{-3}
to 55° C	0.743×10^{-3}
Evaporation rate (n-butyl acetate—1.0)	0.01
Fire point, ASTM open cup	225° F
Flash point, Cleveland open cup	210° F
Freezing point	-60 (sets to glass below this temperature)
Heat of combustion at 25° C	5728 cal./g. 10,312 Btu/lb.
Heat of vaporization at boiling point at 1 atm.	168.9 cal./g. 304 Btu/lb.
Ignition temperature	421° C
Molecular weight, calculated	76.094
Pour point	-59.5° C
Refractive index, n_D 20° C	1.4326
Specific heat at 20° C	0.593 cal./g./°C
Specific gravity, 20/20° C	1.0381
Δ Specific gravity/Δtemperature, 0 to 40° C	0.00073/°C
Surface tension at 25° C	72.0 dynes/cm.
Vapor density (air—1.0)	2.52
Vapor pressure at 20° C	0.05 mm. Hg 0.08 mm. Hg
Viscosity at 0° C	243 cp.
20° C	56 cp.
40° C	18 cp.
Weight per gallon at 25° C	8.64 lb.

Table 18. Propylene Glycol Specifications*

	Standard Grade	U.S.P. Grade	Air-Treatment Grade	Special Grade
Specific gravity at 20/20° C	1.0370 to 1.0390	1.0375 to 1.0400	1.0375 to 1.0400	1.0380 to 1.0390
Distillation at 760 mm. Hg	Lbp, 185° C, max. 95 ml. 109° C, max. Dp, 194° C, max.	†	†	‡
Propylene glycol, min.	—	97.5% by wt.	97.5% by wt.	99.0% by wt.
Acidity, max.	0.005% by wt.§	0.005% by wt.§	0.005% by wt.§	0.005% by wt. #
Refractive Index at 20° C, n_D	—	—	1.4316 to 1.4335	—
Solubility	—	●	▲	—
Chlorides, max. (as Cl)	0.001% by wt.	0.001% by wt.	0.001% by wt.	0.001% by wt.
Oxidizing substances	—	—	—	none
Carbonyl groups	—	—	—	shall pass test
Sulfates	—	none	—	—
Heavy metals, max. (as Pb)	—	5 ppm	—	—
Lead, max. (as Pb)	—	—	—	0.0003% by wt. **
Arsenic, max. (As_2O_3)	—	1 ppm	—	0.001% by wt. ††
Water, max.	0.5% by wt.	0.2% by wt.	0.5% by wt.	—
Ash, max.	0.005% by wt.	0.005% by wt.	0.007% by wt.	—
Color, max. (Pt-Co Scale)	10	10	15	15
Odor	—	mild	—	mild
Suspended matter	substantially free	substantially free	substantially free	substantially free

*Courtesy of Union Carbide Chemicals Co.

†Shall entirely distill within a 5° C range which shall include 187.3° C.

‡Shall entirely distill within a 5° C range, and 90 ml. shall distill within a 2.2° C range.

§Calculated as acetic acid. This is equivalent to 0.047 mg. KOH per g. sample.

#Calculated as hydrochloric acid. This is equivalent to 0.077 mg. KOH per g. sample.

●Miscible in all proportions with water, acetone, and chlorform at 25° C.

▲Completely miscible in all proportions with water at 20° C.

**This is equivalent to 3 ppm.

††This is equivalent to 10 ppm.

Table 19. Solubility of Some Substantially Pure Compounds in Propylene Glycol*

Compound	Solubility at 25° C, g./100 g. of glycol
Antipyrine	25
Benzene	23.8
Benzocaine	very soluble in dilute aqueous solutions
Benzyl alcohol	25
Bis(2 chlorethyl) ether	144
Bismuth hydroxide	soluble
Bismuth thioglycolate	10.4
Camphor	10.8
Carbon tetrachloride	30.5
Chlorobenzene	29.0
Chlorothymol	soluble
Desoxycorticosterone acetate	soluble
Dibutyl phthalate	8.8
o-Dichlorobenzene	24.1
Diethanolamine	∞
Diothane	5
Ethyl ether	∞
Glycol stearate	very slightly soluble
Hexylresorcinol	soluble
α-Ionone	∞
Methanol	>50
Methyl salicylate	24.7
Monoethanolamine	∞
Paraldehyde	very soluble
Perchlorethylene	11.7
Phenobarbital	soluble
Phenol	∞
Phenothiazine	soluble
Salicyl alcohol	4.2
Sodium bismuth thioglycolate	10.4
Sodium iodobismuthite	6.4
Sulfadiazine	0.3
Sulfanilamide	11.1
Sulfapyridine	3.1
Sulfathiozole	3.1
Thymol	soluble
Toluene	14.0
Trichloro-tert-butanol	>60
Vitamin A	soluble
Vitamin D	soluble

*Courtesy of Reinhold Publishing Corp.

Table 20. Solubility of Miscellaneous Materials in Propylene Glycol*

Material	Solubility at Room Temperature, g./100 g. of Glycol
Animal glue	very slightly soluble
Cassia oil	∞
Castor oil	0.8
Cellulose acetate	insoluble
Clove oil	∞
Coconut oil	insoluble
Cottonseed oil	insoluble
Dextrin	slightly soluble
Dextrin (10% in water)	∞
Glycol distearate	very slightly soluble
Gum damar	slightly soluble
Hydrous wool fat	slightly soluble
Kauri gum	slightly soluble
Lard oil	insoluble
Lemon oil	0.81
Linseed oil	slightly soluble
Methyl orange	0.6
Nitrocellulose	insoluble
Nutmeg oil	1.53
Olive oil	insoluble
Orange oil	0.26
Paraffin oil	insoluble
Pine oil	∞
Rosin	slightly soluble
Rubber	insoluble
Sassafras oil	2.02
Shellac	very slightly soluble
Soy bean oil	insoluble
Sperm oil	insoluble
Sudan III	slightly soluble
Tall oil	9.9
Tung oil	insoluble
Turkey red oil	3.7
Urea	26.0
Bakelite Vinyl Resin AYAF	insoluble
Bakelite Vinyl Resin VYHH	insoluble

*Courtesy of Union Carbide Chemicals Co.

Table 21. Solubility of Flavoring Materials in Aqueous Propylene Glycol Solutions*

Material	Glycol, % by Volume				
	100	80	60	40	20
	Solubility at 25° C, % by Weight Solute in Final Mixture				
Amyl acetate	∞	∞	∞	1.48	1.34
Benzaldehyde	∞	18.97	4.62	1.80	0.82
Cassia oil	∞	3.13	0.85	0.69	0.21
Citral	∞	0.35	0.17	0.10	0.04
Clove oil	∞	1.19	0.26	0.24	0.12
Ethyl acetate	∞	∞	∞	11.65	8.09
Ethyl formate	∞	∞	∞	—	17.45
Ethyl vanillin	14.20	10.80	5.20	1.84	0.79
Eucalyptol	19.90	4.75	1.73	0.35	0.25
Isoamyl formate	∞	5.22	4.51	1.68	1.53
Lemon oil	0.81	0.52	0.32	0.13	0.03
Methyl anthranilate	∞	∞	∞	—	—
Nutmeg oil	1.53	0.34	0.17	0.14	0.11
Orange oil	0.26	0.13	0.08	0.06	0.03
Phenyl ethyl alcohol	∞	∞	∞	18.95	3.11
Sassafras oil	2.02	1.21	0.20	0.12	0.08
Vanillin	20.20	20.10	12.60	5.85	2.09

*Courtesy of Reinhold Publishing Corp.

Propylene glycol is completely soluble in water, alcohol, and ether, and in most nitrogen- and oxygen-containing aliphatic compounds of low molecular weight. It is miscible with acetone and chloroform and only partly miscible with aromatic and halogenated compounds. It dissolves many essential oils, some water-soluble vitamins, dyes, and some perfumes. It is a solvent for drugs containing tannins, saponins, and anthraquinone derivatives, and for morphine. It is a solvent for coal tar, Stockholm tars, calophony, and zein, and is a good solvent for rosin. It partly dissolves shellac and kauri gum and is only slightly soluble in hydrocarbons and raw linseed oil. Propylene glycol will not dissolve vegetable oils, cellulose esters, vinyl resins, polyvinyl chloride, acetate or chloracetate, ester gum, dammar, and rubber. It does not form an azeotrope with water.

Propylene glycol is used as a solvent, humectant, and preservative in food products. It is a good solvent for flavorings, extracts, and food colors, and is therefore widely used in confectionery and bakery products. It is a solvent in elixirs and pharmaceutical preparations in which some water-soluble ingredients are present. It is a solvent and coupling agent in sun-screen lotions, shampoos, shaving creams, and similar products. It is considered to be a

Table 22. Constant Boiling Mixtures*

Components			Azeotrope		
Compound	Specific Gravity at 20/20° C	Boiling Point, °C at 760 mm. Hg	Boiling Point, °C at 760 mm. Hg.	Relative Volume of Layers at 20° C	Specific Gravity at 20/20° C
Propylene glycol dibutyl ether	1.0381 0.7694	187.4 142.1	136	Upper layer 93 Lower layer 7	
Propylene glycol di-(2-ethylhexy) ether	1.0381 0.8121	85† 135†	84†		‡
Propylene glycol toluene	1.0381 0.8683	187.4 110.6	108	Upper layer 98 Lower layer 2	

*Courtesy of Union Carbide Chemicals Corp.
†At 10 mm. Hg.
‡Heterogeneous at 20° C.

more suitable solvent in nasal inhalants and throat sprays than mineral oil, since the latter is found to be dangerous if it lodges in the lungs.

The acceptance of propylene glycol in food products makes it a preferred solvent for high-speed, steam-set inks used for printing paper and cloth wrappers used for packaged foods. Valued for its mutual solubility with water and various oils, greases and organic compounds, propylene glycol is employed as a coupling and blending agent for cosmetics, toilet goods, and textile lubricants and penetrants.

This glycol is also used as a low-temperature heat-transfer medium in brewing and dairy cooling systems and other refrigeration equipment in direct contact with foods and beverages. It is employed in hydraulic fluids as a solvent and coupling agent, where, at the same time, it inhibits the rubber swelling caused by other ingredients present. It is effective in hydraulic liquid formulations based on either castor oil, modified castor oil, or "Ucon" fluids.

Aqueous solutions of propylene glycol are used as permanent antifreeze for automobiles, airplane, and railroad car water systems, and for deicing airplane surfaces and automobile windshields. It is claimed to be superior as an antifreeze to ethylene glycol, on the basis that it is less corrosive and in aqueous solutions forms slushes at much lower temperatures, thus permitting more efficient circulation of coolant.

Propylene glycol is useful in the form of a fine spray to be applied as a nontoxic, bactericidal agent for sterilizing chambers where crowds collect, such as in shelters. [21] It finds further application as a humectant and preservative in the tobacco industry and as an intermediate for the production of resins and plasticizers. As an inhibitor of mold growth and fermentation, it is comparable to ethyl alcohol, and is therefore a valuable preservative, particularly for moisture-containing foods, pharmaceuticals, [11, 98] and cosmetics.

Toxicity studies [22] have revealed that, while the use of propylene glycol as a solvent is apparently justifiable for oral administration in humans, it has produced convulsions when injected in mice. Therefore it is suggested that more thorough investigation is appropriate.

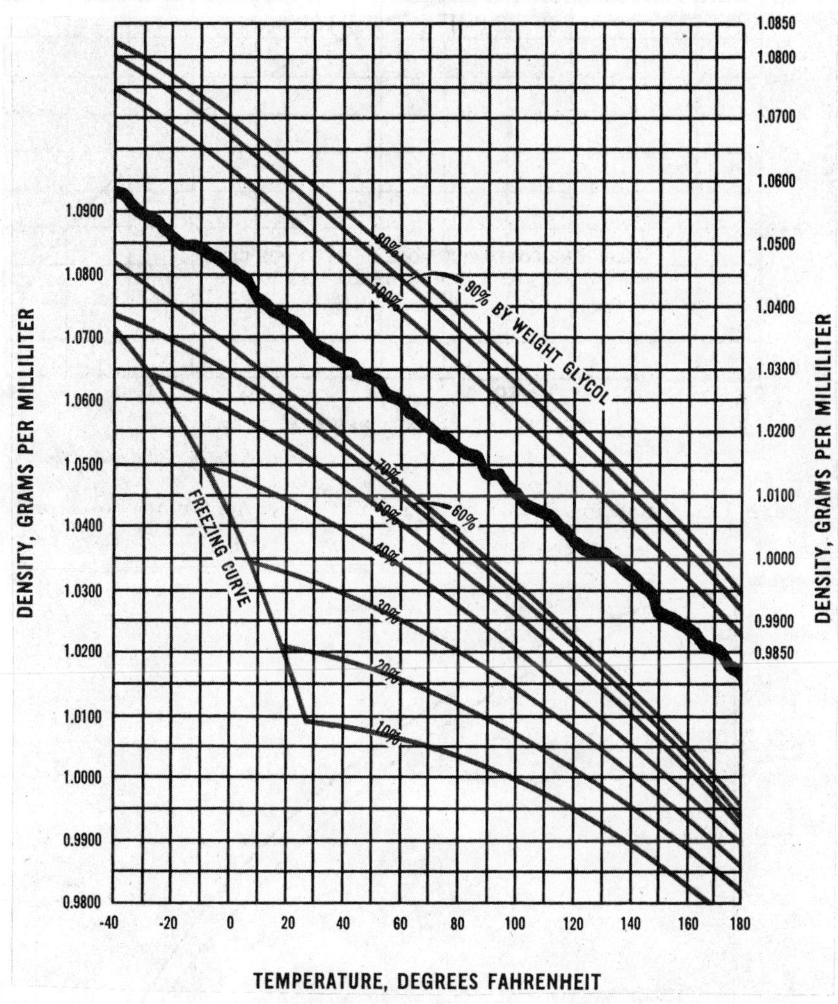

Courtesy of Dow Chemical Co.

Figure 13. Density of Aqueous Propylene Glycol Solutions (Per Cent by Weight).

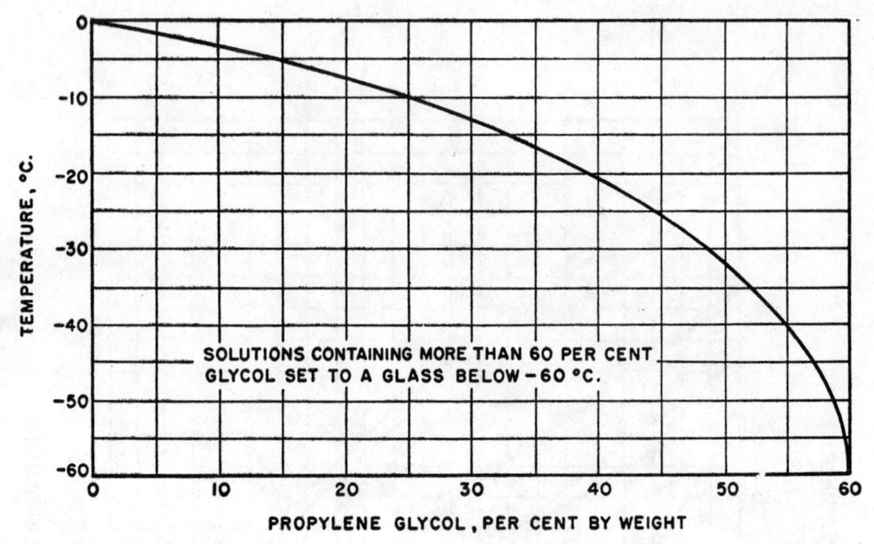

Courtesy of Union Carbide Chemicals Co.

Figure 14. Freezing Points of Aqueous Propylene Glycol Solutions.

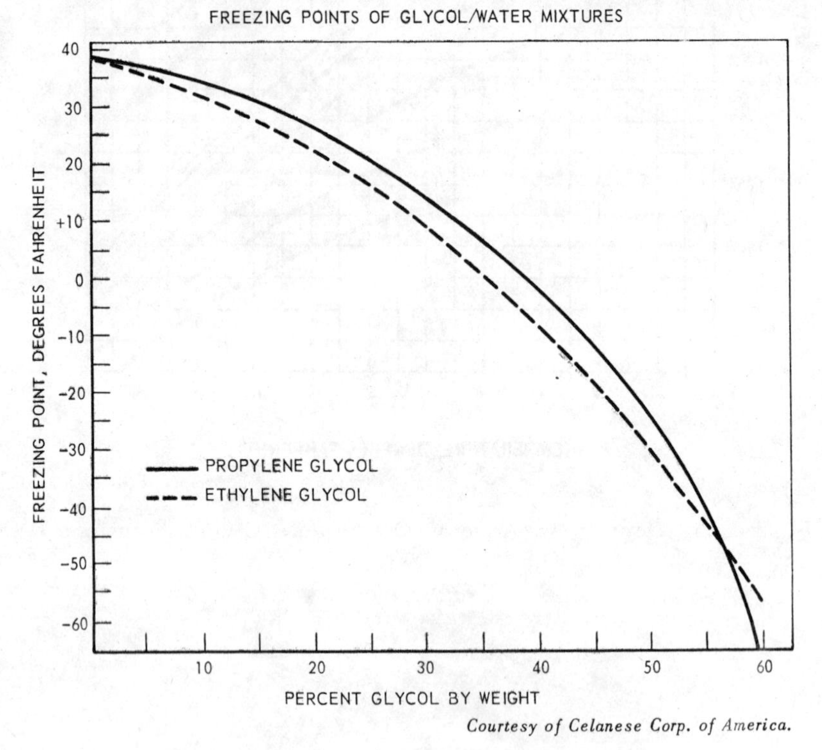

Courtesy of Celanese Corp. of America.

Figure 15. Permanent Type Antifreeze.

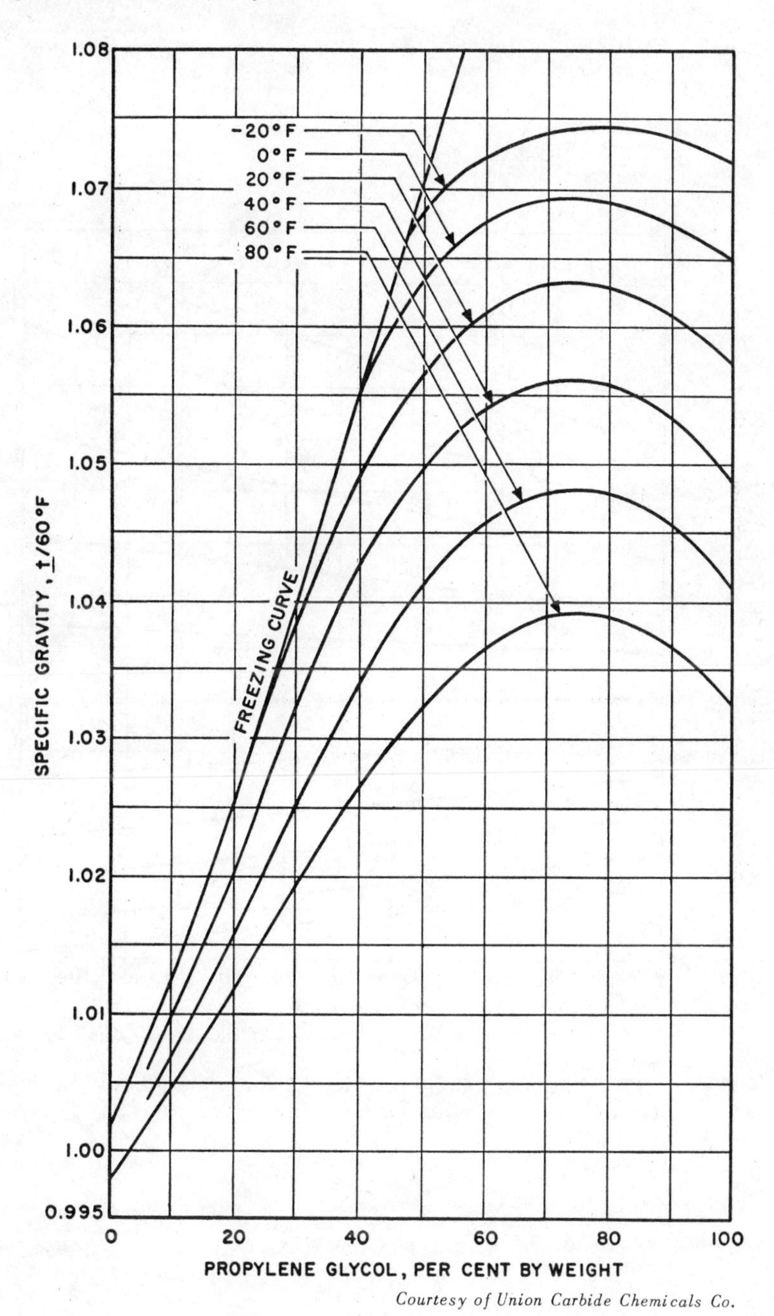

Courtesy of Union Carbide Chemicals Co.

Figure 16. Specific Gravity of Aqueous Propylene Glycol Solutions at Various Temperatures.

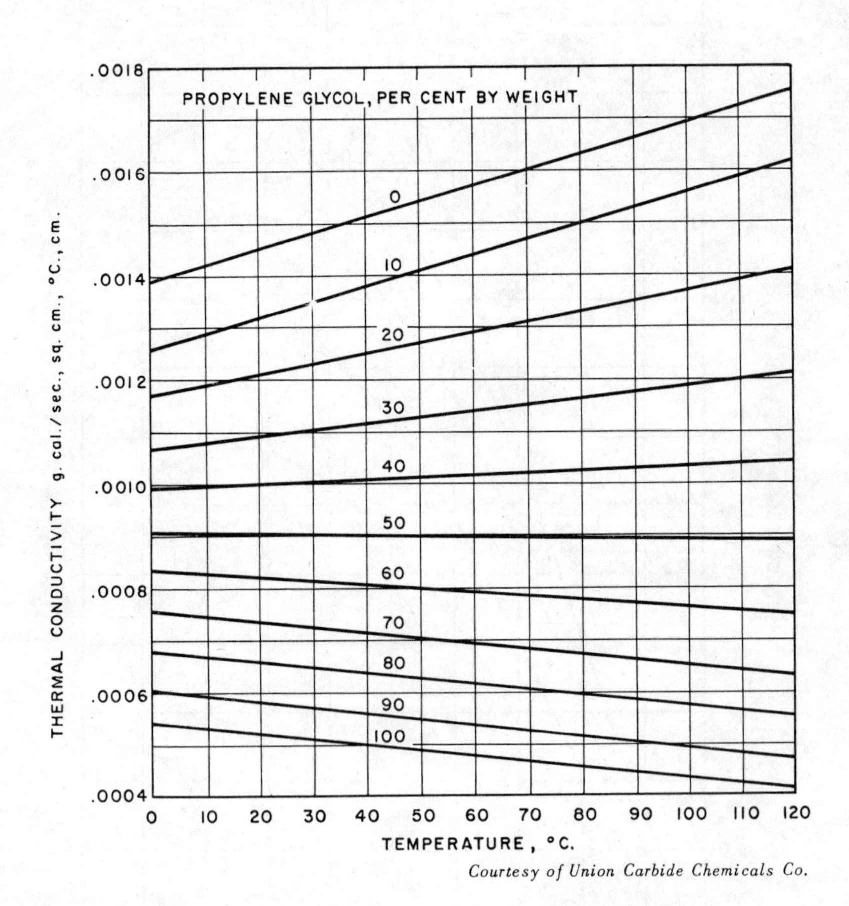

Courtesy of Union Carbide Chemicals Co.

Figure 17. Thermal Conductivity of Aqueous Propylene Glycol Solutions at Various Temperatures.

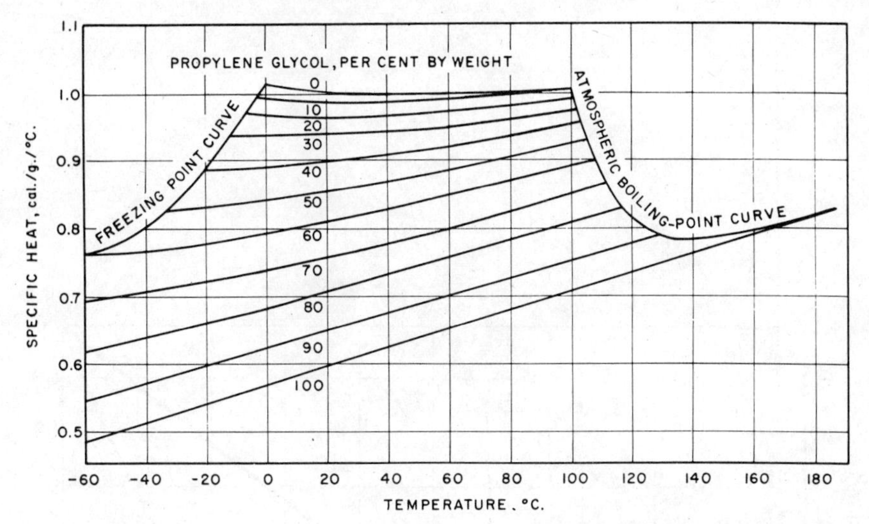

Courtesy of Union Carbide Chemicals Co.

Figure 18. Specific Heat of Aqueous Propylene Glycol Solutions.

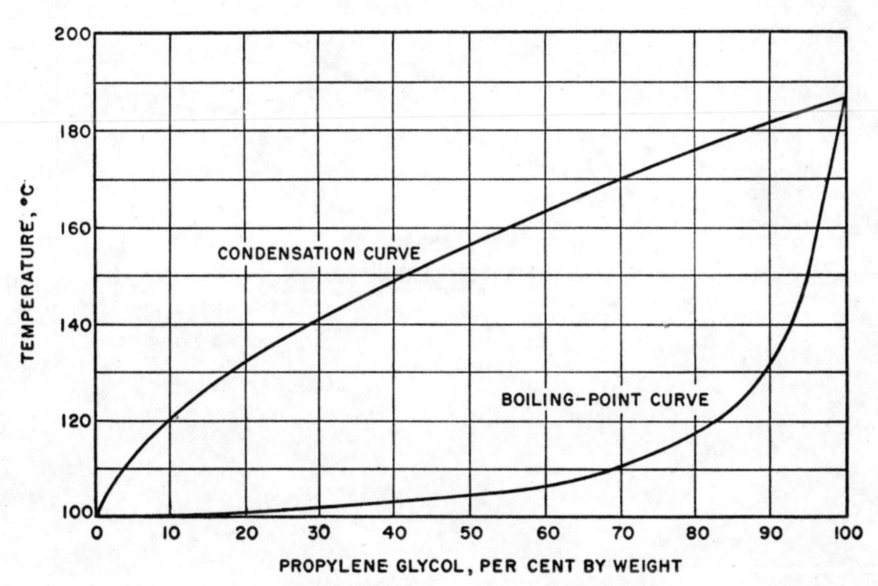

Courtesy of Union Carbide Chemicals Co.

Figure 19. Boiling Points of Aqueous Propylene Glycol Solutions.

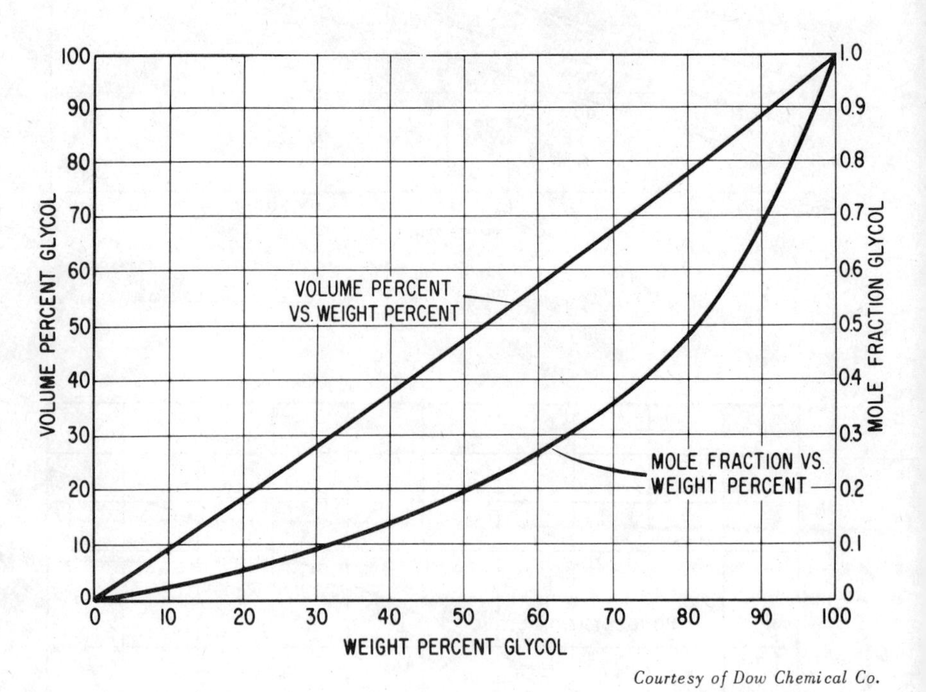

Courtesy of Dow Chemical Co.

Figure 20. Conversion Chart for Aqueous Propylene Glycol Solutions.

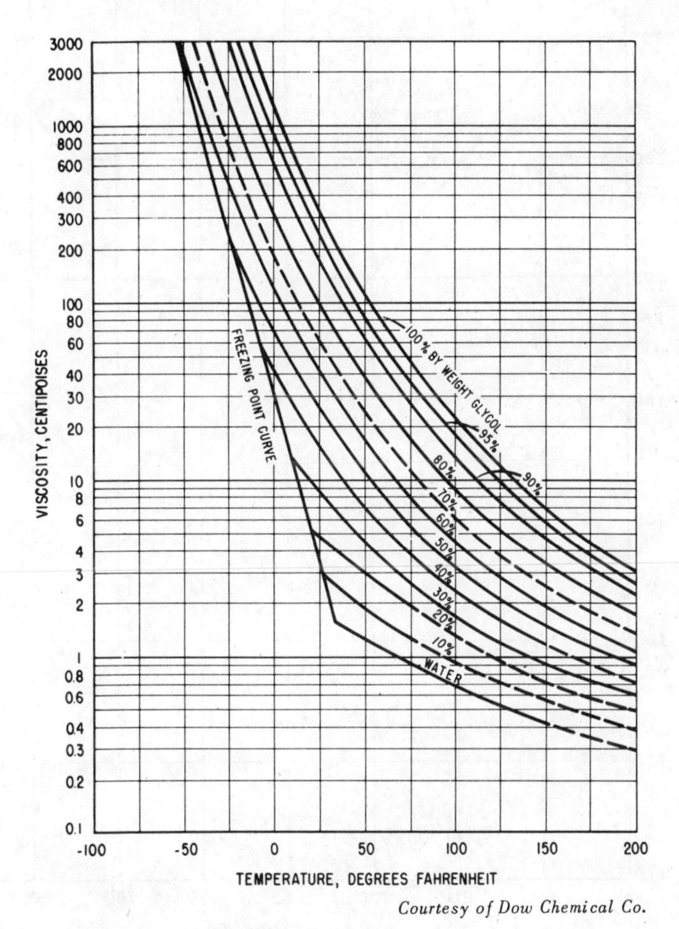

Courtesy of Dow Chemical Co.

Figure 21. Viscosities of Aqueous Propylene Glycol Solutions.

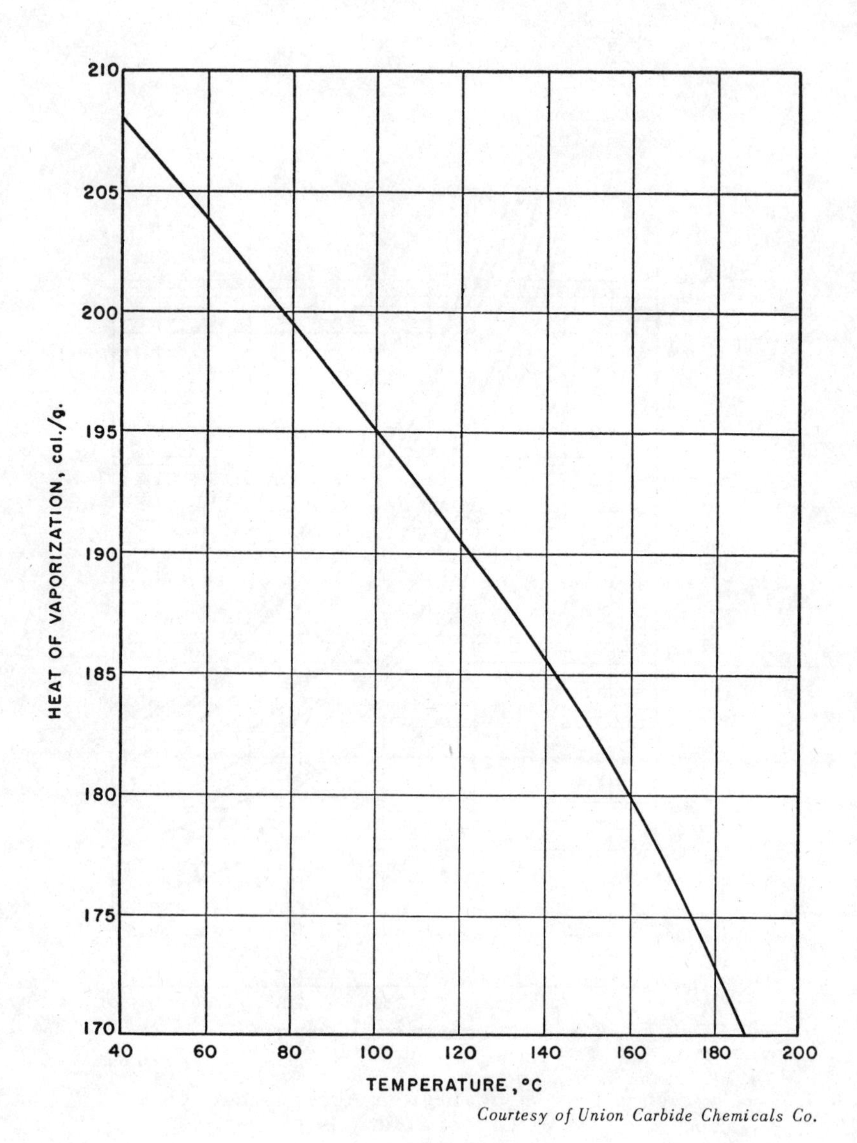

Courtesy of Union Carbide Chemicals Co.

Figure 22. Heat of Vaporization of Propylene Glycol at Various Temperatures.

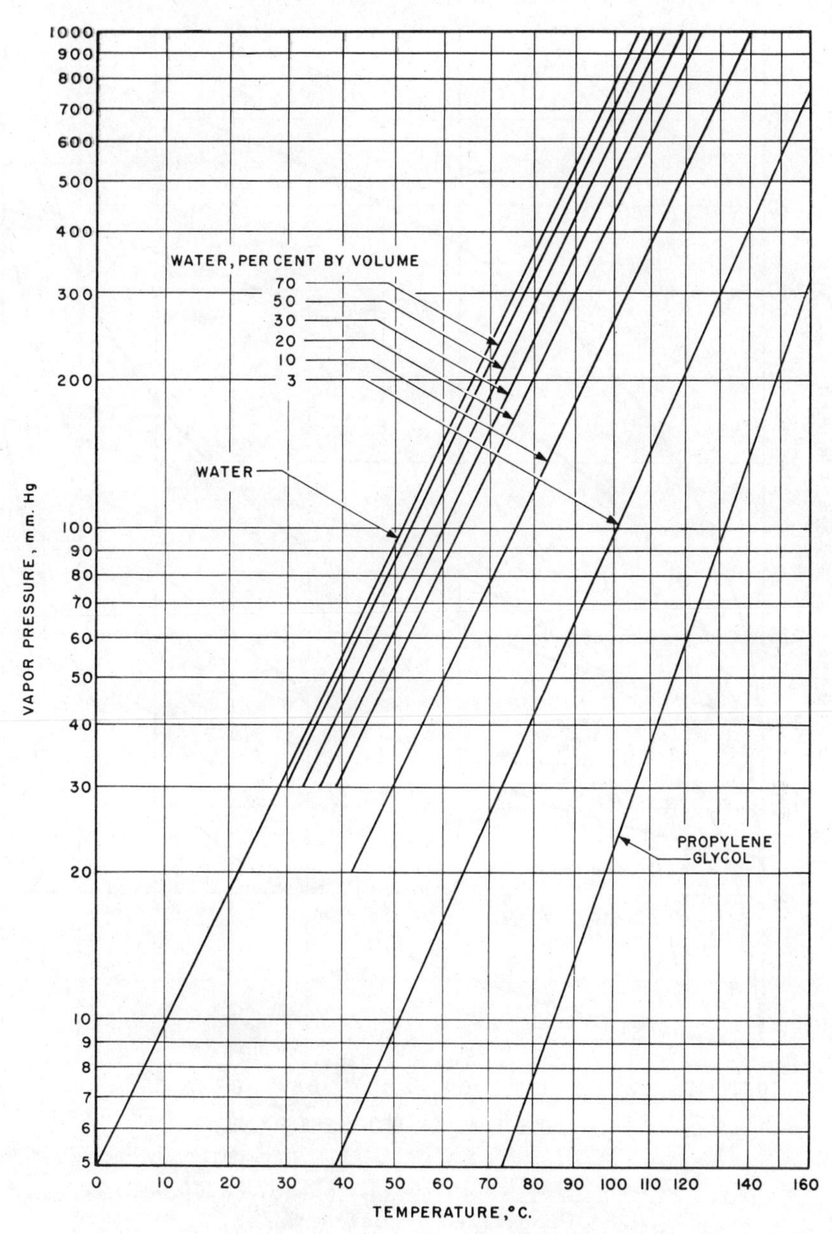

Courtesy of Union Carbide Chemicals Co.

Figure 23. Vapor Pressures of Aqueous Propylene Glycol Solutions.

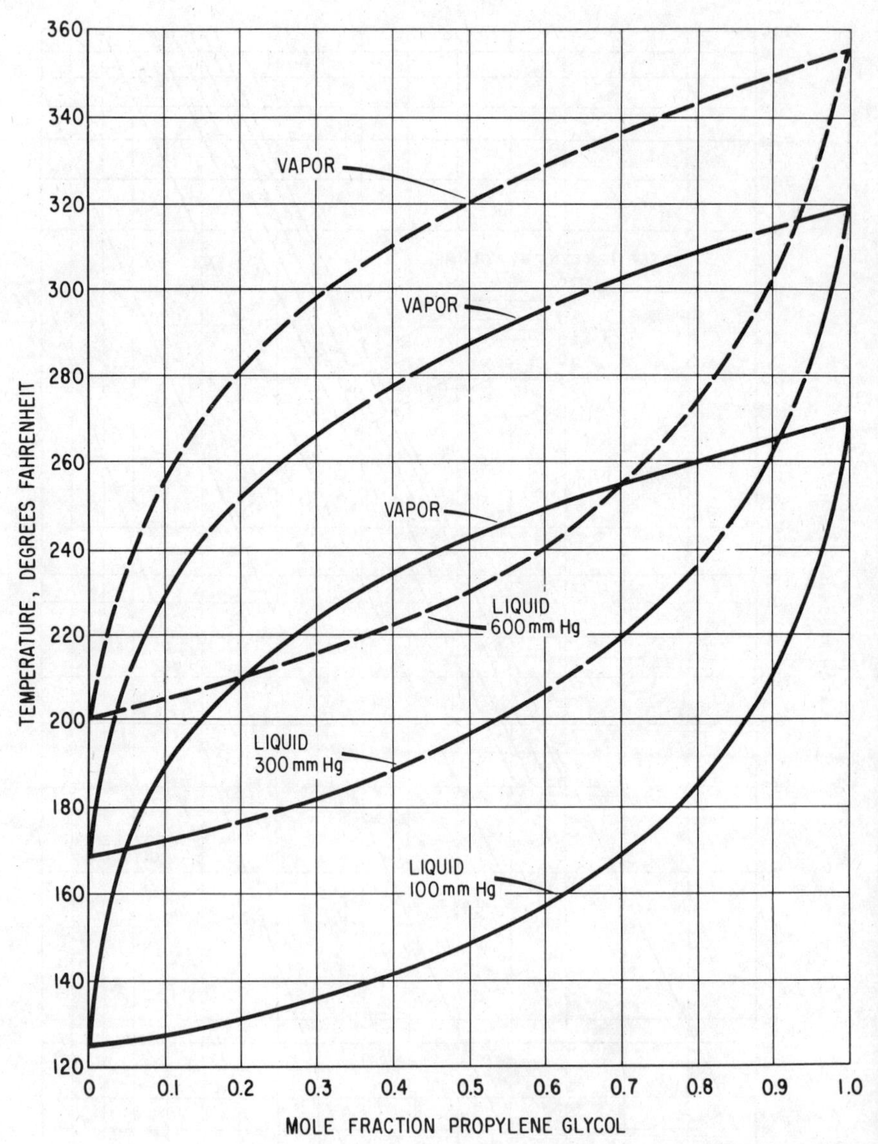

Courtesy of Dow Chemical Co.

Figure 24. Vapor-Liquid Composition Curves For Aqueous Propylene Glycol Solutions.

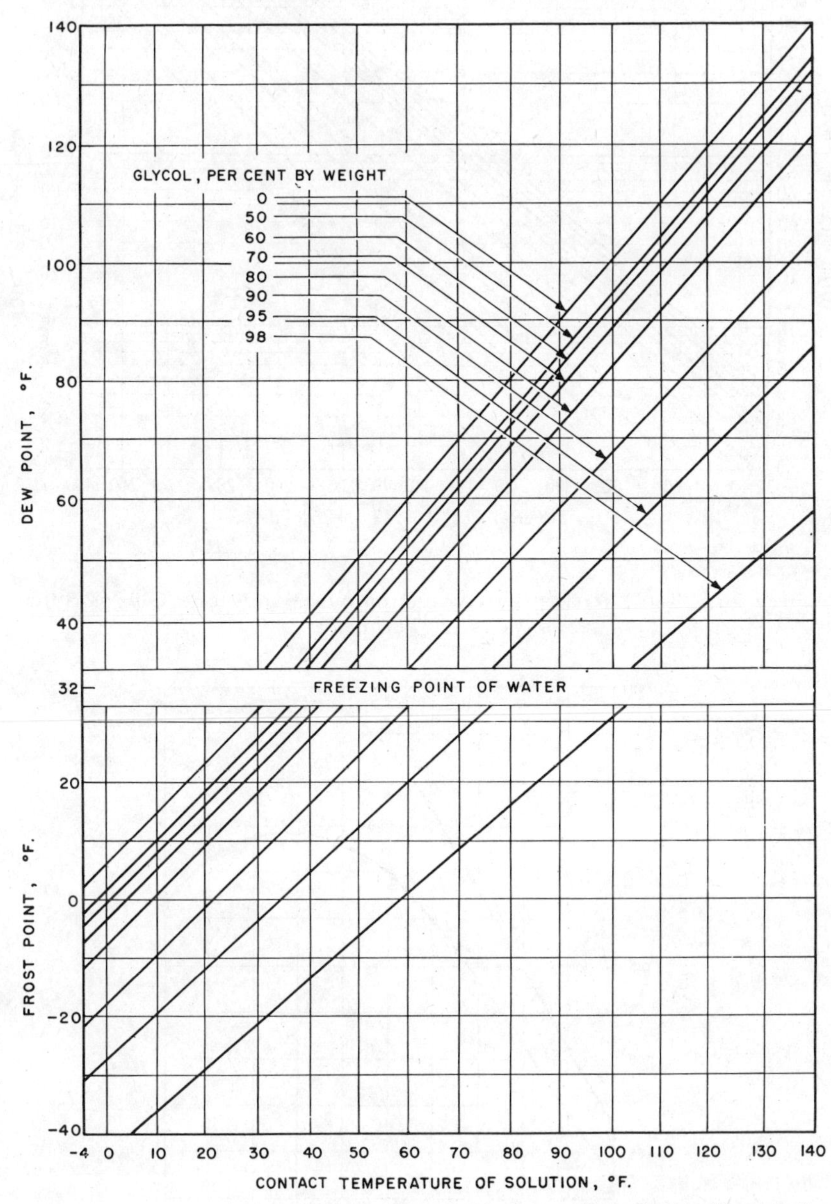

Courtesy of Union Carbide Chemicals Co.

Figure 25. Effect of Aqueous Propylene Glycol Solutions on Dew Points at Various Contact Temperatures.

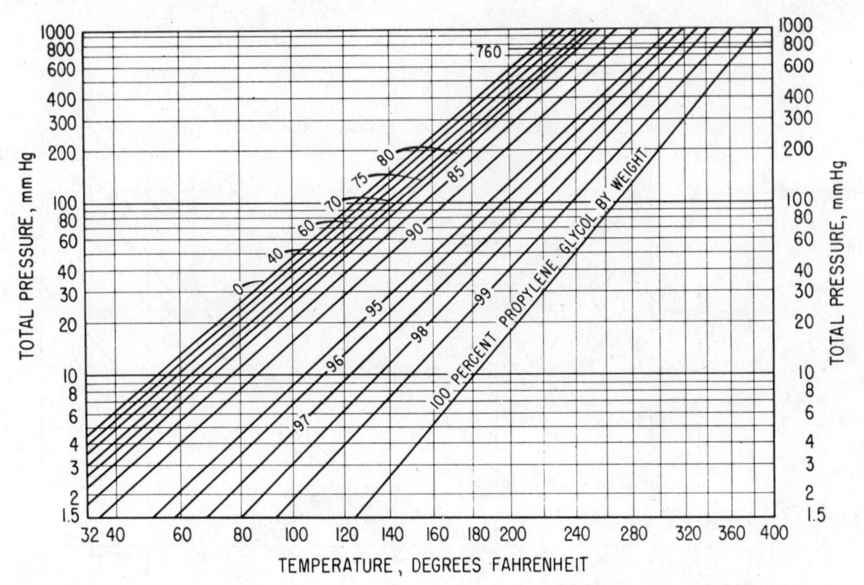

Courtesy of Dow Chemical Co.

Figure 26. Total Pressure Over Aqueous Propylene Glycol Solutions Versus Temperature.

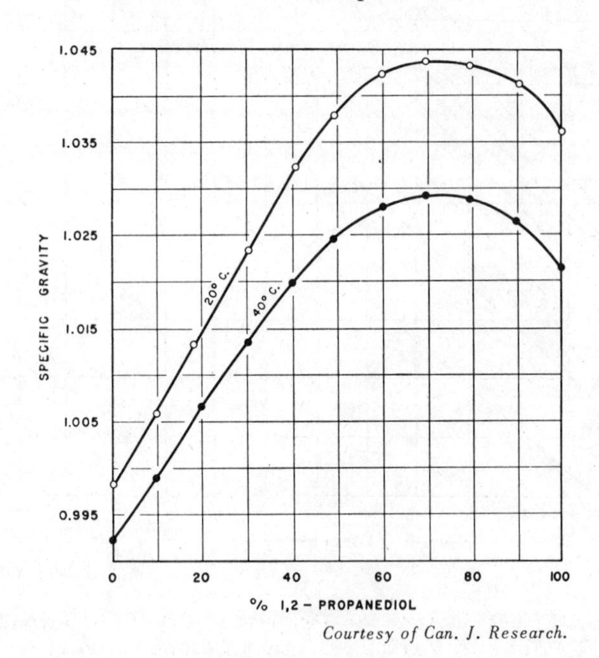

Courtesy of Can. J. Research.

Figure 27. Specific Gravity of Aqueous 1,2-Propanediol Solutions at 20° and 40° C.

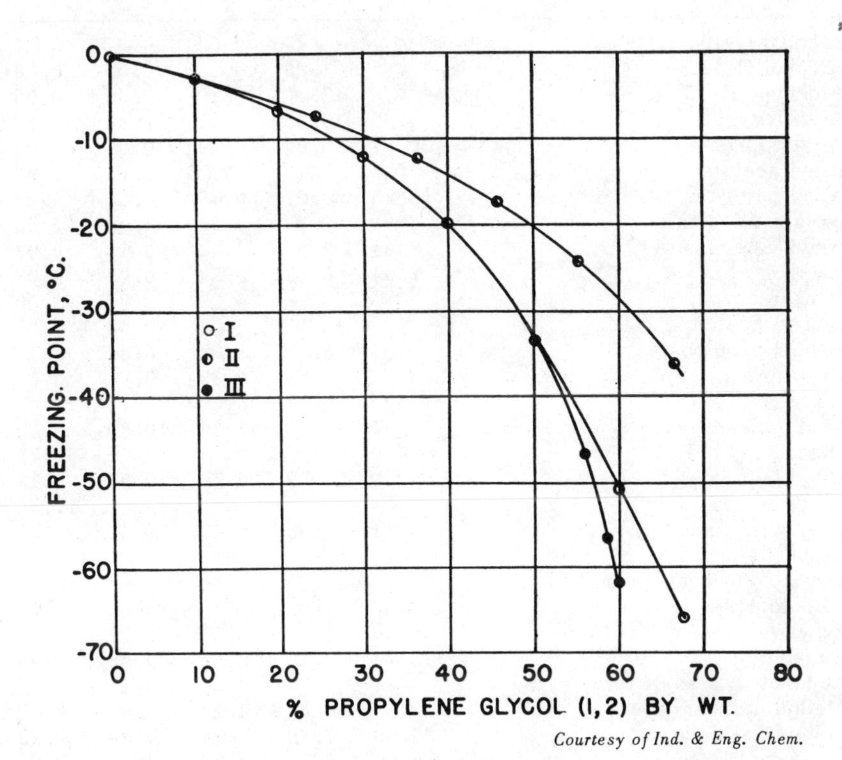

Courtesy of Ind. & Eng. Chem.

Figure 28. Freezing Points of Propylene Glycol (1,2-Propanediol)-Water Mixtures. (I) Observed; (II) Theoretical, without hydration; (III) Theoretical, with complete hydration.

Table 23. Solubility of Synthetic Aromatics in Propylene Glycol-Water Mixtures at 77° F*

Flavorings	Per Cent	Propylene		Glycol	
	100	80	60	40	20
	Solubility in Fluid Ounces Per Gallon of Solvent				
Alcohol C-10	∞	∞	0.52	0.07	0.03
Alcohol C-12	∞	1.29	0.16	<0.03	<0.03
Aldehyde C-16	∞	2.89	0.10	0.06	0.05
Allyl butyrate	45.37	10.35	2.32	0.95	0.50
Allyl caproate	20.87	3.00	0.49	0.06	0.04
Amyl acetate	∞	∞	∞	2.33	1.99
Amyl butyrate	18.25	3.07	0.63	0.25	0.08
Iso amyl formate	∞	8.34	7.20	2.60	2.55
Amyl valerianate	12.04	2.50	0.42	0.12	0.07
Anethol	7.04	0.89	0.34	0.05	<0.03
Benzaldehyde	∞	29.84	6.09	2.32	1.00
Benzyl acetate F. F. C.	∞	10.75	2.55	0.53	0.35
Benzyl propionate	∞	5.30	1.02	0.31	0.14
Cinnamic aldehyde (99-100% pure)	∞	2.24	0.39	0.07	0.03
Citral	∞	0.45	0.30	0.15	0.06
Cyclotene	24.07	23.00	18.86	10.83	6.02
Diacetyl (100%)	∞	∞	∞	∞	26.79
Ethyl butyrate	∞	17.08	4.76	0.43	0.11
Ethyl acetate	∞	∞	∞	19.03	12.79
Ethyl cinnamate	22.96	3.99	0.59	0.10	0.04
Ethyl formate	∞	∞	∞	∞	30.01
Ethyl oxyhydrate (conc. special colorless)	∞	∞	∞	∞	4.46
Ethyl valerate	38.30	11.10	3.51	1.06	1.04
Eucalyptol	35.70	7.16	2.52	0.58	0.43
Eugenol U. S. P. XII	∞		49.2	0.16	0.06
Methyl anthranilate	∞	30.8	4.14	0.57	0.45
Methyl salicylate	24.50	4.79	1.14	0.34	0.22
Palatone	5.89	5.28	4.28	3.14	2.27
Phenethyl alcohol	∞	∞	∞	30.80	4.10
Phenethyl formate	26.20	4.47	0.71	0.18	0.04
Phenethyl propionate	∞	8.55	1.21	0.42	0.25

*Courtesy of Dow Chemical Co.

Table 24. Solubility of Essential Oils and Resins in Propylene Glycol-Water Mixtures at 77° F*

Flavorings	Per Cent Propylene Glycol				
	100	80	60	40	20
	Solubility in Fluid Ounces Per Gallon of Solvent				
Cassia oil	∞	4.06	1.01	0.89	0.25
Clove oil	∞	1.53	0.38	0.25	0.12
Lemon oil	1.25	0.78	0.47	0.20	0.05
Nutmeg oil	0.73	0.446	0.25	0.21	0.14
Ocotea cymbarum	11.58	1.46	0.25	<0.03	<0.03
Oil anise, star U.S.P. XII	3.81	0.80	0.26	0.06	0.03
Oil bay, N.F. VII	1.24	0.23	0.07	0.03	<0.03
Oil bay (terpeneless)	∞	4.36	0.17	0.06	0.03
Oil caraway	3.59	0.71	0.06	0.04	0.04
Oil cassia (terpeneless)	∞	6.75	1.15	0.13	0.07
Oil cloves (terpeneless)	∞	2.88	0.04	0.05	0.04
Oil dill weed	1.71	0.06	0.04	<0.03	<0.03
Oil ginger	<0.30	—	—	—	—
Oil lime (distilled)	2.34	0.23	0.04	0.03	<0.03
Oil mace (distilled) (so-called)	1.605	0.42	0.07	0.04	0.03
Oil peppermint	∞	0.40	0.06	0.03	<0.03
Oil peppermint (terpeneless)	∞	0.73	0.07	0.04	<0.04
Oil petitgrain (terpeneless)	∞	0.98	0.17	0.06	0.03
Oil pimento leaf	∞	1.24	0.21	0.08	0.04
Oil sage (spanish)	2.42	0.28	0.14	0.06	0.03
Oil spearmint U.S.P. XII	1.07	0.06	0.05	0.03	0.03
Oil thyme, white (high-test N.F. VII)	∞	1.35	0.31	0.10	<0.03
Oil wormseed (American chenopodium U.S.P. XII)	13.46	1.07	0.16	0.06	0.04
Oleo resin celery	0.15	0.05	<0.03	<0.03	<0.03
Oleo resin ginger	Immisc.	—	—	—	—
Oleo resin red pepper	Immisc.	—	—	—	—
Orange oil	0.20	0.21	0.13	0.09	0.05
Sassafras oil	2.50	1.56	0.25	0.15	0.10

*Courtesy of Dow Chemical Co.

Table 25. Solubility of Pharmaceuticals in Propylene Glycol, N. F.
(Temperature = 77 °F)*

Material	% Solubility
Drugs and Medicinals	
Acetanilide	2.09
Acetarsone	0.52
Acetphenetidine	2.10
Aloin	4.37
Antipyrine	>55.00
Caffeine	0.77
Chloral hydrate	>89.00
Ethyl carbamate	>57.00
Glycine	< 0.45
Hexamethylene tetramine	11.22
o-Hydroxybenzul alcohol	44.10
Paraldehyde	∞
Pepsin	< 0.08
Phenobarbital (luminal sodium)	>49.00
Resorcinol	55.70
Sodium bismuth thioglycolate	9.4
Sodium iodobismuthite	6.
Sulfadiazine	0.3
Sulfanilamide	7.25
Sulfapyridine	0.50
Sulfathiazole	1.71
Terpin hydrate	18.20
Urea	22.20
Local Anesthetics	
Benzocaine	12.20
Benzyl alcohol	∞
Diothane	5.
Salicyl alcohol (saligenin)	4.
Antiseptics	
Camphor	9.80
Calcium sulfocarbolate	>30.00†
Chlorothymol	70.00
Hexylresorcinol	>80.00†
Menthol	>50.00
Merthiolate	>29.00
Metaphen	< 0.27
Salol	10.50
Thymol	>50.00
Trichloro-tert-butanol	>60.00
Zinc sulfocarbolate	>39.00†
Vitamins and Hormones	
a-Estradiol mg. per cc.	0.5
Ascorbic acid	8.16
Calcium pantothenate	2.04
Nicotinic acid	0.88
Pyridoxine hydrochloride	2.73
Riboflavin	< 0.006
Thiamine hydrochloride	5.14
Vitamin A (12% in oil)	Insol.
Organic Substances	
Acacia gum	< 0.16
Calcium glycerophosphate	< 0.07
Cetyl alcohol	0.23
Pectin	Insol.
Phenothiazine (purified)	< 1.15
Sodium citrate	0.23
Tannic acid	>45.20†
Inorganic Substances	
Arsenious acid	Insol.
Cupric oxide	Insol.
Ferric oxide	Insol.

*Courtesy of Dow Chemical Co.
†Viscosity of solutions prevented further additions of solid.

Table 26. Relative Humectant Values of Propylene Glycol, N.F. (values are given as the per cent by weight of glycol in water solutions that will be in equilibrium with air of various temperatures and humidities)*

Temperature of Air	RELATIVE HUMIDITIES							
	20%	30%	40%	50%	60%	70%	80%	90%
0° F	93.0	88.0	78.0	73.7	70.0	62.5	45.0	
10° F	93.5	87.5	78.0	73.7	70.5	63.0	46.0	30.0
20° F	93.0	87.5	78.5	73.7	71.0	63.0	47.0	30.0
30° F	92.7	88.0	79.5	74.0	71.0	62.0	48.0	30.0
40° F	93.0	89.5	81.0	76.0	71.5	64.0	50.0	30.0
50° F	93.5	90.5	83.0	77.5	72.0	66.0	51.0	31.0
60° F	93.7	90.8	84.0	78.0	72.0	66.0	52.0	32.0
70° F	94.0	91.0	85.0	78.5	73.0	66.5	52.5	33.0
80° F	94.3	91.2	85.0	79.0	73.0	66.0	52.5	34.0
90° F	94.4	91.2	85.5	79.5	73.5	67.0	53.0	35.0
100° F	94.4	91.25	85.8	80.5	74.0	67.0	53.0	35.0
110° F	94.4	91.26	86.0	81.0	75.0	67.5	53.0	33.0
120° F	94.4	91.27	86.5	81.3	75.0	68.0	54.0	33.0

*Courtesy of Dow Chemical Co.

1,3-PROPANEDIOL

Trimethylene glycol

1,3-Dihydroxpropane $CH_2OHCH_2CH_2OH$

B-Propylene glycol

Trimethylene glycol is a colorless to pale-yellow high-boiling liquid, sweet in taste, viscid, and miscible in all proportions with water. It is obtained in commercial quantities as a by-product in the production of glycerol by either saponification or fermentation. Although this solvent was known for many years, it was considered an undesirable impurity in crude glycerol obtained from soap-lye, especially when this mixture was used in making dynamite. The dinitro derivative of 1,3-propanediol is much more sensitive to shock than is trinitroglycerol. It is a good solvent for many organic compounds. [71]

To assess the value of this viscous glycol as a high-temperature coolant, Clendenning [90] blended trimethylene glycol, ethylene glycol, and tetrahydrofurfuryl alcohol. The illustrations that follow indicate the freezing-point data of these anhydrous glycol solutions and the resulting viscosities [91] that were determined.

Physical Properties of 1,3-Propanediol*

Property			
Boiling point at 760 mm. Hg	214° C (210-211° C)		
Freezing points of aqueous solutions, °C			
10%	-2.86		
20%	-6.5		
30%	-11.8		
40%	-18.8		
50%	-27.7		
60%	-40.0		
Molecular weight	78.1		
Refractive indices of aqueous solutions at 20, 30, and 40° C	n_D^{20}	n_D^{30}	n_D^{40}
11.0%	1.3433	1.3430	1.3410
20.0%	1.3540	1.3528	1.3511
30.2%	1.3654	1.3640	1.3623
40.3%	1.3770	1.3755	1.3735
50.0%	1.3880	1.3861	1.3839
60.3%	1.3997	1.3975	1.3951
70.2%	1.4103	1.4080	1.4065
79.9%	1.4205	1.4183	1.4155
89.7%	1.4300	1.4276	1.4250
100.0%	1.4389	1.4364	1.4332
Specific gravity at 20/20° C	1.0554		
at 0° C	1.0625		
at 214° C	0.9028		
Thermal expansion of aqueous solutions between 20 and 40° C (α x 10^3)			
20%	0.39		
40%	0.47		
60%	0.55		
80%	0.60		
100%	0.61		
Isothermal contraction in volume on mixing with water between 20 and 40° C (ml. contraction per 100 ml. of initial volume)	20° C	40° C	
20%	0.37	0.29	
40%	0.90	0.81	
60%	1.19	1.07	
80%	1.01	0.89	

*Courtesy of Can. J. Research.

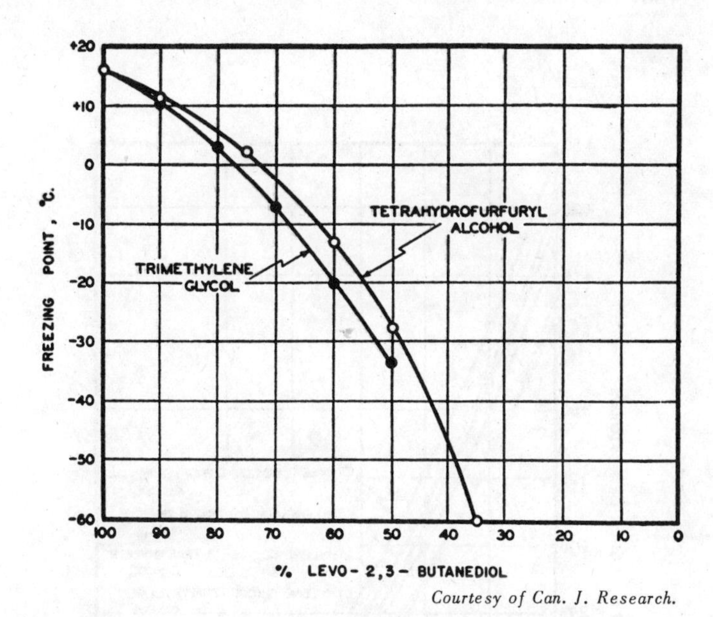

Courtesy of Can. J. Research.

Figure 29. Freezing Points of Anhydrous ℓ-2,3-Butanediol and Trimethylene Glycol Solutions (1,3-Propanediol).

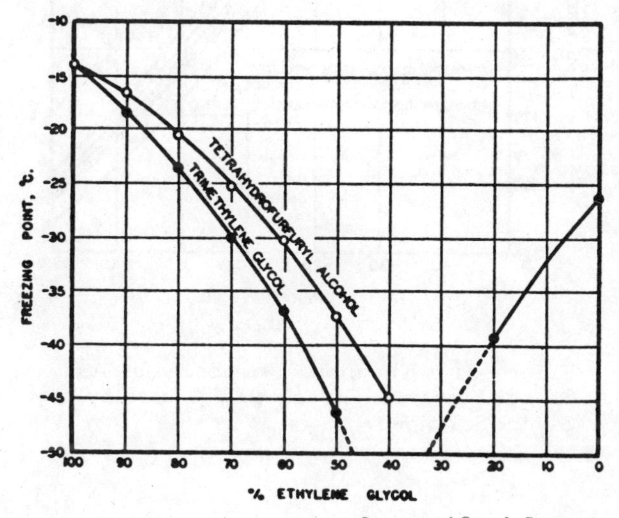

Courtesy of Can. J. Research.

Figure 30. Freezing Points of Anhydrous Ethylene Glycol and Trimethyl Glycol Solutions.

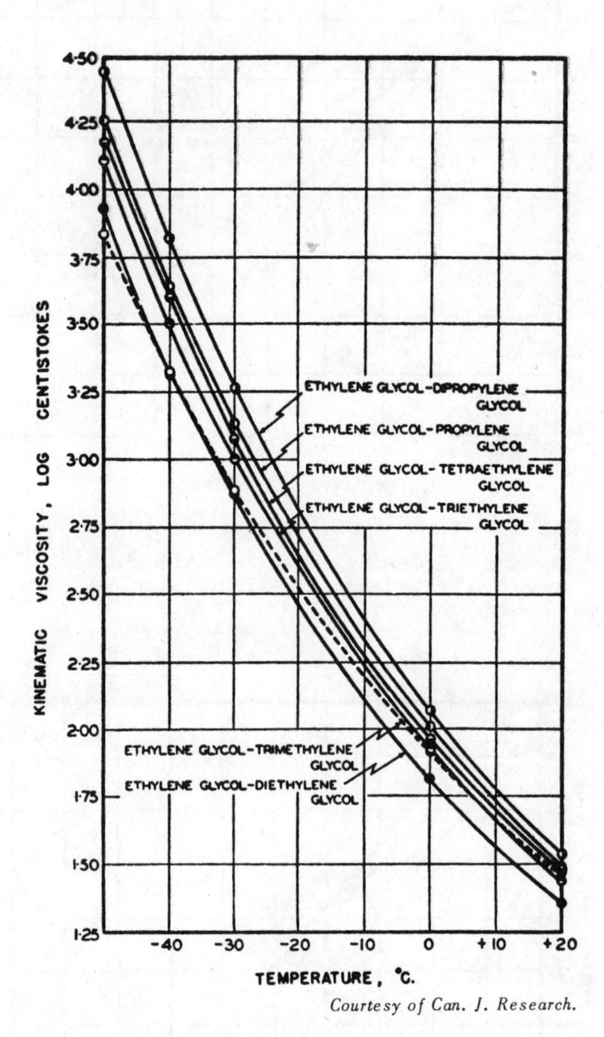

Courtesy of Can. J. Research.

Figure 31. Kinematic Viscosity of Anhydrous Ethylene Glycol and Trimethylene Glycol Solutions.

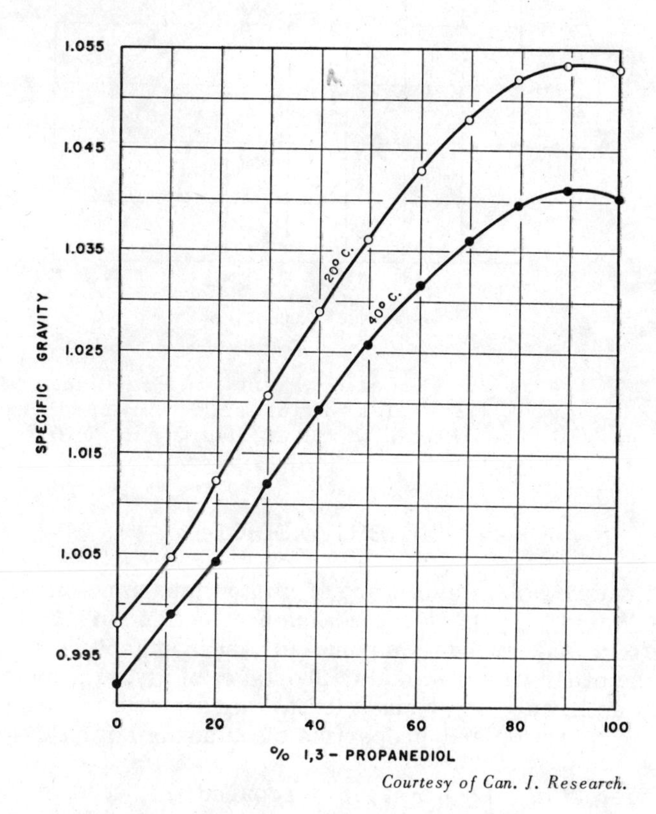

Courtesy of Can. J. Research.

Figure 32. Specific Gravity of Aqueous 1,3-Propanediol Solutions at 20° and 40° C.

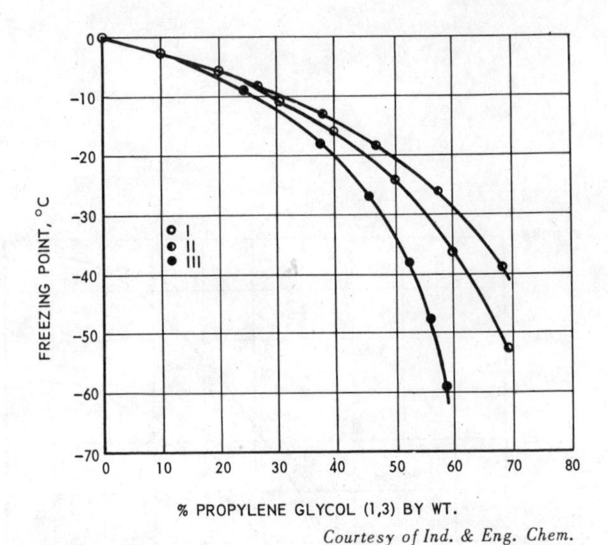

Courtesy of Ind. & Eng. Chem.

Figure 33. Freezing Points of Propylene Glycol (1,3)-Water Mixtures. (I) Observed; (II) Theoretical, without hydration; (III) Theoretical, with complete hydration.

THE BUTANEDIOLS

The butanediols, which were of minor importance until the outbreak of World War II, attracted much attention during the war as a source of a four-carbon compound for the manufacture of synthetic rubber and other war chemicals. Shortages of glycerol and ethylene glycol as antifreeze compounds led to more intensive investigations into the preparation and properties of butanediol for this purpose.

Fulmer *et al.*, [23] in 1933, prepared this type of glycol by bacterial fermentation, and the process was considered to be practicable for producing large quantities of 2,3-butanediol. [74] Fermentation processes were also more compelling, since they could be applied to surplus agricultural products, and thus provide a practical and economical source of appreciable quantities of this compound during a time of emergency. The United States government therefore established a project in which fermentation methods were developed for preparing 2,3-butanediol. This was initiated at the Northern Regional Research Laboratories of the Department of Agriculture in Peoria, Illinois. An exchange of information was made possible with our allies, and similar projects were carried out in government laboratories in Ottawa, Canada, and Australia. Valuable assistance was provided by Joseph E. Seagram & Company, Louisville, Kentucky, and Distillers Corporation, LaSalle, Quebec.

Extensive work followed in which Aerobacter and Aerobacillus fermentations were explored. The bacteria which were found to produce 2,3-butanediol included Aerobacter aerogenes, Bacillus polymyxa, Aeromonas hydrophilia, Bacillus subtilis, and Serratia marcescens. The Aerobacillus polymyxa produced successful fermentations of whole wheat, [24] starch, [25] and barley, [26] forming the pure ℓ-2,3-butanediol isomer as the principal product, and a smaller amount of ethyl alcohol, though in sufficient quantity to make recovery of interest. The use of Aerobacter aerogenes produced a larger quantity of 2,3-butanediol and a smaller quantity of ethyl alcohol, but this diol was a mixture of the meso, racemic, and dextro isomers. [27]

At the close of the war, the high cost of grain and starch discouraged further work in such fermentation processes and cheaper raw materials were investigated. Sugar-beet molasses as a raw material proved to be an excellent substrate when fermented by Aerobacter aerogenes. The fermentation of sulfite waste liquor [28] was also a source of experimentation, and good yields of butanediol and ethanol being obtained with the Pseudomonas hydrophila organism. This produces a mixture of meso, racemic, and levo isomers of 2,3-butanediol. [29]

Because Aerobacter aerogenes will ferment both hexose and pentose sugars, Perlman [30] found it particularly suitable in the fermentation of wood sugar solutions, producing, among other products, 2,3-butanediol. Wood sugar from the hydrolysis of Douglas fir was shown [31] to be suitable for the production of glycols and glycerol by hydrogenation.

Butanediols have long been known to be formed in small amounts during yeast fermentation of glucose. French chemists during the 1880's recorded the isolation of butanediol from yeast-fermented solutions. [32, 33, 34] Neish [35] found the 2,3-butanediol produced by yeast to be a mixture of the levorotatory (at least 67 per cent) and the meso isomers, with the possible presence of a small amount of the racemic form.

Despite the interest and information gathered from investigations of fermentation processes, butanediols are at present prepared on a commercial scale by synthetic methods. In the United States, the isomers available are 2,3-butanediol, 1,3-butanediol, and 1,4-butanediol.

Table 27. Comparison of Butanediol and Ethanol Production and Sugar Consumption by Pseudomonas hydrophila 491 and Aerobacter aerogenes M148 Grown on Normal Strength and Concentrated Liquor "C" Treated with Ammonium Hydroxide. Time = 72 hr. (Yields expressed as g. per 100 ml. of medium)*

Treatment of SWL	Yields		Initial Sugar, %	Residual Sugar, %	Sugar Fermented, %	G. Diol Per G. Sugar Fermented	Diol: Ethanol Ratio	Diol Yield, % of Theory
	Diol	Ethanol						
Pseudomonas hydrophila†								
Normal SWL, pH 6.5	1.27	0.30	3.81	0.79	79.2	0.42	4.25	84.1
Normal SWL, pH 8.5	1.24	0.24	3.81	1.18	69.0	0.47	5.17	94.3
Concentrated SWL, pH 8.5	2.14	0.39	6.89	1.42	75.3	0.39	5.49	78.2
Aerobacter aerogenes†								
Normal SWL, pH 6.5	1.02	0.31	3.80	1.10	71.1	0.33	3.29	75.6
Normal SWL, pH 8.5	0.90	0.33	3.80	0.15	69.7	0.34	2.77	67.9
Concentrated SWL, pH 8.5	1.85	0.54	6.27	2.20	63.3	0.41	3.44	91.0

*Courtesy U. S. Dept. of Commerce.
†No growth occurred in the concentrated medium set at pH 6.5.

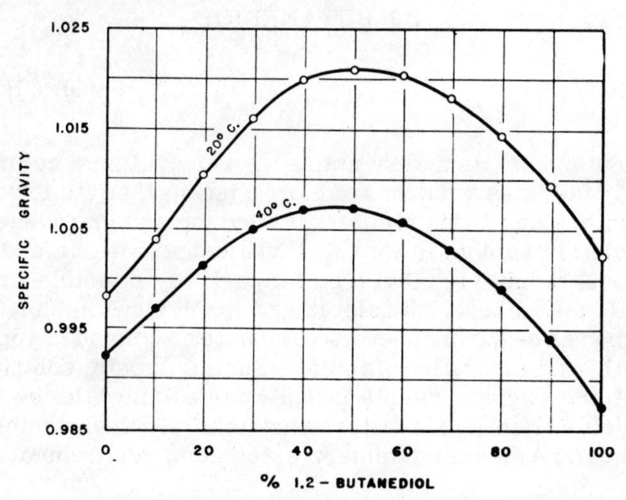

Courtesy of Can. J. Research.

Figure 34. Specific Gravity of Aqueous 1,2-Butanediol Solutions at 20° and 40° C.

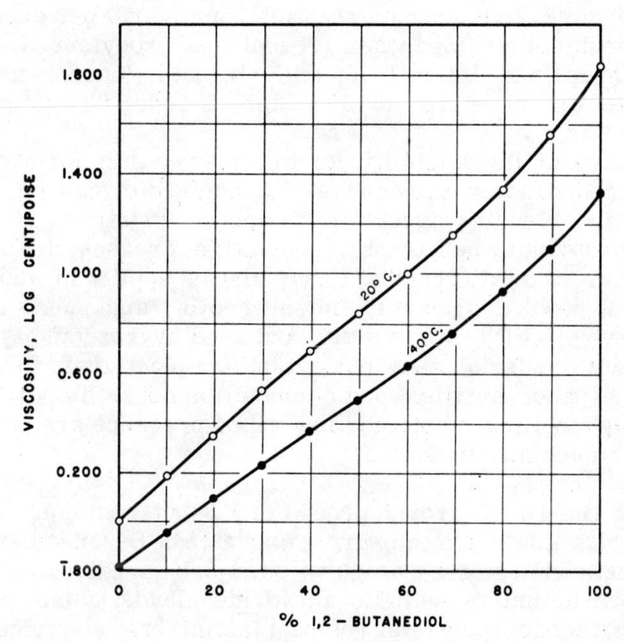

Courtesy of Can. J. Research.

Figure 35. Absolute Viscosity of Aqueous 1,2-Butanediol Solutions at 20° and 40° C.

1,3-BUTANEDIOL

1,3-Butylene glycol $CH_3 \cdot CHOH \cdot CH_2 \cdot CH_2OH$

1,3-Butanediol is a very stable, syrupy, almost colorless and odorless liquid, less volatile and more viscous than its lower homologues, with solubilities similar to ethylene and propylene glycols. It is completely soluble in water, ethyl alcohol, acetone, and methylethyl ketone; soluble in ethyl acetate; partially miscible with ether, castor oil, and dibutyl phthalate; and insoluble in toluol, aliphatic hydrocarbons, benzene, phenol, carbon tetrachloride, mineral oil, linseed oil, and monoethanolamine. Shellac, rosin, colophony, and cumarone are slightly soluble in 1,3-butanediol, while the following are insoluble: cellulose esters and ethers; vinyl resins VYHH, VYNS, and AYAF; gum dammar; ester gum; and rubber chloride.

Celanese Corporation synthesizes 1,3-butanediol by hydrogenating aldol obtained from the hydrogenation of diacetone alcohol, which in turn has been prepared by the aldol condensation of acetone. A method has been developed [36, 75] which converts propylene directly to 1,3-butanediol at temperatures above 70° C with proper control of acid strength and reaction time. A 70 per cent yield of 1,3-butanediol is obtained when 1.4 moles of propylene, 1.0 mole of formaldehyde, and 0.2 mole of sulfuric acid (3 per cent solution) are heated for 17 hours at 130 to 135° C under 830 psi pressure.

Because of its solubility for water as well as for a variety of solvents and organic substances, 1,3-butanediol can be used as a coupling and blending agent for ointments, printing pastes, dyes, textile lubricants, penetrants, protective greases, liquid soaps, hand lotions, and toilet goods. It may also be applied in wood stains, emulsions, wool lubricants, finishing oils, and metal cleaners. Having low volatility, low toxicity, and good hygroscopicity characteristics, it is useful as a humectant and plasticizer for tobacco, cosmetics, paper, textiles, and composition cork. Its solvent properties, high boiling point, and low vapor pressure are used to advantage in specialty inks.

Since the two hydroxyl groups of 1,3-butanediol are not adjacent, dehydration or ring closure is prevented. Because of its longer chain length and steric configuration, 1,3-butanediol is of interest in the production of phthalic anhydride alkyds; fumeric, adipic, maleic, and sebacic polyester resins; plasticizers; electrical potting compounds; cloth, paper, and glass fiber laminates; rosin acid resins for paints, varnishes, and lacquers; and nonionic detergents. It is also of interest in the preparation of the Desmophens, which are diisocyanate polyester hard resins.

Physical Properties and Specifications of 1,3-Butanediol

Acid as acetic	0.005% by wt., max.
Boiling point	207.5° C
Color, APHA	15, max.
Distillation range	200-215° C
Flash point, tag open cup	250° F
Freezing point	Below -50° C
Heat of vaporization	155 cal./g.
Hygroscopicity, weight % water absorbed in 144 hours at:	
25-28° C and 81% relative humidity	38.5
25-28° C and 47% relative humidity	12.5
25-28 C and 20% relative humidity	4.3
Molecular weight, calculated	90.12
Purity	95% by wt., min.
Refractive index at 20° C/D	1.4401
Solubility (% by weight)	
in castor oil	18%
in ether	7%
either in	9%
in ethyl acetate	32%
ethyl acetate in	41%
in dibutyl phthalate	2%
Specific gravity at 20/20° C	1.0062
Surface tension at 25° C	37.8 dynes/cm.
Vapor pressure at 20° C	0.06 mm. Hg
Viscosity at 25° C	104 cp.
at 35° C	89 cp.
Water	0.5% by wt., max.
Weight per gallon at 20° C	8.38 lb.

Table 28. Refractive Index and Freezing Point of Aqueous Solutions of 1,3-Butanediol*

Content of 1,3-Butanediol, % by Weight	$n_D^{25°C}$	Freezing Point °C	Freezing Point °F
19.4	1.3561	-4	+25
39.4	1.3806	-15.5	+4
49.3	1.3922	-25	-13
58.5	1.4032	-37	-35
64.5	1.4093	-42	-44
69.0	1.4138	-51	-60
79.5	1.4237	Viscous	
89.0	1.4319	liquid	

*Courtesy of Can. Chem. Process Inds.

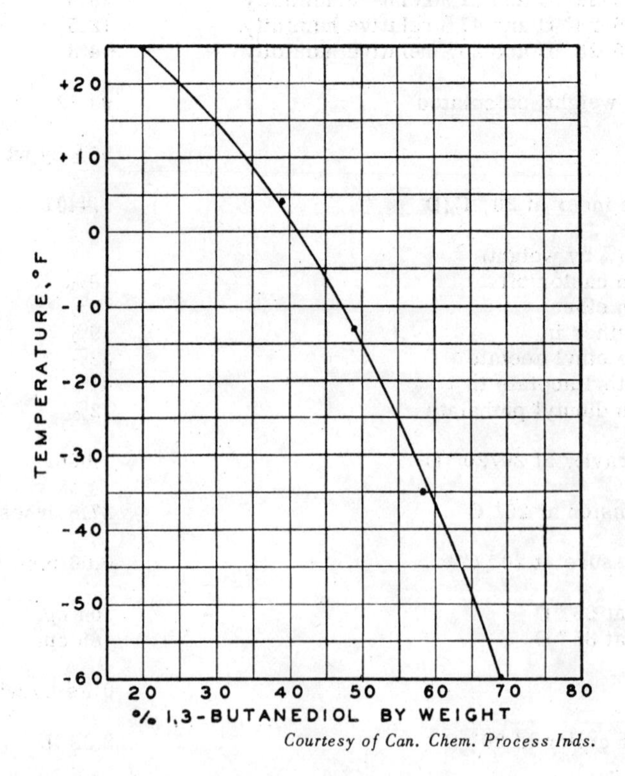

Courtesy of Can. Chem. Process Inds.

Figure 36. Freezing Point of Aqueous Solutions of 1,3-Butanediol.

Table 29. Viscosity of Aqueous Solutions of 1,3-Butanediol*

Content of 1,3-Butanediol, % by Weight	Viscosity, centipoises		
	25.0° C	-171° ± C	-37 ± 1° C
19.4	2.1		
39.4	4.7		
49.3	6.7	95	
58.5	10.2	172	
69.0	16.7	304	
79.5	27.7	620	7,000
89.0	50.8	1,360	18,500
100.0	98.3	3,150	35,000

*Courtesy of Can. Chem. Process Inds.

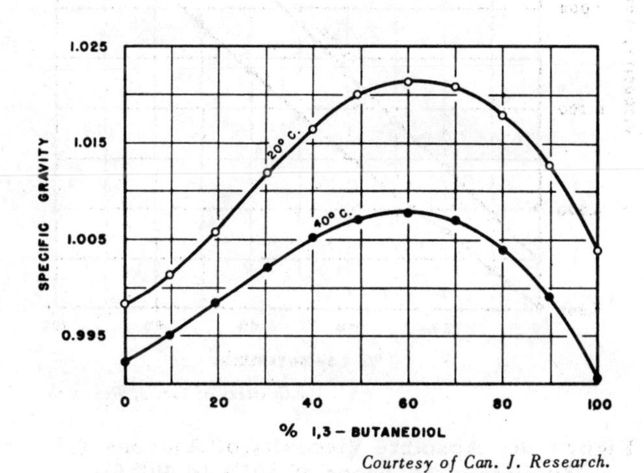

Courtesy of Can. J. Research.

Figure 37. Specific Gravity of Aqueous 1,3-Butanediol Solutions at 20° and 40° C.

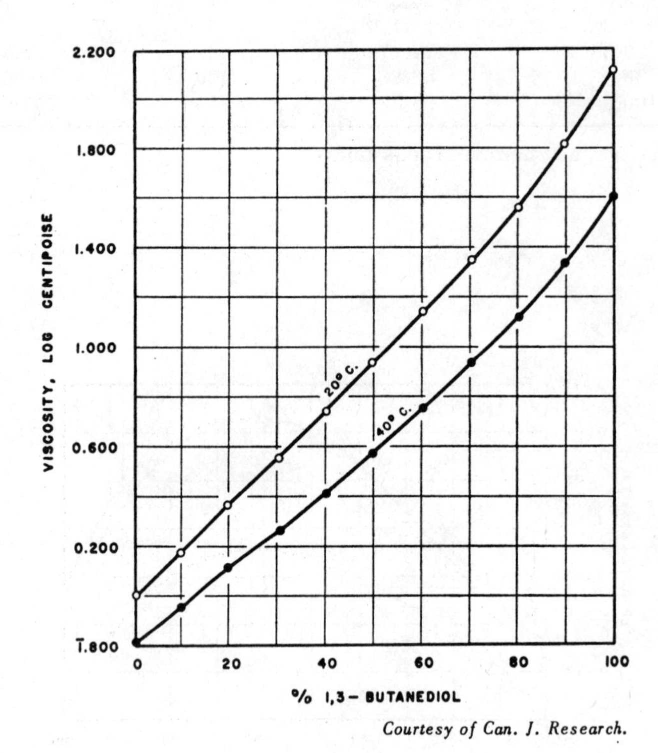

Courtesy of Can. J. Research.

Figure 38. Absolute Viscosity of Aqueous 1,3-Butanediol Solutions at 20° and 40° C.

1,2-BUTANEDIOL

Physical Properties of 1,2-Butanediol

Freezing points of aqueous solutions, °C	
10%	-2.6
20%	-6.0
30%	-11.0
40%	-16.5
50%	-22.4
60%	-29.0

Refractive indices of aqueous solutions at 20, 30, and 40° C	n_D^{20}	n_D^{30}	n_D^{40}
10.13%	1.3452	1.3436	1.3420
19.69%	1.3572	1.3553	1.3534
29.72%	1.3693	1.3672	1.3650
39.79%	1.3813	1.3788	1.3760
49.68%	1.3920	1.3892	1.3865
59.88%	1.4027	1.4000	1.3966
69.37%	1.4120	1.4090	1.4058
79.73%	1.4211	1.4185	1.4165
69.40%	1.4297	1.4265	1.4230
100.0%	1.4375	1.4347	1.4310

Viscosity of aqueous solutions at 20 and 40° C, in centistokes	20° C	40° C
10.125%	1.520	0.910
19.7%	2.187	1.243
29.7%	3.310	1.690
39.8%	4.802	2.311
49.7%	6.739	3.088
59.9%	9.72	4.227
36.4%	13.82	5.744
79.7%	21.37	8.372
89.4%	35.54	12.59
100.0%	68.0	21.25

Thermal expansion of aqueous solutions between 20 and 40° C ($\alpha \times 10^3$)	
20%	0.454
40%	0.654
60%	0.726
80%	0.765
100%	0.775

Isothermal concentration in volume on mixing with water between 20 and 40° C (ml. contraction per 100 ml. of initial volume)	20° C	40° C
20%	1.12	1.01
40%	1.96	1.67
60%	1.92	1.65
80%	1.27	1.10

2,3-BUTANEDIOL

2,3-Butylene glycol $CH_3OH(OH) \cdot CH(OH)CH_3$

Preparation

2,3-Butanediol, a glycol having two secondary hydroxyl groups, appeared in commercial quantities for the first time in 1951, manufactured by the Celanese Corporation of America. It can be prepared by the hydrogenation of the aldehyde and acetaldol. The product has the approximate composition of 85 per cent meso and a 15 per cent mixture of the dextro and levo forms.

It is also prepared by the fermentation of sugars and starch. The production of ℓ-2,3-butanediol on a pilot-plant scale, [42] employing fermentation of whole wheat and barley mashes by *Bacillus polymyxa*, is graphically described in Figure 39. Good yields of butanediol from beet molasses, fermented by the three organisms *Bacillus polymyxa*, *Aerobacter aerogenes*, and *Pseudomonas hydrophila*, have been reported. Since poor results were obtained in preliminary pilot-plant trials with *B. polymyxa*, the other two organisms were used in these tests. A mixture of the meso, racemic, and dextro isomers of 2,3-butanediol were produced by *A. aerogenes*, and a mixture of meso, racemic, and levo isomers were formed with *P. hydrophila*. *B. polymyxa* will produce essentially the pure levo isomer.

Factors affecting the Ford-type strains of Bacillus subtilis fermentation of sugar are complex, and the optimum conditions for a high yield of the desired products are shown to include a temperature of 45° C, 5 to 10 per cent fermentable carbohydrate, nutrients, anaerobic conditions, and agitation. [43]

The fermentation yield of 2,3-butanediol and ethanol varies considerably with the use of different varieties of wheat. In experiments [44] made with these different types and the three strains of *A. polymyxa*, the latter showed individual preferences among different varieties. All of the strains used gave positive correlation coefficients between total yield and starch content, but the coefficient showed significance at the 5 per cent level for only one strain of *A. polymyxa*.

The bacteria which produce 2,3-butanediol by fermentation of carbohydrates also yield some organic acid during the process that inhibits the growth of the organism when allowed to accumulate. It is therefore necessary to neutralize these acids as they are formed by the addition of an excess of calcium carbonate to the medium. This maintains the pH reasonably constant in the range 5.6 to 5.8. [45]

ℓ-2,3-Butanediol, ethanol, and residual solids are the recoverable products of a grain mash fermented by *Aerobacillus polymyxa*. *Aerobacter aerogenes* is used to produce a greater quantity of diol than ethanol. The diol is predominantly the mesoisomer.

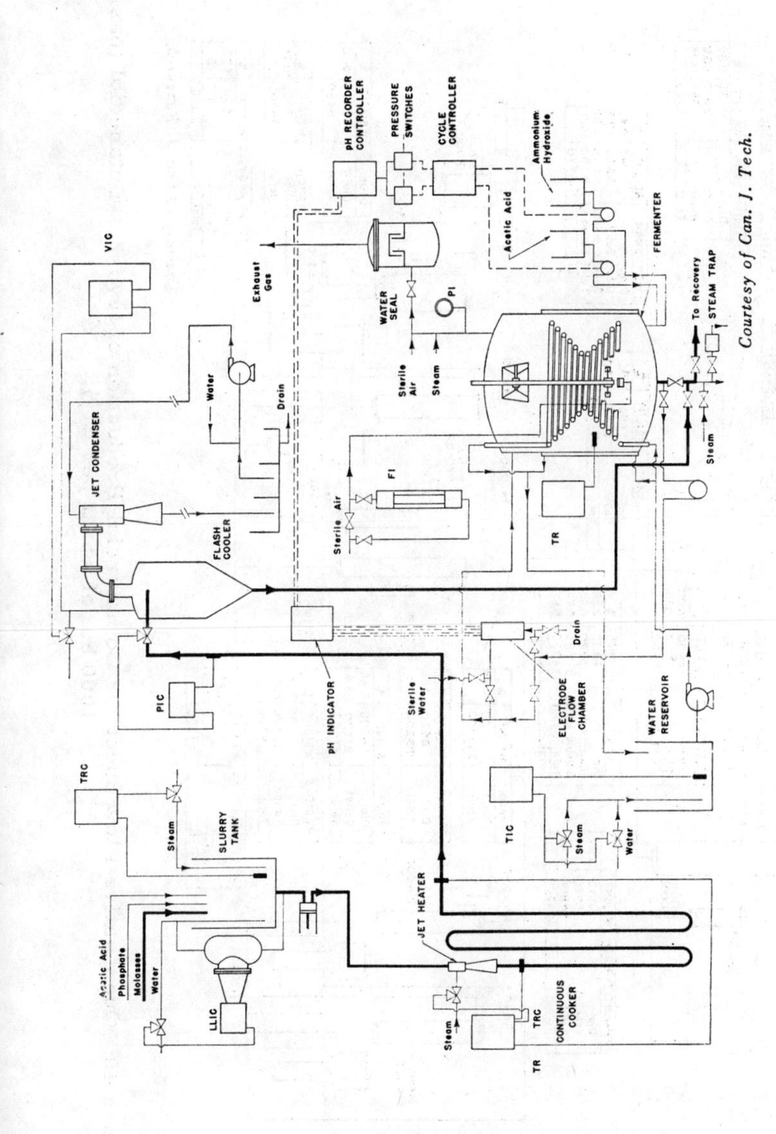

Courtesy of Can. J. Tech.

Figure 39. Flow Sheet of Levo-2,3-Butanediol Production. Flow sheet for fermenter and continuous cooker. T = temperature, P = pressure, F = flow, LL = liquid level, I = indicator, R = recorder, C = controller.

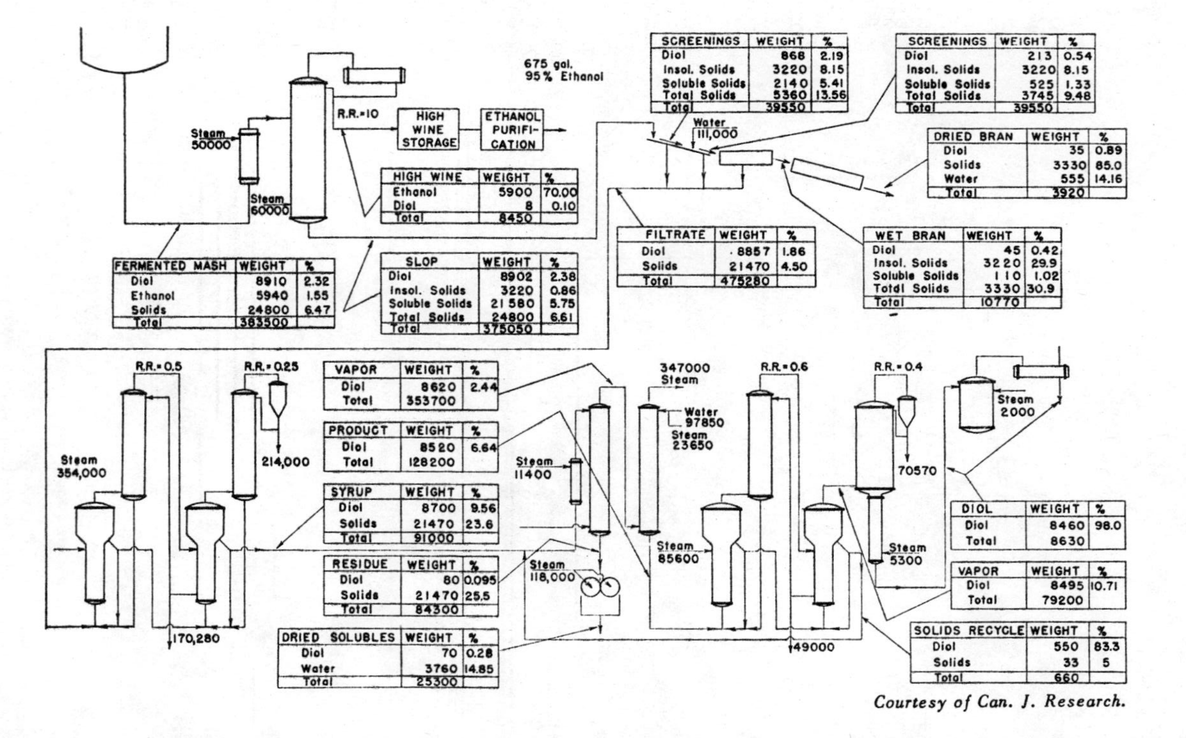

Courtesy of Can. J. Research.

Figure 40. Quantitative Flow Sheet for Commercial Production of levo-2,3-Butanediol (basis: 1000 bu. of wheat per day).

Table 30. Effect of Temperature on the Yield of Products*

	mM. Product per 100 mM. Glucose Dissimilated									
	5% Initial Glucose					10% Initial Glucose				
	Temperature, °C									
Product	30	35	40	45	47.5	30	35	40	45	47.5
Acetion	2.52	8.58	11.90	9.96	7.58	1.81	3.46	1.26	10.95	10.44
2,3-Butanediol	56.97	55.38	50.20	52.88	58.38	59.06	62.52	65.62	58.54	57.92
Glycerol	53.45	46.51	46.22	47.05	44.11	54.94	44.93	44.93	38.70	36.43
Ethanol	11.25	11.23	9.25	10.27	8.31	8.30	10.05	10.51	10.50	9.95
n-Butyric acid	0.21	Trace	0.13	0.22	Trace	0.11	0.24	0.27	0.40	0.38
Acetic acid	0.16	4.58	2.13	1.80	1.20	0.09	0.84	1.16	3.49	3.74
Formic acid	2.00	3.52			3.09	2.73	0.29	2.00		1.34
Succinic acid	0.39	0.57	0.01	0.10	0.45	0.32	0.08	0.35	0.30	0.26
Lactic acid	6.05	8.16	7.07	9.21	8.61	8.81	6.00	5.07	3.46	5.45
Fermentation time, days	6	4	3.5	2.5	2	8	6.5	4	3.5	3
Glucose dissimilated, %	99.8	99.8	99.8	99.7	99.9	98.0	99.6	99.8	99.0	99.9
Glucose accounted for, %	95.4	98.8	94.2	97.0	97.2	97.2	97.0	98.0	97.6	96.1
(D + A)/G ratio†	1.1	1.4	1.3	1.3	1.5	1.1	1.5	1.5	1.8	1.9

*Courtesy of Can. J. Research.

†(D + A)/G ratio = $\frac{\text{Diol + acetion}}{\text{glycerol}}$ ratio. Conditions: Culture No. 453 was grown without shaking with 150 ml. of medium in one liter Erlenmeyer flasks.

Table 31. Fermentation of Mashes Containing 15 g. Wheat/100 ml. Water*

Wheat	Locality	Moisture (%)	Starch (%)	Nitrogen (%)	GS(2) Fermentation		C3(1) Fermentation		GS(7) Fermentation	
					Total Products (%)	Diol/Ethanol	Total Production (%)	Diol/Ethanol	Total Production (%)	Diol/Ethanol
Bencubbin	Georgetown	9.19	51.3	2.122	2.47	0.94	3.49	1.47	3.78	1.50
Bencubbin	Yeelanna	10.36	51.5	1.502	2.56	2.16	3.29	1.46	3.92	1.60
Wango	Georgetown	10.05	47.5	2.316	3.32	1.79	3.73	1.96	3.59	1.59
Wango	Yeelanna	10.81	55.0	1.542	3.60	2.08	3.30	1.29	3.72	1.56
Scimitar	Roseworthy	10.31	55.6	2.461	3.29	1.59	3.40	1.46	3.67	1.78
Scimitar	Sandalwood	10.37	56.7	1.844	3.24	1.75	3.77	1.50	3.76	1.53
Seewari	Georgetown	10.10	50.8	2.428	2.29	1.52	3.62	1.94	3.66	1.62
Seewari	Yeelanna	10.27	59.1	1.654	3.40	2.44	3.32	1.11	4.29	1.52
Ridley	Georgetown	10.42	56.1	2.222	3.23	1.96	3.68	1.56	4.07	1.61
Ridley	Yeelanna	10.63	52.6	1.645	2.35	2.41	3.73	1.46	4.28	1.63
Rapier	Georgetown	9.83	51.0	2.538	3.11	1.66	3.62	1.81	3.57	1.45
Rapier	Yeelanna	10.93	57.8	1.633	3.23	2.23	3.55	1.37	4.10	1.52
Ford†	Georgetown	10.40	49.1	2.673						
Ford	Yeelanna	10.47	59.3	1.822	3.45	2.00	3.60	1.47	3.82	1.77
Dirk	Georgetown	9.58	53.0	2.603	3.14	1.45	3.31	1.63	3.63	1.56
Dirk	Yeelanna	10.68	56.1	1.561	2.84	3.06	3.75	1.76	3.62	1.74
Dundee	Georgetown	11.48	54.4	2.423	3.04	1.90	3.17	1.73	3.38	1.54
Dundee	Yeelanna	10.67	56.8	1.718	3.14	2.11	3.96	1.67	3.62	1.40
Javelin	Georgetown	10.29	56.5	2.030	3.38	2.31	3.79	1.65	3.75	1.68
Javelin	Yeelanna	10.08	59.7	1.651	3.65	2.65	4.15	1.73	4.13	1.53

*Courtesy of Can. J. Tech.

†Mashes prepared from this wheat sample were partly lost due to excessive frothing.

Table 32. Anaerobic Dissimilation of Glucose by Bacillus polymyxa (all fermentations were incubated at 30° C using a medium containing 5.0% glucose and 0.5% yeast extract. The pH was controlled by automatic addition of ammonium hydroxide while anaerobic conditions were maintained by bubbling purified nitrogen through the medium.)*

Product	pH 5.40	pH 5.80	pH 6.20	pH 6.47	pH 6.80	pH 7.17	pH 7.60
	Millimoles per 100 Millimoles of Glucose Dissimilated						
2,3-Butanediol	43.3	51.3	50.5	49.7	44.2	33.2	11.3
Acetoin	2.32	1.77	2.36	1.88	3.48	2.88	4.90
Ethanol	67.4	71.4	73.1	69.3	67.3	75.0	78.9
Glycerol	2.90	3.39	2.84	2.24	3.23	2.02	2.39
Acetone	2.23	0.34	0.38	0.21	Nil	0.33	Nil
Butyric acid	Nil	Nil	Nil	Nil	Nil	Nil	Nil
Acetic acid	1.85	2.11	3.15	6.32	16.59	26.45	46.7
Formic acid	0.47	0.22	2.76	1.61	3.56	4.81	82.6
Succinic acid	1.68	0.79	0.64	0.21	1.67	6.65	4.45
Lactic acid	0.75	1.67	2.12	1.67	1.84	3.20	6.52
Carbon dioxide	183.9	186.5	183.1	187.1	175.3	161.2	78.9
Hydrogen	89.2	68.0	70.4	78.0	84.1	82.1	46.0
Glucose carbon assimilated	32.8	---	---	---	31.9	---	29.6
Fermentation time, hr.	53	30	26	26	26	28	53
% glucose used†	99.6	100.0	100.0	100.0	100.0	99.9	9.44
% carbon accounted for	93.9	94.1	94.8	93.5	98.8	95.0	91.6
O/R index	1.01	1.00	0.97	1.01	0.99	0.98	0.99

*Courtesy of Can. J. Research.

†Determined by direct estimation of the glucose before and after fermentation.

Table 33. Dissimilation of Glucose Under Aerobic Conditions by Strains of Bacillus subtilis*

Product	mM. Product Per 100 mM. Glucose Dissimilated		
	B42†	B43†	B2†
2,3-Butanediol	30.41	30.65	33.35
Acetoin	24.61	30.08	33.63
Glycerol	2.27	1.97	3.66
Ethanol	Nil	Nil	7.38
Formic acid	0.19	0.31	1.03
Acetic acid	4.23	3.64	4.89
n-Butyric acid	8.05	6.52	1.24
Lactic acid	1.76	1.25	1.77
Carbon assimilated	---	---	34.00
Carbon dioxide	285.0	284.0	207.58
Hydrogen	Nil	Nil	Nil
Time of fermentation, days	7	7	8
Glucose dissimilated, %	53.4	53.4	98.9
Carbon recovered, %	93.6	98.3	93.0

*Courtesy of Can. J. Research.

†Named cultures previously described, B42 and B43, Marburg, B2, Ford strain. Conditions: Grown at 30° C using 150 ml. medium in a 1000 ml. Erlenmeyer. Carbon-dioxide-free air was bubbled through at 12 to 14 ml. per min.

Table 34. 2,3-Butanediol Production by Aerobacter Aerogenes (A-5)*

Initial Sucrose Concentration	Sucrose Utilized	Fermentation Time	2,3-Butanediol Yield		
				Per Cent of Theory	
				Sugar Utilized†	Sugar Added‡
1 Per Cent $CaCO_3$ Added With Inoculum					
gm per cent	per cent	hr.	gm per cent		
4.22	90.0	24	1.54	77.3	69.5
5.66	71.0	24	2.01	95.4	67.4
7.35	92.8	48	2.01	56.2	52.1
9.23	90.8	72	2.22	50.5	45.7
10.60	82.5	72	2.16	46.9	38.8
12.10	72.8	72	2.71	58.5	42.7
14.15	63.6	72	3.18	67.0	42.7
16.40	45.2	72	3.64	62.2	42.2
16.40	68.0	96	---	---	---
1 Per Cent $CaCO_3$ Added 91 Hours After Inoculum					
5.76	100.0	191	2.87	94.7	94.7
7.90	95.3	191	3.44	85.8	82.8
10.10	92.3	191	3.89	79.4	73.3
11.80	92.0	236	4.12	72.2	66.4
14.20	65.3	236	3.18	65.2	42.6
15.40	61.6	236	3.67	73.5	45.3
18.50	58.2	236	4.34	76.5	44.5

*Courtesy of Applied Microbiology.
†Based on actual sucrose fermented.
‡Based on initial sucrose concentration.

Table 35. Analyses of Pilot-Plant and Commercial Residues*

	Dried Stripper Residue		Dried Screen Solids	Distillers Grains from Rye	Brewers Grains over 25% Protein	Strained Distillery Slop†
	No. 1	No. 2				
Butanediol, %	1.27	1.58	0.53			
Moisture, %	8.42	11.8	10.7	7.2	7.5	10.0
Soluble solids, %	59.4	55.6	0.0			
Ash, %	11.7	13.5	1.65	3.9	3.5	6.6
Total nitrogen, %	5.59	6.02	1.21	3.7	4.24	4.91
Water soluble nitrogen, %	4.05	4.40	0.21			
Total P_2O_5, %	2.33	2.96	1.33	0.83	0.99	
Available P_2O_5, %	2.21	2.82	1.13			
Total K_2O, %	0.11	0.10	0.07	0.24	0.09	
Total CaO, %	5.4	5.5	0.74		0.16	
Crude protein, % N x 6.25	34.9	37.6	7.56	23.1	26.5	30.7
Fat, %	5.1	5.0	3.4	7.8	6.9	15.4
Fiber, %	2.0	2.3	27.0	10.9	14.6	4.4
Nitrogen free extract, %	37.9	29.8	49.5	47.1	41.0	32.9
Thiamine, p.p.m.	0.0		0.0			
Riboflavin, p.p.m.	1.64		1.3			
Nicotinic acid, p.p.m.	88		6.4			

*Courtesy of Can. J. Research.
†Calculated to a 10% moisture basis.

Characteristics and Uses

2,3-Butanediol, a high-boiling solvent, is an almost colorless and odorless viscous liquid or solid, depending on the isomeric form, with solvent properties similar to its lower homologues, ethylene glycol and 1,2-propylene glycol.

It is completely soluble in water, ethanol, acetone, and methylethyl ketone, and partly soluble in ethyl ether, ethyl acetate, castor oil, and dibutyl phthalate. Is is insoluble in toluol, aliphatic hydrocarbons, benzene, phenol, carbon tetrachloride, mineral oil, linseed oil, and monoethanolamine. Shellac and rosin are slightly soluble in 2,3-butanediol, while the following are insoluble: cellulose nitrate; the vinyl resins VYHH, VYNS, and AYAF; gum dammar; and ester gum.

The mutual solubility of 2,3-butanediol with water and various organic substances suggests its use as a coupling and blending agent for ointments, printing pastes, dyes, textile lubricants, penetrants, emulsions, wood stains, finishing oils for leather, cutting oils, and in metal cleaners. Also, the solubility, low volatility, high boiling point and hygroscopic properties suggest its application as a humectant, plasticizer, and solvent for paper coatings, adhesives, gummed paper, stencil paper, composition cork, shoe cements, artificial leather, abrasive polishes, rust preventatives, warp sizes, dyestuffs, printing pastes, steam set inks, textile lubricants, and specialty soaps.

Its use as a nonvolatile antifreeze has been explored, and a ternary antifreeze solution [37] found to be most effective for this purpose is composed of 40 per cent butanediol-20 methanol-40 water, which can be used at temperatures as low as -50° C. The levo isomer is superior for this purpose, since a 50 per cent aqueous solution freezes at -30° C, as compared to the meso form, which in a 50 per cent aqueous solution freezes at +14° C.

The ability of 2,3-butanediol to dissolve castor oil, and its satisfactory rubber-swell properties, suggest its use as the glycol component of castor oil brake fluids. 2,3-Butanediol is of interest as an intermediate for the production of diacetyl, a flavoring and coloring agent; polyester and alkyd resins; surface active agents; and as the glycol component of rosin and tall oil resins used in paints, lacquers, and varnishes. Since the toxicity of 2,3-butanediol is similar to that of ethylene glycol, it should not be a component in preparations for internal use.

As an antifreeze, a 60 to 70 per cent ℓ-2,3-butanediol solution provides protection against freezing down to -40° C. Among the third components used with ℓ-2,3-butanediol, methanol was found most effective as an accessory freezing point depressant and thinning agent. The other compounds used were ethanol, ethylene glycol, and tetrahydrofurfuryl alcohol. [37]

Physical Properties and Specifications of 2,3-Butanediol

Acidity as acetic	0.005% by wt., max.
Boiling point at 760 mm. Hg	182.5° C
Color, APHA	15 max.
Density of liquid	1.048
Distillation range	175-195° C
Flash point, tag open cup	185° F
Freezing point	19° C (5% water lowers F. P. to +10° C)
Hygroscopicity (% water pickup-400 hrs.)	
25° C and 50% rel. hum.	24
25° C and 75% rel. hum.	33
Molecular weight	90.12
Purity	95% by wt., min.
Refractive index, n_D^{20}	1.4377
Solubility (1% by weight)	
in castor oil	78%
in ether	5%
ether in	5%
in ethyl acetate	14%
ethyl acetate in	9%
in dibutyl phthalate	2%
Specific gravity at 20/20° C	1.0093
Specific heat at 30° C	0.60 cal./g.
Specific tension at 25° C	36 dynes/cm.
Vapor pressure at 20° C	17 mm. Hg
Viscosity at 25° C	121 cp.
at 35° C	90 cp.
Water content	0.5% by wt., max.
Weight per gallon	8.41 lb.

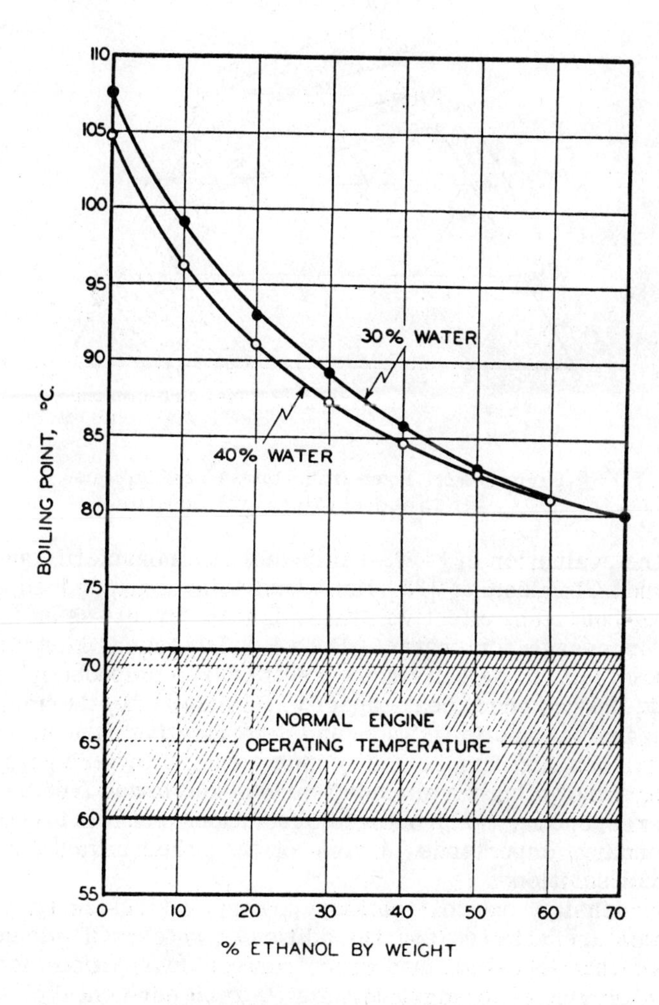

Figure 41. Boiling Points of Aqueous Levo-2,3-Butanediol-Ethanol Solutions.

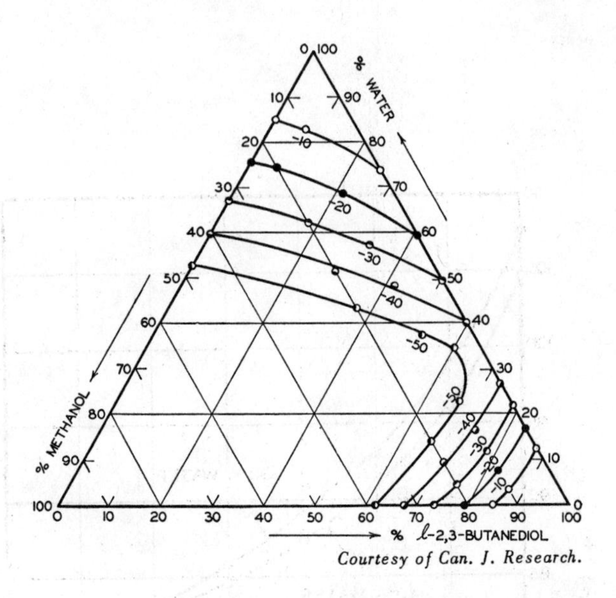

Figure 42. Freezing Points of Aqueous ℓ-2,3-Butanediol-Methanol Solutions.

In the evaluation of ℓ-2,3-butanediol as a nonvolatile antifreeze compound, Clendenning [38] has found this compound superior to glycerol—but less effective than ethylene glycol—as a freezing-point depressant for water. Both ℓ-2,3-butanediol and ethylene glycol are found to be satisfactory antifreeze compounds, judged by stability, permanence, heat capacity, flammability, thermal expansion, expansion on solidification, and deteriorative action on metals, metal finishes, and rubber hose connections. Ethylene glycol solutions have shown higher surface tensions and lower freezing points than corresponding ℓ-2,3-butanediol solutions, but this is considered of secondary importance in view of the other advantages of the butanediol solutions.

The density, optical rotatory power, and refractivity of 2,3-butanediol are affected by the addition of water. Clendenning [41] observed that the levo and meso isomers in solution increase in specific gravity to a maximum in a 50 to 60 per cent diol solution. Higher concentrations cause a gradual reduction. The contraction occurring when 2,3-butanediol is mixed with water is due to temperature, and the levo form contracts slightly more than the meso isomer. The former has a higher coefficient of thermal expansion than the latter. In solution, the levo isomer shows a reduction of specific rotation value from -13° C of the anhydrous compound to -9° C for solutions containing 40 to 70 per cent water. A rise in the specific rotation value is evident on further dilution. An increase in temperature will reduce the optical rotatory power of the anhydrous levo isomer, whereas aqueous solutions of from 30 to 90 per cent show an increase. These experiments indicate that the hydration tendencies are approximately the same in both isomers.

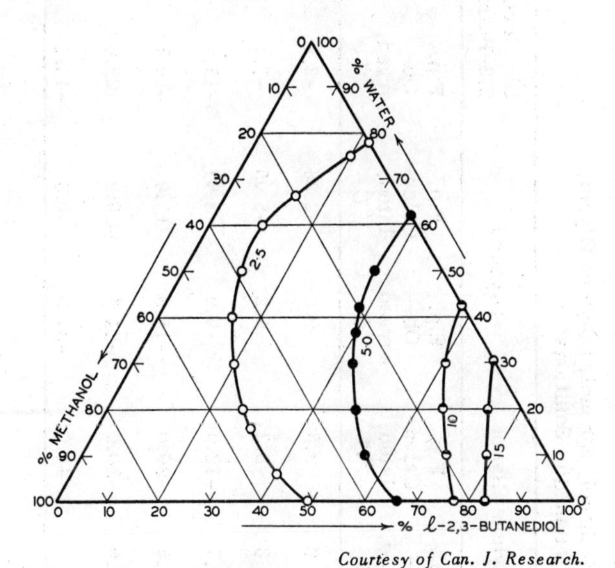

Courtesy of Can. J. Research.

Figure 43. Kinematic Viscosity of Aqueous ℓ-2,3-Butanediol-Methanol Solutions at 20° C, Expressed in Centistokes.

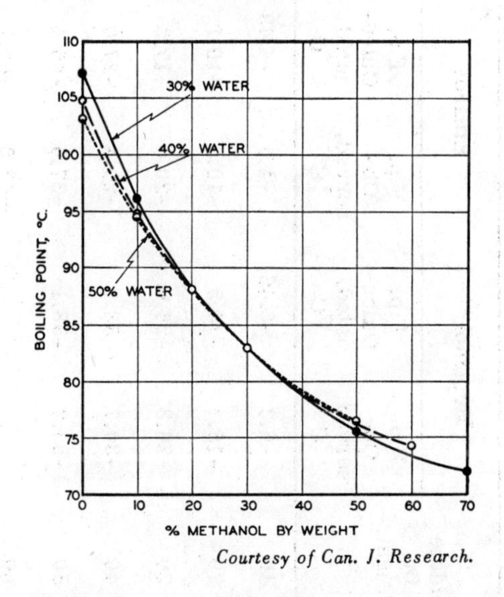

Courtesy of Can. J. Research.

Figure 44. Boiling Points of Aqueous ℓ-2,3-Butanediol-Methanol Solutions.

Table 36. Freezing-Point Data for Methanol, Ethanol, Ethylene Glycol, Glycerol, and levo-2,3-Butanediol Solutions*

Solute by Weight, %	Methanol		Ethanol		Ethylene Glycol		Glycerol		levo-2,3-Butanediol	
	F.p. Observed, °C	F.p. Calculated, °C	F.p. Observed, °C	F.p. Calculated, °C	F.p. Observed, °C	F.p. Calculated, °C	F.p. Observed, °C	F.p. Calculated, °C	F.p. Observed, °C	F.p. Calculated, °C
10	-6.3	-6.46	-4.5	-4.49	-3.6	-3.33	-2.0	-2.25	-3.1	-2.30
20	-15.3	-14.5	-10.5	-10.1	-8.3	-8.27	-5.2	-5.05	-7.1	-5.17
30	-26.3	-24.9	-20.0	-17.3	-14.7	-12.9	-9.9	-8.67	-12.4	-8.85
40	-39.7	-38.8	-29.4	-27.0	-23.5	-20.0	-15.9	-12.0	-19.4	-14.3
50	-55.2	-58.1	-37.0	-40.4	-35.0	-30.0	-24.6	-20.2	-29.6	-20.7
60			-43.8	-60.7	-50	-45.0	-37.9	-30.3	-40.4	-31.0

*Courtesy of Can. J. Research.

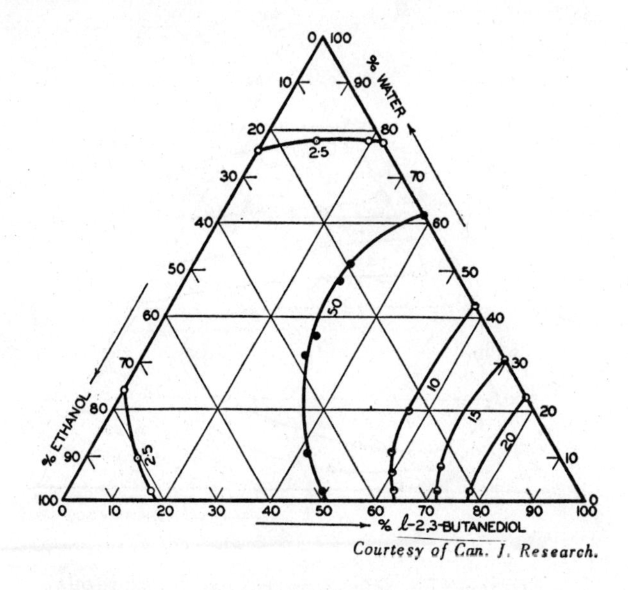

Courtesy of Can. J. Research.

Figure 45. Kinematic Viscosity of Aqueous l-2,3-Butanediol-Ethanol Solutions at 20° C, Expressed in Centistokes.

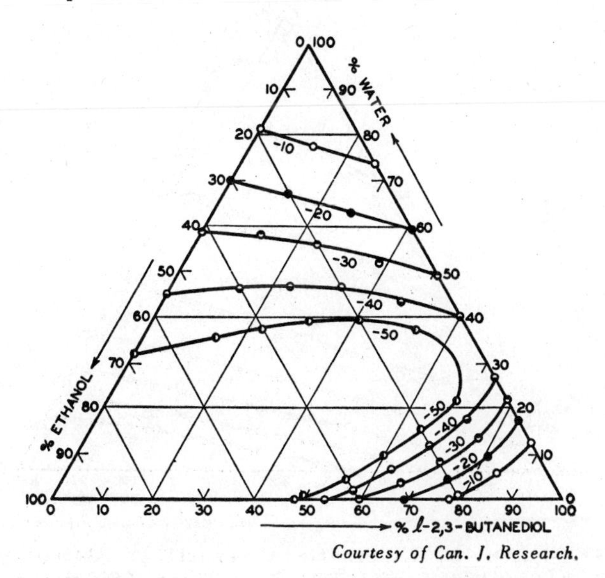

Courtesy of Can. J. Research.

Figure 46. Freezing Points of Aqueous l-2,3-Butanediol-Ethanol Solutions.

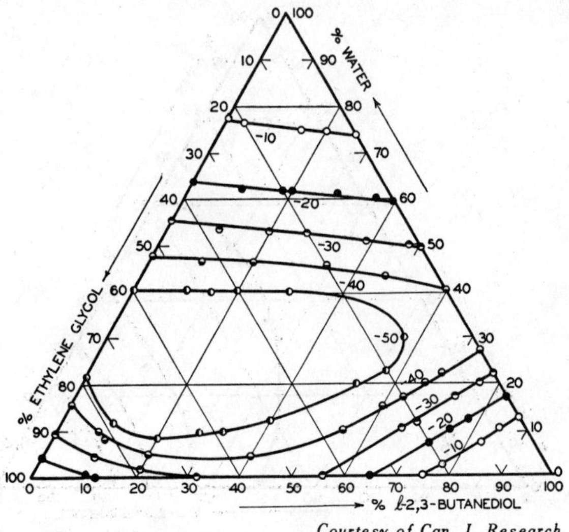

Figure 47. Freezing Points of Aqueous ℓ-2,3-Butanediol-Ethylene-Glycol Solutions.

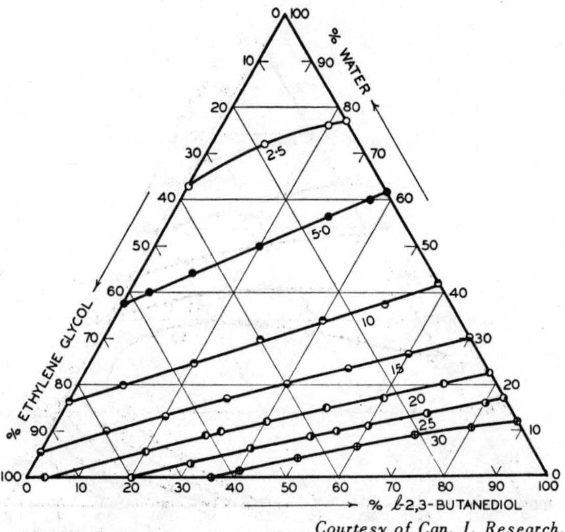

Figure 48. Kinematic Viscosity of Aqueous ℓ-2,3-Butanediol-Ethylene-Glycol Solutions at 20° C, Expressed in Centistokes.

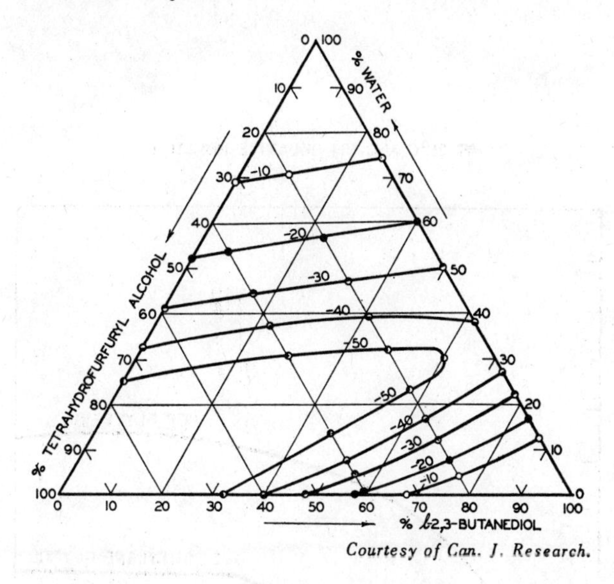

Courtesy of Can. J. Research.

Figure 49. Freezing Points of Aqueous ℓ-2, 3-Butanediol-Tetrahydrofurfuryl-Alcohol Solutions.

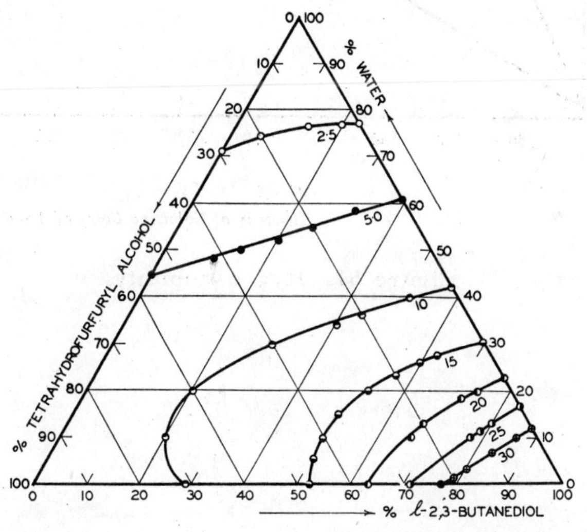

Courtesy of Can. J. Research.

Figure 50. Kinematic Viscosity of Aqueous ℓ-2,3-Butanediol-Tetrahydrofurfuryl Alcohol Solutions at 20° C, Expressed in Centistokes.

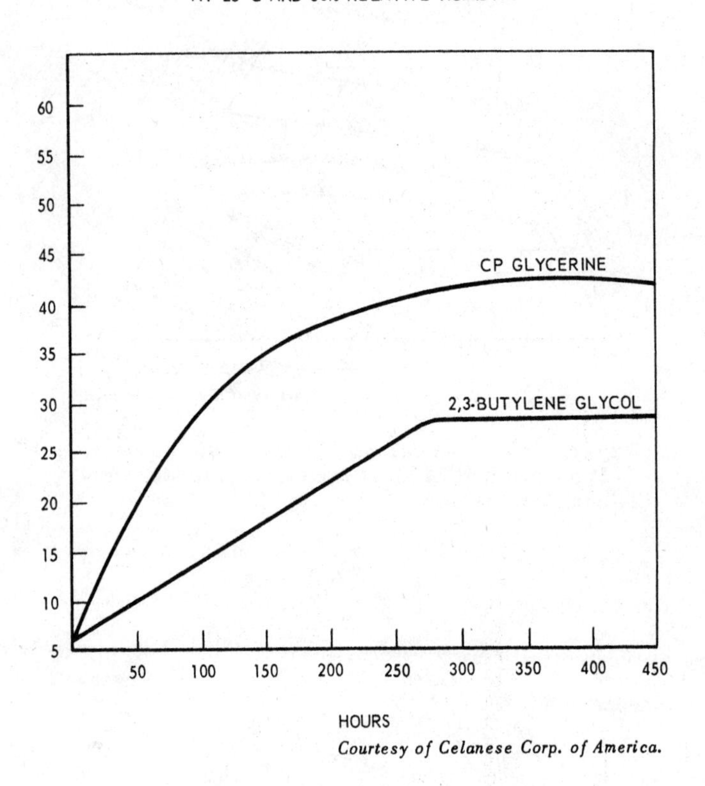

Courtesy of Celanese Corp. of America.

Figure 51. Hygroscopicity.

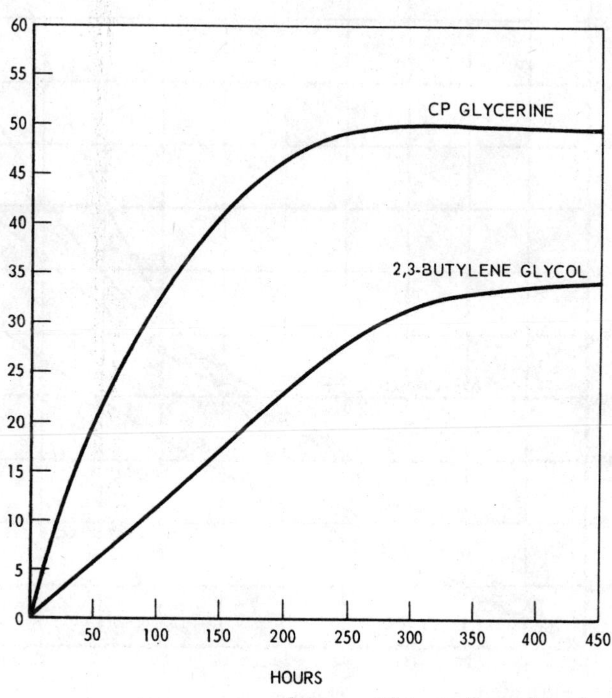

Courtesy of Celanese Corp. of America.

Figure 52. Hygroscopicity.

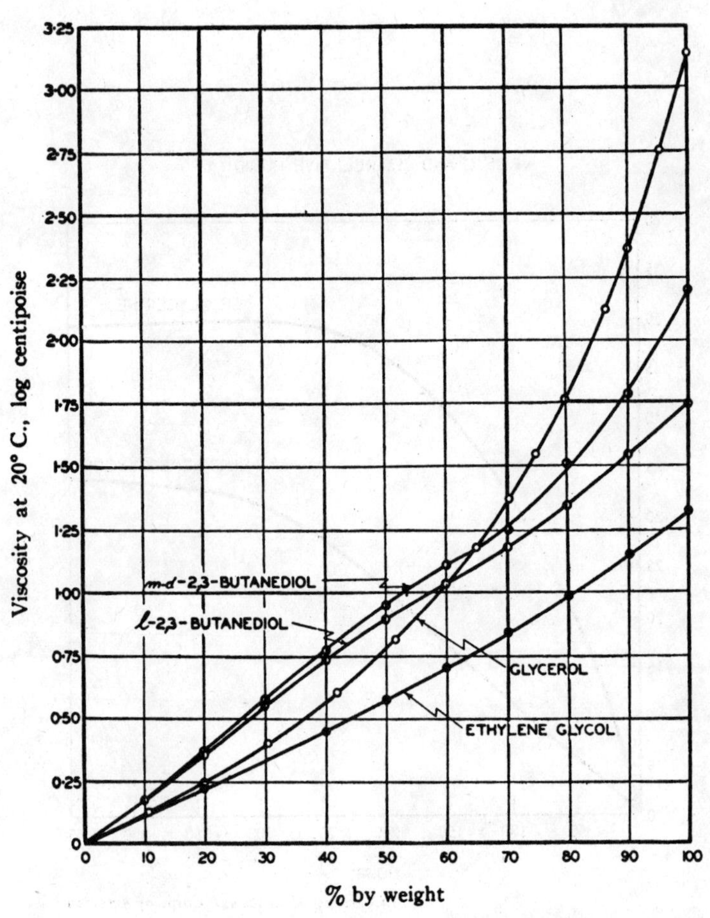

Courtesy of Can. J. Research.

Figure 53. Absolute Viscosity of Aqueous Solutions of Ethylene Glycol, levo-2,3-Butanediol, Meso-dextro-2,3-Butanediol, and Glycerol at 20° C.

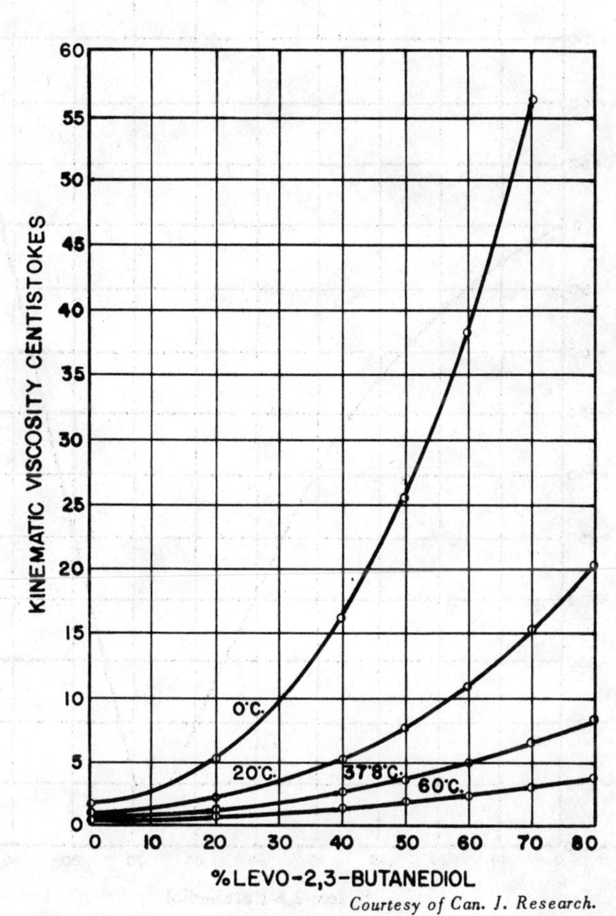

Courtesy of Can. J. Research.

Figure 54. Kinematic Viscosity of Aqueous levo-2,3-Butanediol Solutions in Relation to Concentration and Temperature.

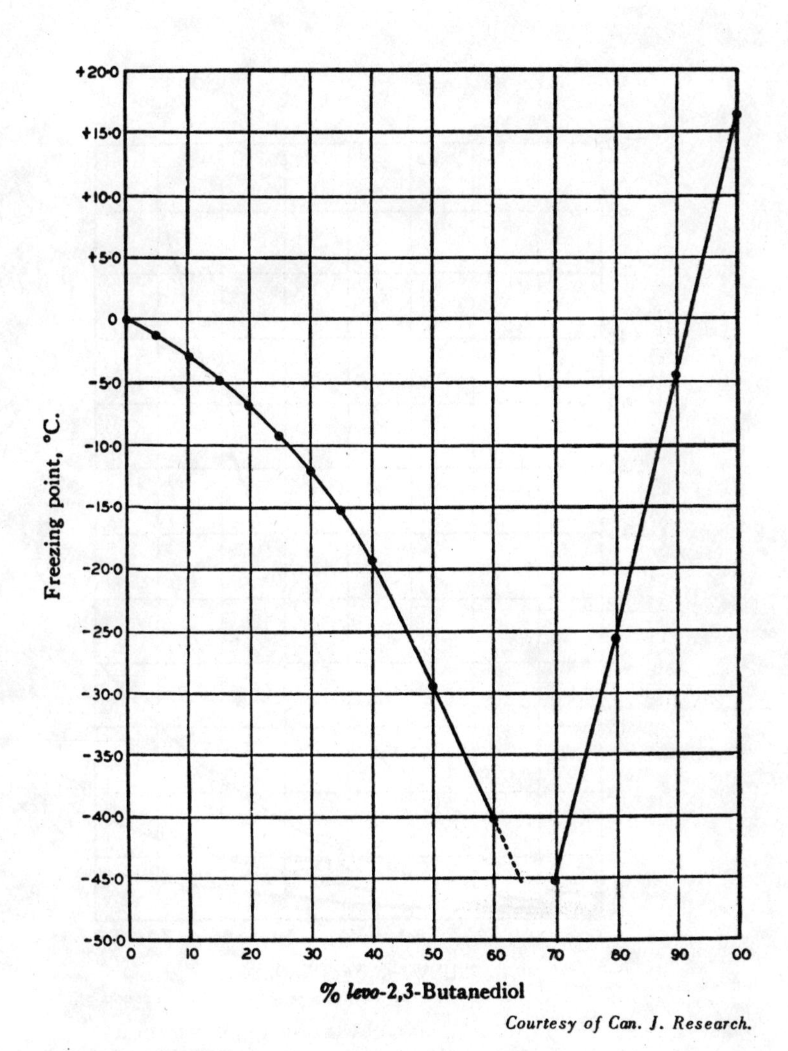

Figure 55. Freezing Points of Aqueous levo-2,3-Butanediol Solutions.

Table 37. Effect of meso-2,3-Butanediol on the Freezing Point of Aqueous levo-2,3-Butanediol Solutions Having Water Contents of 40 and 60%

Composition of Diol	40% Water	60% Water
100% levo	-40.4° C	-19.4° C
95% levo 5% meso	-37.0	-21.0
90% levo 10% meso	-28.2	-21.0
85% levo 15% meso	-18.6	-17.2
80% levo 20% meso	-14.0	-12.4
50% levo 50% meso	+1.55	+1.55

*Courtesy of Can. J. Research.

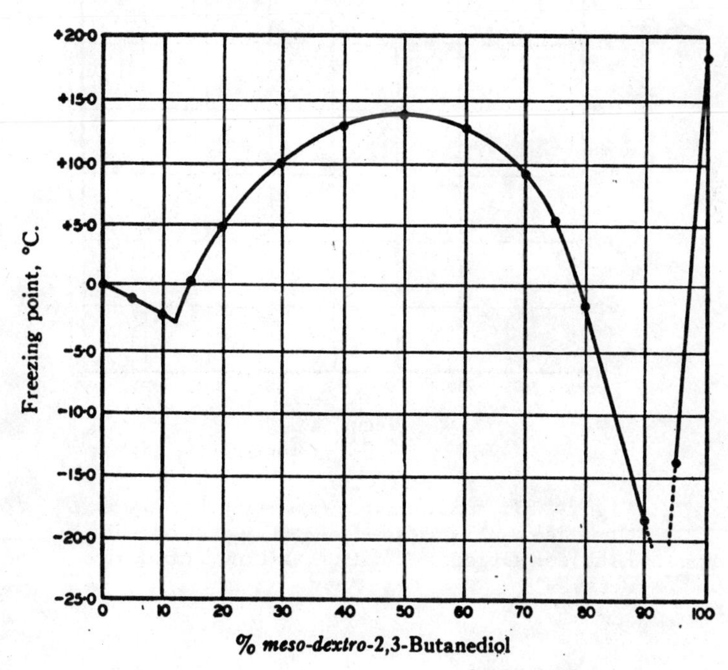

Courtesy of Can. J. Research.

Figure 56. Freezing Points of Aqueous meso-dextro-2,3-Butanediol Solutions.

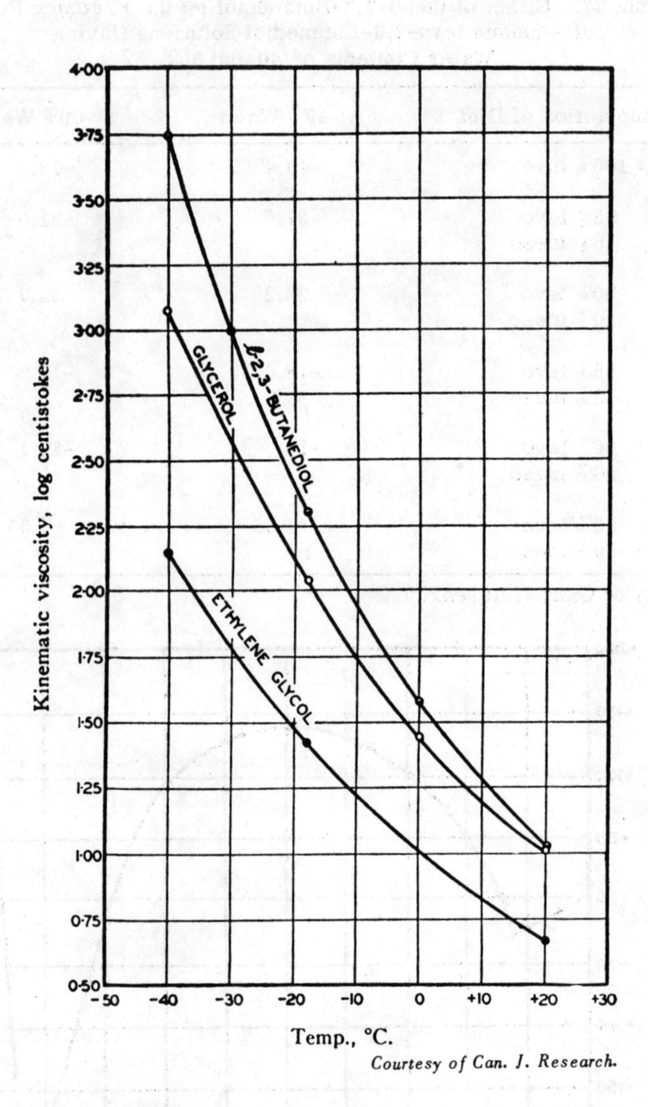

Courtesy of Can. J. Research.

Figure 57. Kinematic Viscosity of 60 Per Cent levo-2,3-Butanediol, Glycerol, and Ethylene Glycol Solutions at Low Temperatures.

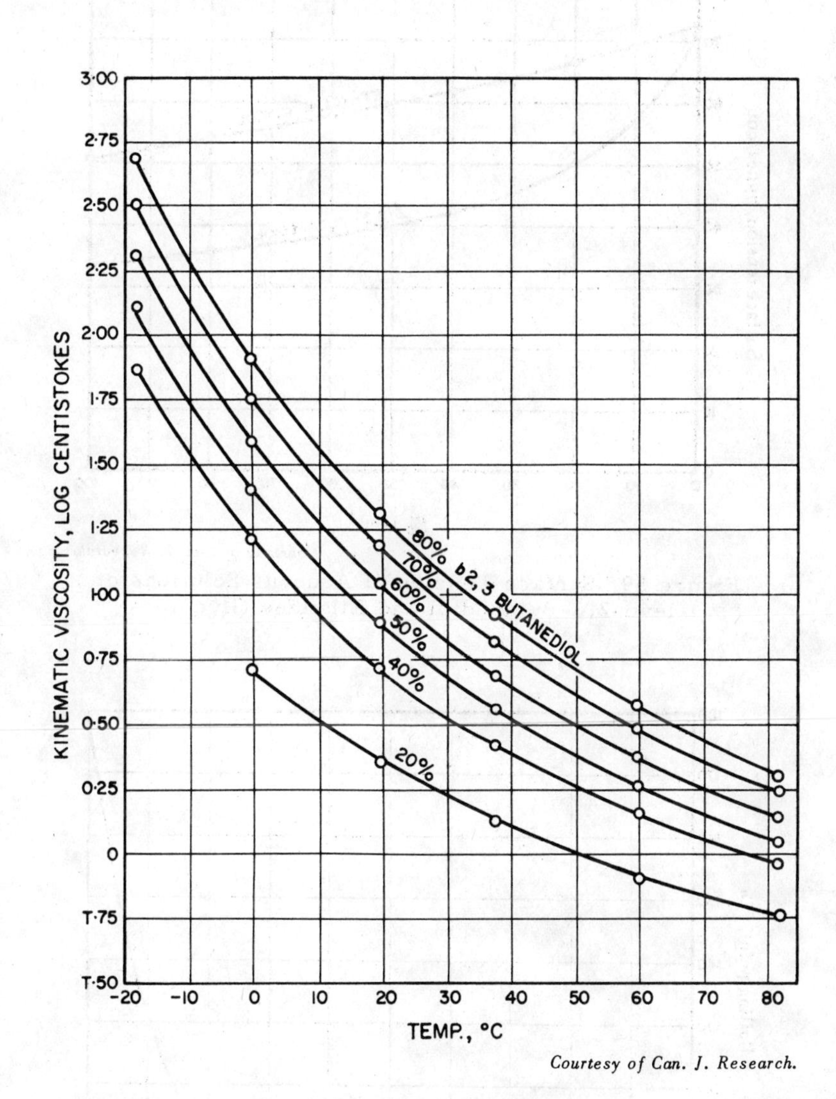

Courtesy of Can. J. Research.

Figure 58. Kinematic Viscosity of Aqueous levo-2,3-Butanediol Solutions, Expressed Logarithmically, as a Function of Concentration and Temperature.

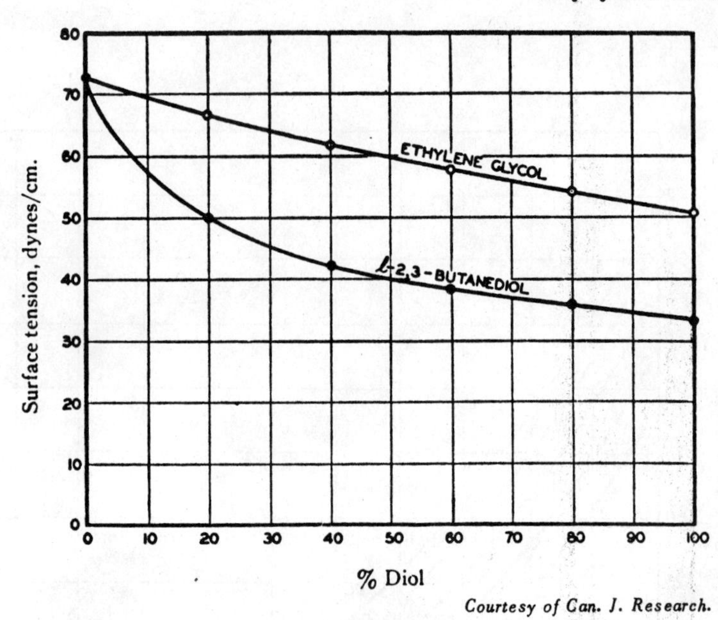

Courtesy of Can. J. Research.

Figure 59. Surface Tension of Aqueous Solutions of levo-2,3-Butanediol and Ethylene Glycol.

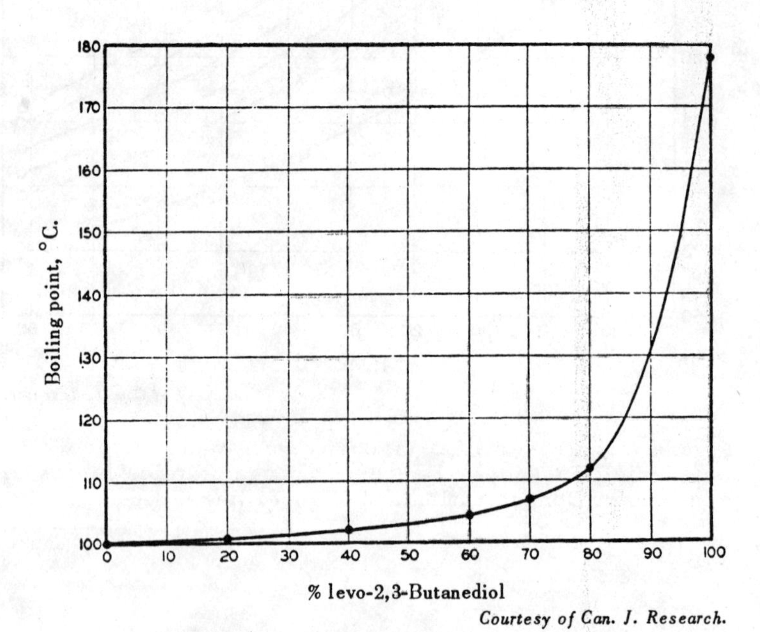

Courtesy of Can. J. Research.

Figure 60. Boiling Points of Aqueous levo-2,3-Butanediol Solutions at Atmospheric Pressure.

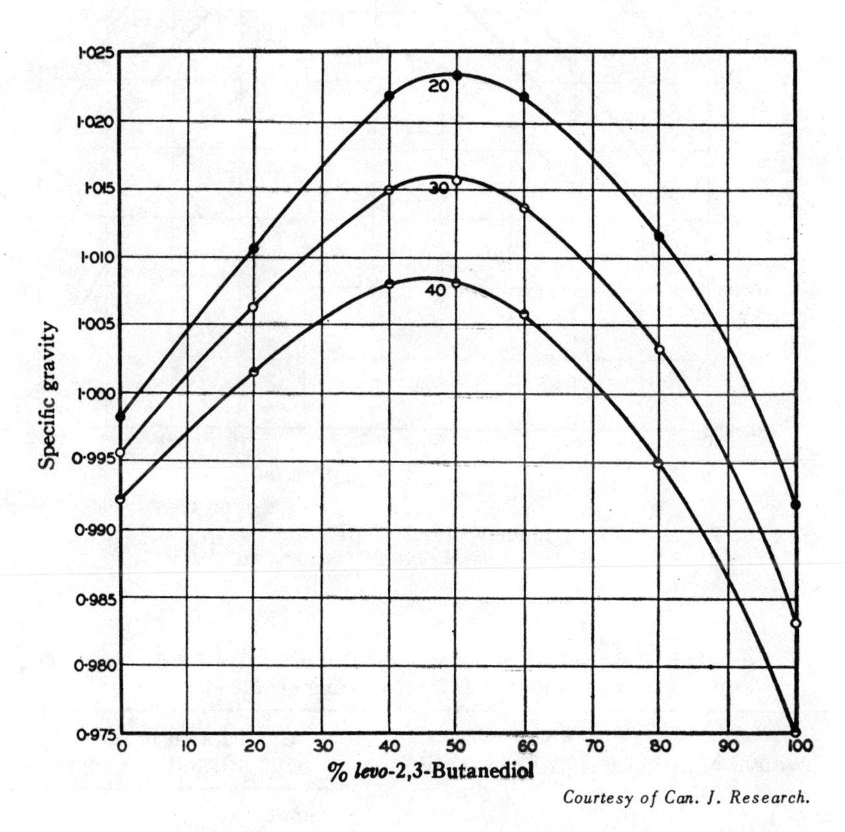

Courtesy of Can. J. Research.

Figure 61. Specific Gravity of Aqueous levo-2,3-Butanediol Solutions at 20°, 30°, and 40° C.

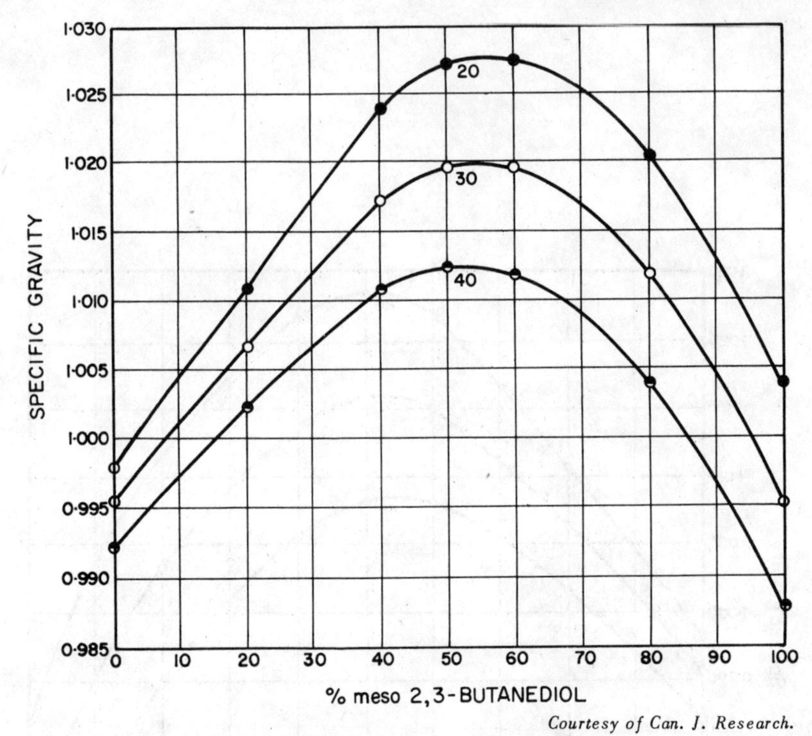

Courtesy of Can. J. Research.

Figure 62. Specific Gravity of Aqueous meso-2,3-Butanediol Solutions at 20°, 30°, and 40° C.

Table 38. Contraction in Volume on Mixing meso-2,3-Butanediol with Water at Different Temperatures*

Weight of glycol, gm.	Weight of water, gm.	Contraction in ml. per 100 ml. Initial Volume		
		20 C	30 C	40 C
10.0141	40.0192	1.14	1.10	1.10
19.9990	30.2180	2.28	2.11	2.02
25.0276	25.0238	2.51	2.31	2.18
30.0111	20.2621	2.49	2.31	2.21
40.0242	10.0277	1.74	1.60	1.52

*Courtesy of Can. J. Research.

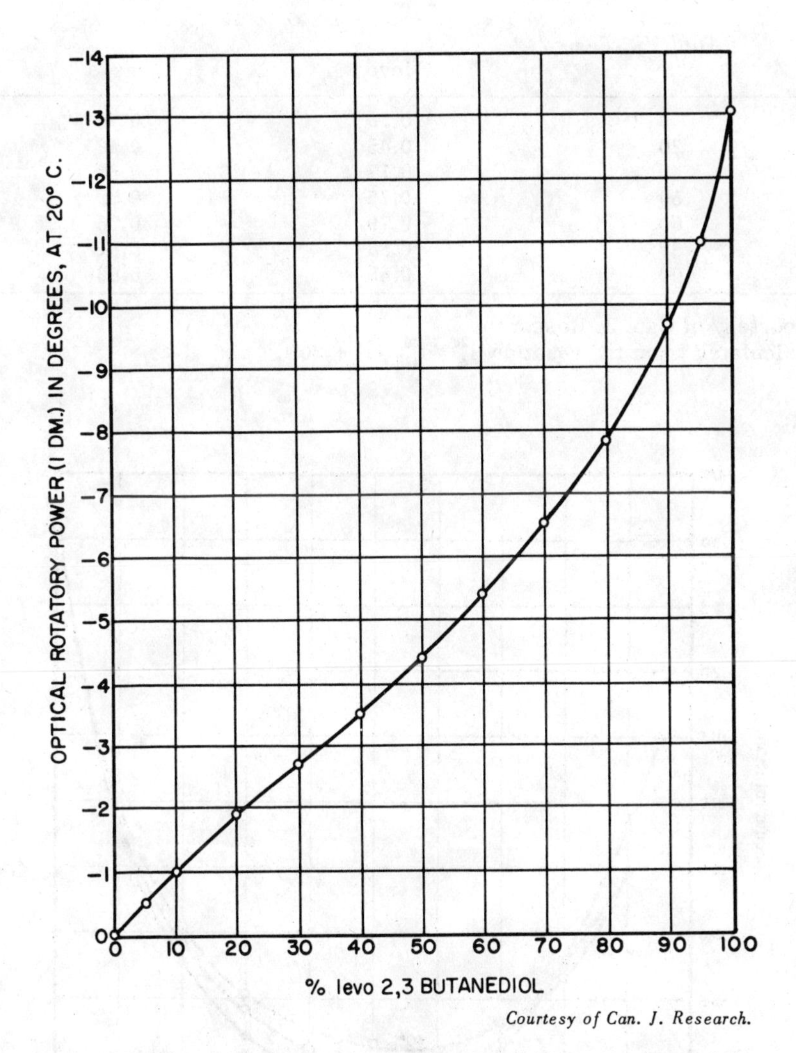

Courtesy of Can. J. Research.

Figure 63. Optical Rotatory Power of Aqueous levo-2,3-Butanediol Solutions at 20° C.

Table 39. Thermal Expansion of Aqueous 2,3-Butanediol Solutions Between 20° and 40° C*

Diol, %	$\alpha \times 10^3$†	
	levo	meso
0	0.30	0.30
20	0.45	0.42
40	0.77	0.65
50	0.75	0.72
60	0.79	0.76
80	0.83	0.81
100	0.85	0.82

*Courtesy of Can. J. Research.
†Calculated from the equation $d_4^{20}/d_4^{40} = 1 + 20\alpha$.

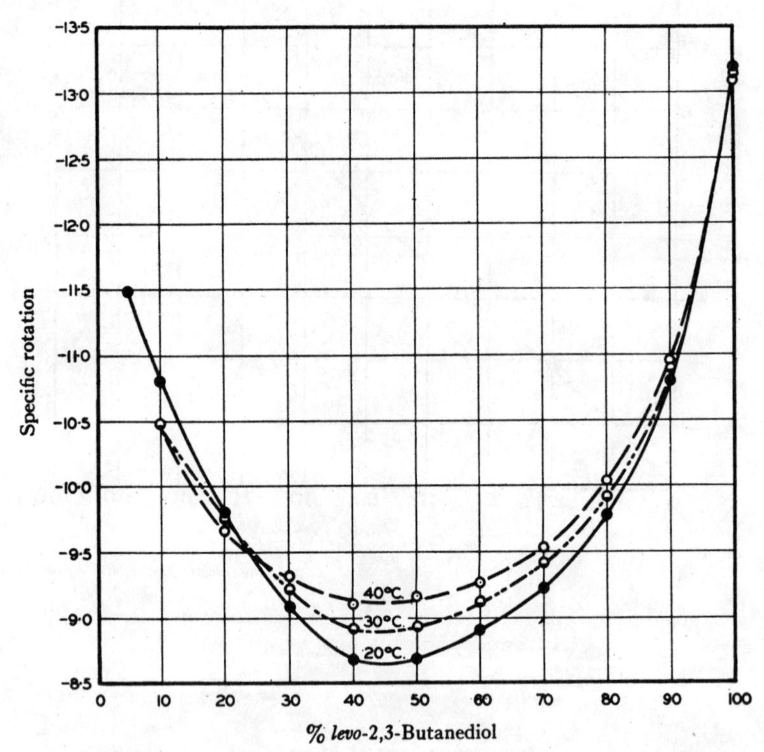

Courtesy of Can. J. Research.

Figure 64. Effects of Concentration and Temperature on the Specific Rotatory Power of levo-2,3-Butanediol in Aqueous Solution.

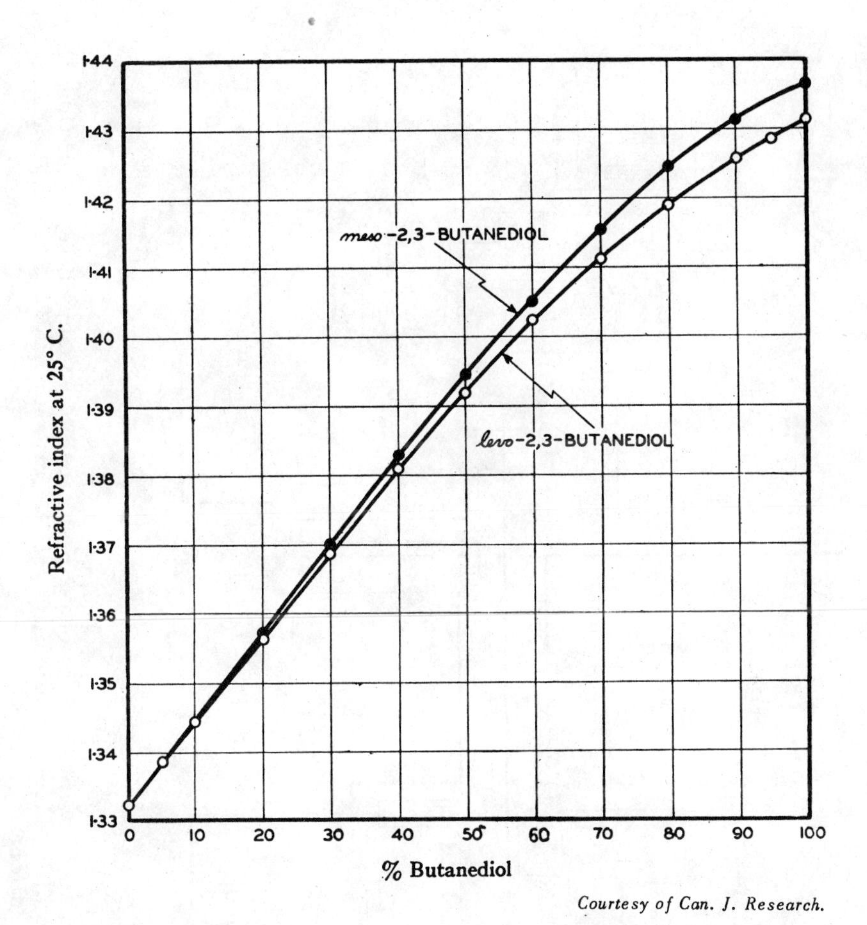

Courtesy of Can. J. Research.

Figure 65. Refractive Indices of Aqueous Solutions of meso- and levo-2,3-Butanediol at 25° C.

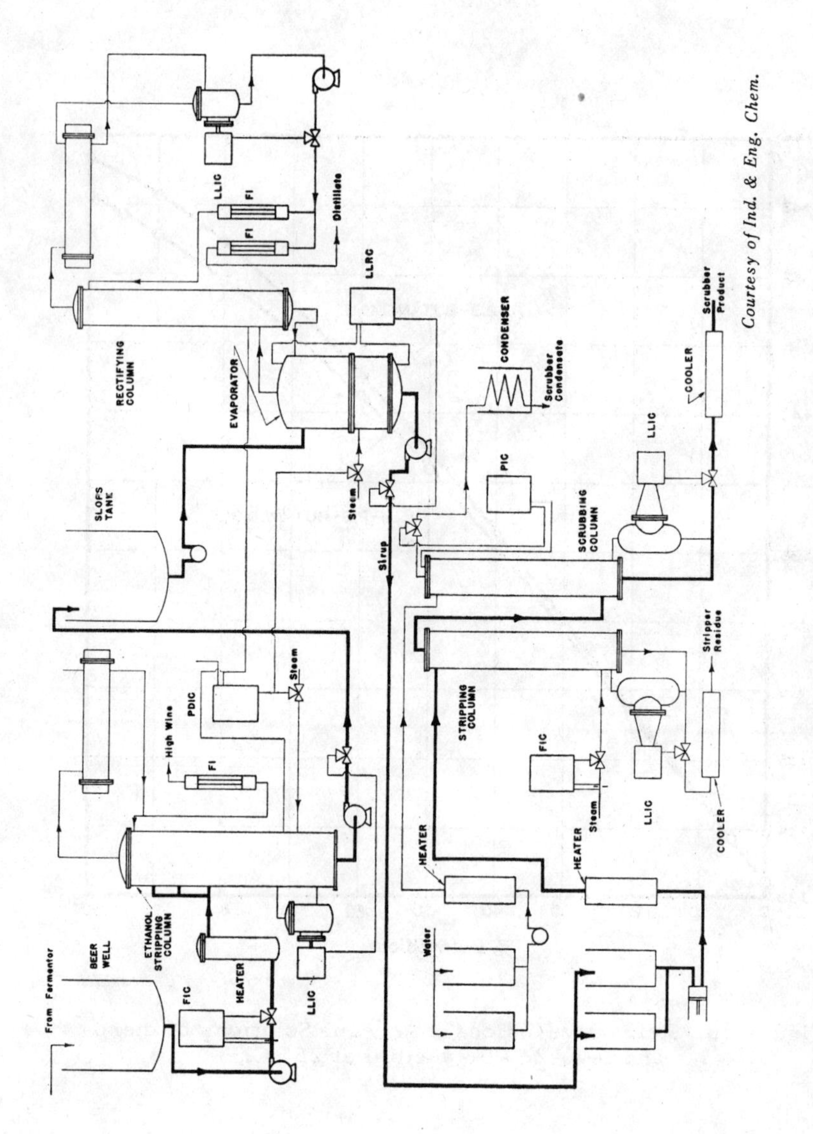

Courtesy of Ind. & Eng. Chem.

Figure 66. Flow Sheet for levo-2,3-Butanediol Manufacture. F = flow, PD = pressure difference, LL = liquid level, P = pressure, I = indicator, R = recorder, C = controller.

Table 40. Refractive Indices of Aqueous levo-2,3-Butanediol Solutions at Different Temperatures*

Diol, %	Temperature, °C			
	20	25	30	35
0	1.3330	1.3325	1.3319	1.3312
10.0	1.3450	1.3445	1.3437	1.3429
19.9	1.3574	1.3566	1.3557	1.3549
29.9	1.3700	1.3689	1.3677	1.3666
39.9	1.3820	1.3807	1.3793	1.3779
49.9	1.3930	1.3915	1.3900	1.3885
59.6	1.4027	1.4012	1.3997	1.3982
70.0	1.4115	1.4098	1.4082	1.4065
79.7	1.4197	1.4180	1.4162	1.4146
89.7	1.4264	1.4247	1.4229	1.4212
99.5	1.4322	1.4302	1.4283	1.4264

*Courtesy of Can. J. Research.

1,4-BUTANEDIOL

$HOCH_2CH_2CH_2CH_2OH$

This saturated glycol is produced in commercial quantities by Antara Chemicals. It is made by the hydrogenation of 1,4-butynediol, the hydrogenation taking place at 70 to 140° C under 300 atmospheres pressure in the presence of a catalyst composed of nickel, copper, and manganese. [76, 77] The technical grade, being somewhat unstable, should be purified by vacuum distillation.

1,4-Butanediol is a viscous and almost colorless and odorless liquid, freely soluble in water, methanol, ethyl alcohol, and acetone, but only partly soluble in ethyl acetate, ethyl ether, petroleum ether, chlorobenzene, carbon tetrachloride, and benzene. It is readily compatible with casein, animal glue, and gelatin. It is proposed as a solvent for printing inks, gums, and resins.

Considering its physical properties, this glycol should find application as a solvent, moistener, softener, size component, and lubricant. The miscibility, viscosity, and humectant properties of 1,4-butanediol suggest its use as a rayon lubricant; warp size component; additive for sizing and finishing baths; as a softener for gelatin, casein, cellophane, parchment, tissue paper "Glassine," and gummed paper; and as a moistener for glues, stencil paper, and stamp pad inks. It may also be used as a heat-transfer liquid, and as a component for brake fluids.

This glycol is used in the preparation of polyurethane resins, synthetic fibers, bristles, films, artificial leather, solvents, plasticizers, softening agents, binding agents, plastics, synthetic rubbers, casting and laminating resins, pharmaceuticals, and so forth.

Physical Properties and Specifications of Commercial 1,4-Butanediol

Acetals (as CH_2O)	Less than 0.8%
Acidity (as HCO_2H)	Less than 1%
Ash	0%
Boiling range	221-231° C
1-Butanol	Less than 0.5%
Flash point (ASTM open cup)	More than 250° F
Free aldehyde as CH_2O	Less than 0.1%
Freezing point range	18-19.5° C
Purity	Over 96%
Refractive index, n_D^{25}	1.4435-1.4445
Specific gravity, d_4^{25}	1.012-1.016
Unsaturation (as butendiol)	Less than 1%
Viscosity, 25° C	65-70 cp.
Water content	Less than 0.8%

Pure 1,4-Butanediol

Boiling point at 10 mm. Hg	118° C
20 mm. Hg	133° C
100 mm. Hg	170° C
200 mm. Hg	187° C
760 mm. Hg	228° C
Freezing point	20.9 ° C
Refractive index, n_D^{25}	1.4446
Solubility at 25° C (g./100 ml. solvent)	
in water	Infinite
in methanol	Infinite
in ethanol	Infinite
in acetone	Infinite
benzene	0.3
carbon tetrachloride	0.4
chlorobenzene	0.4
ethyl acetate	14.1
ethyl ether	3.1
petroleum ether (35-60° C)	0.9
Specific gravity, d_4^{25}	1.0154

% Water in 1,4-Butanediol	Freezing Point (°C)	Viscosity (cp. at 25° C)
0.0	20.0	71.5
0.1	19.8	71.3
0.5	19.0	70.2
1.0	18.1	68.9

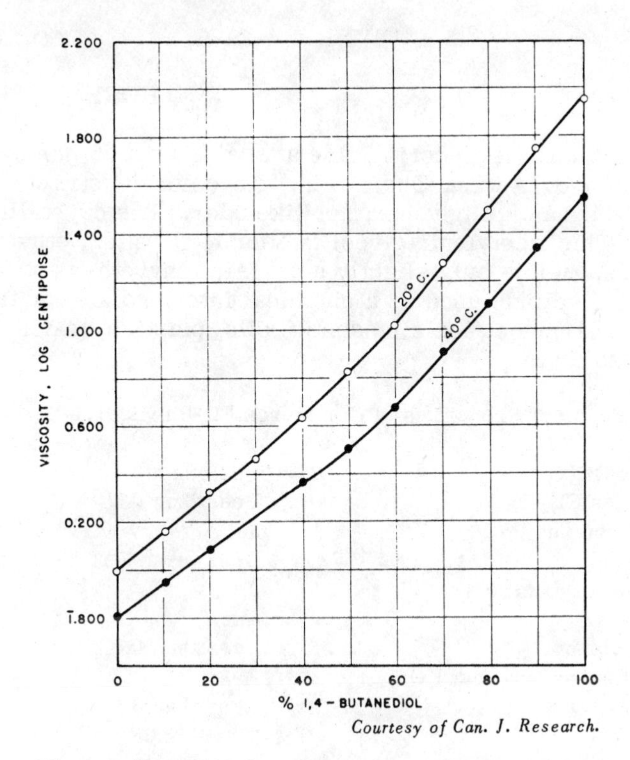

Courtesy of Can. J. Research.

Figure 67. Absolute Viscosity of Aqueous 1,4-Butanediol Solutions at 20° and 40° C.

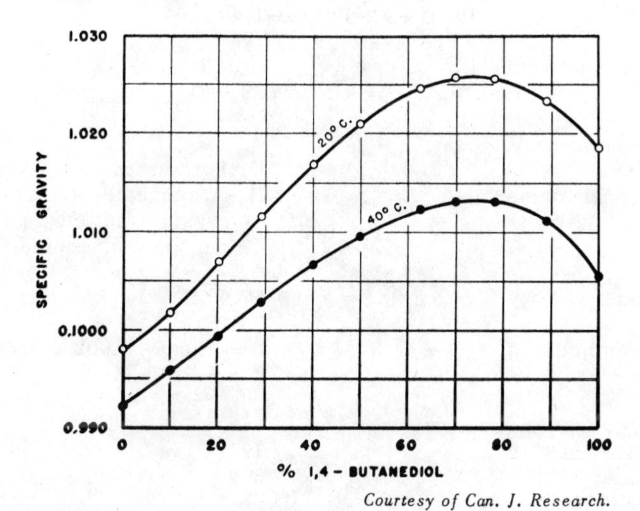

Courtesy of Can. J. Research.

Figure 68. Specific Gravity of Aqueous 1,4-Butanediol Solutions at 20° and 40° C.

2-BUTYNE-1,4-DIOL

$HOCH_2C \equiv CCH_2OH$

This crystalline glycol is made available as a 35 per cent aqueous solution by Antara Chemicals. Its color is straw yellow to amber, and it has a slight caramel-like odor. The crystalline form is toxic. This acetylenic glycol is soluble in water, ethyl alcohol, and acetone, but it is only slightly soluble in ethyl ether and benzene. 2-Butyne-1,4-diol is used as a chemical intermediate for the preparation of pharmaceuticals, essential oils, plastics, textile auxiliaries, and so forth.

Physical Properties of Commercial 2-Butyne-1,4-Diol

Acetals (as CH_2O)	Less than 0.6%
Aldehydes (as CH_2O)	Less than 0.5%
Butynediol content	35 ± 1%
Freezing point	Less than -7° C
Methanol (by distillation)	0.0%
pH	4 to 6
Propargyl alcohol	Less than 0.5%
Saponification No. (as mg. KOH/g. product)	Less than 6
Specific gravity, d_4^{25}	1.04 to 1.05
Weight per gallon	8.7 lb.

Purified 2-Butyne-1,4-Diol

Boiling point at 10 mm. Hg	140° C
100 mm. Hg	194° C
Crystal structure	
system	Orthorhombic
principal forms	Basal pinacoids and prisms with crystals flattened parallel to the basal pinacoids
Melting point	57.5° C
Refractive indices n_D^{25}	α ± 1.450 - 0.002
	β ± 1.528 - 0.002
Solubility (g./100 ml. solvent)	
in water at 0° C	121
in water at 25° C	374
in ethyl alcohol at 25° C	83
in acetone at 25° C	70
in ethyl ether at 25° C	2.6
in benzene at 25° C	0.04

2-BUTENE-1,4-DIOL

Butenediol $HOCH_2CH = CHCH_2OH$

This unsaturated glycol is made available in limited quantities by the General Aniline & Film Corporation. The composition of this product is predominantly the cisisomer; it is about 95 per cent pure and contains 2-butyne-1,4-diol and 1,4-butanediol as the major contaminants. Butenediol has been prepared in both the cis and the transconfiguration. The cisisomer is prepared by the catalytic reduction of 2-butyne-1,4-diol.

It is a colorless essentially odorless liquid, being very soluble in water, methanol, ethyl alcohol, and acetone, but difficultly soluble in benzene. Butenediol is used as a chemical intermediate for the preparation of alkyd resins, plasticizers, solvents for lacquers, nylon, and pharmaceuticals.

Physical Properties of Technical Cis-2-Butene-1,4-Diol

Boiling point range	232-235° C
Fire point (Cleveland open cup)	270° F
Flash point (Cleveland open cup)	263° F
Freezing point range	4.0-7.0° C
Molecular weight	88.1
Refractive index, n_D^{25}	1.476-1.478
Specific gravity at 25/15° C	1.067-1.074
Viscosity at 68° F	22 cp.
100° F	10.8 cp.
210° F	2.5 cp.

Purified Cis-2-Butene-1,4-Diol

Boiling point at 760 mm. Hg	234° C
100 mm. Hg	177° C
20 mm. Hg	140° C
10 mm. Hg	122° C
5 mm. Hg	109° C
Freezing point	12.5° C
Refractive index, n_D^{25}	1.4768-1.4773
Specific gravity at 25/15° C	1.070

1,5-PENTANEDIOL

Pentamethylene glycol $HOCH_2CH_2CH_2CH_2CH_2OH$

1,5-Pentanediol, an acrolein derivative, is a colorless, high-boiling, viscous liquid with a mild odor. It is completely soluble in water, low-molecular-weight alcohols, acetone, and ethyl acetate, and partially soluble in aromatic and aliphatic hydrocarbons. Its solubility in the following at 25° C is by weight: benzene 0.6 per cent; ether 6.0 per cent; heptane 0.6 per cent; and carbon tetrachloride less than 0.01 per cent.

It has been found useful as a solvent for reducing synthetic linear polyamides, such as nylons, to a finely divided powder to be applied as a molding powder or in suspension as a coating material. This glycol is a mutual solvent and blending agent in systems containing such immiscible substances as cutting oils, dry cleaning-soaps, and soluble oils and emulsions. It may be used as a solvent and humectant for inks. It is also proposed as a plasticizer for casein, zein, and other water-soluble resins; adhesives; and cellulose products. This glycol is largely used as an intermediate in the preparation of solvents, polyester resins, plasticizers, high-temperature lubricants, brake fluid components, and insect repellents.

Physical Properties of 1,5-Pentanediol

Boiling point at 760 mm. Hg	242.5° C
50 mm. Hg	166° C
10 mm. Hg	134° C
Coefficient of expansion at 55° C	0.00061/°C
Flash point (open cup)	265° F
Freezing point	-15.6° C
Molecular weight	104.16
Refractive index at 20° C	1.4489
Specific gravity at 20/20° C	0.9921
Surface tension at 20° C	43.2 dynes/cm.
Vapor pressure at 20° C	Less than 0.01
Viscosity at 0° C (absolute)	415 cp.
20° C	128 cp.
40° C	48 cp.
Weight per gallon at 20° C (average)	8.23 lb.

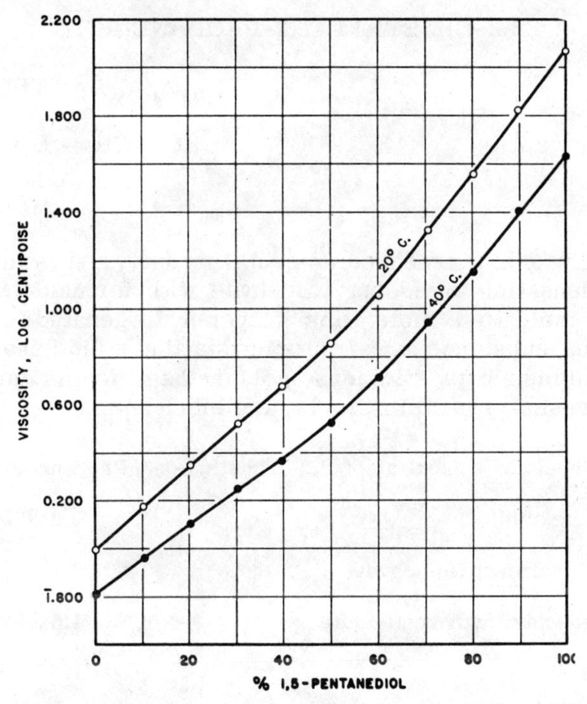

Courtesy of Can. J. Research.

Figure 69. Absolute Viscosity of Aqueous 1,5-Pentanediol Solutions at 20° and 40° C.

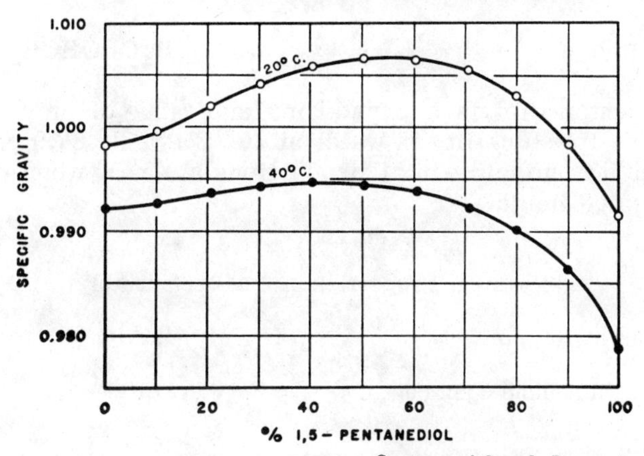

Courtesy of Can. J. Research.

Figure 70. Specific Gravity of Aqueous 1,5-Pentanediol Solutions at 20° and 40° C.

2,2-DIMETHYL-1,3-PROPANEDIOL

Neopentyl glycol

$$HO - CH_2 - \underset{CH_3}{\overset{CH_3}{\underset{|}{\overset{|}{C}}}} - CH_2 - OH$$

This glycol is a recent commercial product, and is made by the aldol condensation of isobutyraldehyde with formaldehyde in the ratio of 1 mole to 1 mole; this is then hydrogenated to neopentyl glycol. The substance is a white crystalline solid used mainly to prepare polymeric plasticizers, polyurethane foams, unsaturated polyester resins, hydraulic fluids, and lubricants.

Physical Properties of 2,2-Dimethyl-1,3-Propanediol

Acid, as acetic acid	0.05% by wt., max.
Aldehyde, as hydroxypivaldehyde	0.7% by wt., max.
Ester, as neopentyl hydroxypivalate	1.5% by wt., max.
Melting point	120-130° C
Water	1.0% by wt., max.

2,4-PENTANEDIOL

Amylene glycol $CH_3CHOHCH_2CHOHCH_3$

2,4-Pentanediol is a crystalline substance of limited interest at present. Its solubility in water at 20° C is only 87.9 per cent by weight, but it is miscible in all proportions at 45° C when it becomes a supercooled liquid.

Physical Properties of 2,4-Pentanediol

Boiling point at 760 mm. Hg	199° C
Flash point, Cleveland open cup	210° F
Melting point	45° C
Molecular weight	104.15
Specific gravity (apparent), 20/20° C	0.964 (supercooled liquid)

2,5-HEXANEDIOL

$CH_3CHOHCH_2CH_2CHOHCH_3$

This six-carbon glycol is the most viscous of the family. It is completely miscible with water.

Physical Properties of 2,5-Hexanediol

Boiling point at 760 mm. Hg	220.8° C
Flash point, Cleveland open cup	220° F
Freezing point	Sets to a glass below -50° C
Molecular weight	118.17
Refractive index at 20° C, n_D	1.4474
Specific gravity (apparent) at 45/15.6° C	0.9617
Viscosity at 20° C	37 cp.

1,6-HEXANEDIOL

$CH_2OHCH_2CH_2CH_2CH_2CH_2OH$

This glycol is very soluble in water.

Physical Properties of 1,6-Hexanediol

Boiling point at 760 mm. Hg	243° C
Flash point, Cleveland open cup	265° F
Melting point	42° C
Molecular weight	118.17
Specific gravity (apparent)	0.958

2-METHYL-2,4-PENTANEDIOL

Hexylene glycol
Methyl amylene glycol
Diacetone glycol

$CH_3COH(CH_3)CH_2CHOHCH_3$

This high-molecular-weight, six-carbon glycol is prepared commercially by the liquid-phase catalytic hydrogenation of diacetone alcohol. It is a mildly hygroscopic, colorless liquid, with a mild, sweetish odor. It has good wetting and dispersing action and a low vapor pressure. It is an excellent solvent for many materials, and it has good compatibility with aliphatic and aromatic hydrocarbons, due to its long chain, and with polar substances such as water, fatty acids, and the lower alcohols, due to its two hydroxyl groups. These solubility characteristics for dissimilar materials are excellently applied as a coupling solvent and blending agent.

Hexylene glycol will dissolve the following diverse materials at 20 to 25° C: acids—acetic, butyric, oleic, and phosphoric; alcohols—butyl, ethyl, isopropyl, methanol, methyl amyl, methyl isobutyl carbinol, n-butyl, and sec-butyl; amines—cyclohexylamine, isopropylamine, morpholine, triethanolamine, and triethylamine; chlorides—carbon tetrachloride, chloroform, ethylene dichlorethane, 1,1,2-trichloroethylene, and 1,2,3-trichloropropane; esters—n-butyl acetate, cellulose acetate, and ethyl acetate; ethers—butyl, ethyl, and isopropyl; glycol ethers—butyl "Carbitol," butyl "Cellosolve," "Carbitol" solvent, "Cellosolve" solvent, and methyl "Cellosolve"; hydrocarbons—benzene, mineral spirits, naphtha, oxtanes, petroleum ether, Stoddard solvent, and toluene; ketones—acetone, diacetone alcohol, dioxane, mesityl oxide, methylethyl ketone, and methyl isobutyl ketone; oils—castor, crude coconut, pine, red, and tall; plasticizers—dibutyl phthalate and dibutyl sebacate, and "Ucon" lubricants.

Over 5 per cent by weight of the following substances are soluble in hexylene glycol: oxalic acid and stearic acid; the aniline dye, para fuchsin; almond oil; such natural resins as Batavia dammar, Singapore-No. 2 dammar, and elemi; such synthetic gums as "Acryloid" B-72 (acrylic copolymers) and ester gum (Hercules 8L); and camphor gum.

Less than 5 per cent by weight of the following substances are soluble in hexylene glycol: asphalts—air blown, 150° F, and paving, 51/60 penetration; aniline dyes, such as acid violet, Amaranth, U.S.P., indigo, orange #1; coal tar dyes, such as alizarin red S, butter yellow, eosine, malachite green, and resorcin brown B; oils, such as A.D.M.-100, raw cottonseed oil, and pure raw linseed oils; natural resins, such as pale bold East India dammar, Philippine Manila copal, Pontianak copal, pale cracked Congo copal, brown kauri copal, white kauri copal, mastic, "Helix" wood and light rosin, and bleached shellac; synthetic resins, such as cellulose triacetate, "Rezyl" 99 (nondrying alkyd), "Teglac" Z 152 (rosin modified maleic alkyd), "Vinylite" XYHL (polyvinyl butyrate) swells, "Vinylite" XYNC (polyvinyl butyral) swells, and "Vinylite" AYAF (polyvinyl acetate); and potassium hydroxide.

The following substances are insoluble in hexylene glycol: quinoline yellow dye; China wood oil; mineral oil, 70/80 viscosity; soybean oil, 2-3 viscosity; synthetic resins, such as cellulose acetate, "Cellolyn" 102, ethyl cellulose, "Formvar" E (polyvinyl formal), "Hercose" CN (cellulose acetate butyrate), raw neoprene, "Styron" YA5-K27 (polystyrene), "Super-Beckacite" 2000 (pure phenolic), "Vinylite" VYNS (vinyl chloride-acetate copolymer); waxes, such as yellow beeswax, carnauba No. 3 N.C., paraffin, white spermaceti; and such materials as cellophane, cerasin, dextrose, egg albumen, gelatin, and lanolin U.S.P.

Hexylene glycol is used as a solvent and coupling agent in castor oil, and by means of its coupling action, prevents water from condensing and seeping into hydraulic systems. It is a good solvent for dyes and for lacquer-type and resin-type inks. In flash-dry and steam-set printing inks, its comparatively low vapor pressure at ordinary temperatures and low degree of hygroscopicity over a wide range of relative humidity, add to good press stability. Under conditions of high temperature, as in flash-dry ink, hexylene glycol volatilizes rapidly to permit a quick drying time and high press speed. It has good penetration for steam-set inks due to the low surface tension of its aqueous solutions. For flash-dry zein inks, mixtures of hexylene glycol and other glycols are used for better solvency and stability.

As a coupling solvent, it is used in soluble cutting oils, either alone or mixed with other glycols; in engine cleaners and degreasing soaps and emulsions; in textile oils, paper coatings, leather oils, and dressings; in prespotting soaps; and in textiles, to which it also contributes humectant properties. It is a good solvent at low temperatures for pentachlorophenol, a wood preservative. It is also used as a moistening and softening agent for composition cork, casein, leather, and paper and textile fibers, and as a penetrant in duplicator fluids, vat-dye pastes, and printing inks. It is a wetting and dispersing agent in polishes and cleaners, a solvent plasticizer for polyvinyl acetate emulsions and other surface coatings, and a grinding and extrusion aid.

Physical Properties and Specifications of 2-Methyl-2,4-Pentanediol

Acidity as acetic acid	0.005% by wt., max.
Boiling point at 760 mm. Hg	198.27° C
	197.1° C
at 50 mm. Hg	125° C
at 10 mm. Hg	94° C
Color, Pt-Co (Hazen) standard	15, max.
Critical properties, P_c	499 psia
T_c	1221° R
V_c	6.78 ft./mole
Density (in air) at 760 mm. Hg	0.928 g./cc.
Density in air at any temp. may be obtained from equation:	$D_t - 0.952 - 4.02 \times 10^4 t$

Density (in vacuo) at 0° C	0.9360 g./cc.
20° C	0.0216 g./cc.
30° C	0.9145 g./cc.
dt/dp at the boiling point	0.045° C/mm.
Flash point, Cleveland open cup	210° F 215° F
Freezing point	Becomes semisolid at -40° C without crystalline formation Sets to glass below -50° C
Distillation range (ASTM D-1078) (95% will distill between 196° C and 199° C)	195 to 200° C
Latent heat of vaporization	12.3×13^3 cal./g.-mole 104.1 g.-cal./g. 208 Btu/lb.
Molecular weight	118.17
Pour point	-37.2° C (35° F)
Refractive dispersion, $(N_F - N_C) \times 10^4$	72.5
Refractive index, n_D^{20}	1.4276
n_D^{30}	1.4243
Specific gravity at 20/4° C	0.9216
20/20° C	0.9234
Δ Sp. Gr./Δ t, 0 to 55° C	0.00097
Surface tension, 20° C	33.1 dynes/cm.
Vapor pressure, 20° C	0.05 mm. Hg
Viscosity (absolute), 20° C	34.4 cp.
Water at 20° C	Miscible without turbidity with 19 vols. of n-heptane
Weight per gallon at 20° C	7.69 lb.

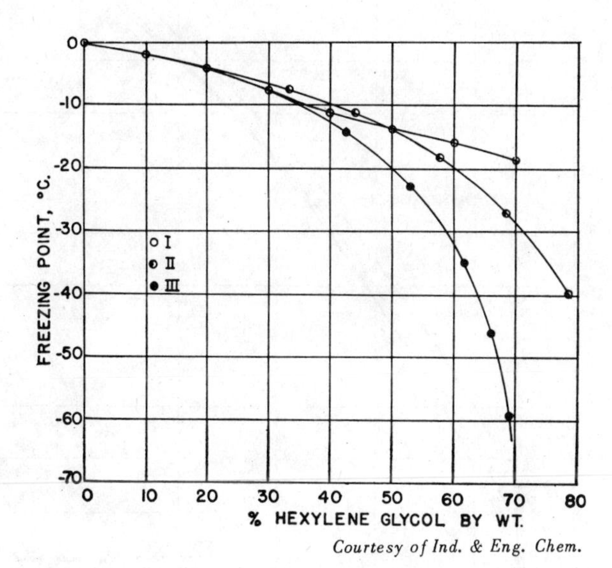

Courtesy of Ind. & Eng. Chem.

Figure 71. Freezing Points of Hexylene Glycol (2-Methyl-2,4-pentanediol)-Water Mixtures. (I) Observed; (II) Theoretical, without hydration; (III) Theoretical, with complete hydration.

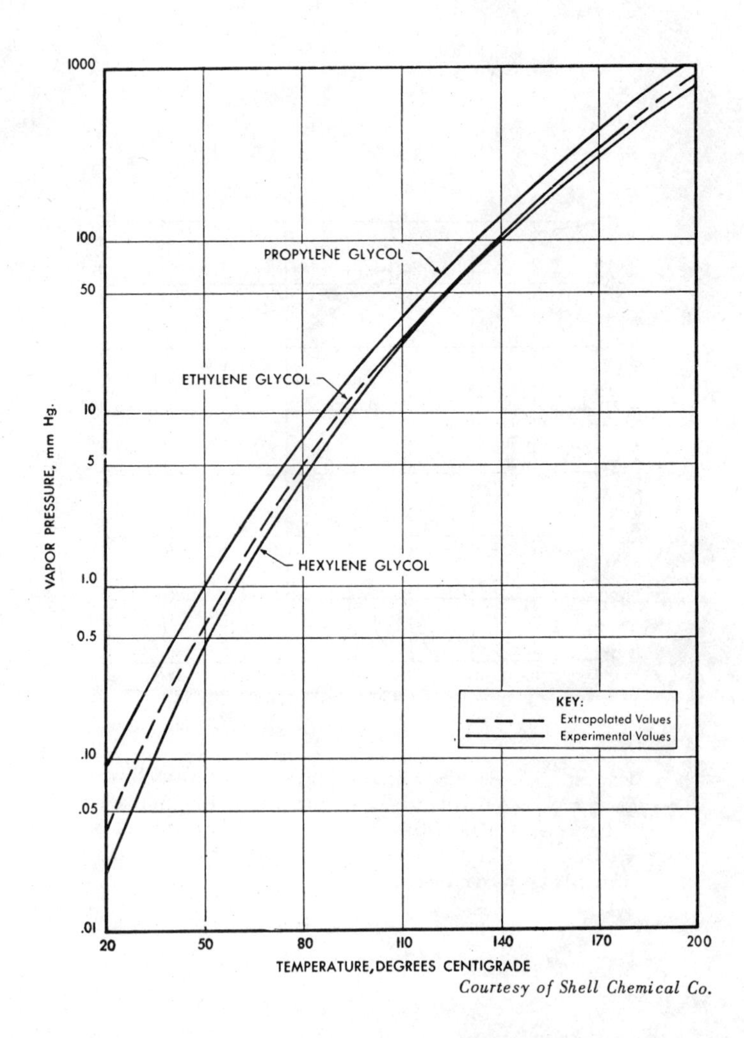

Courtesy of Shell Chemical Co.

Figure 72. Vapor Pressure of Glycols.

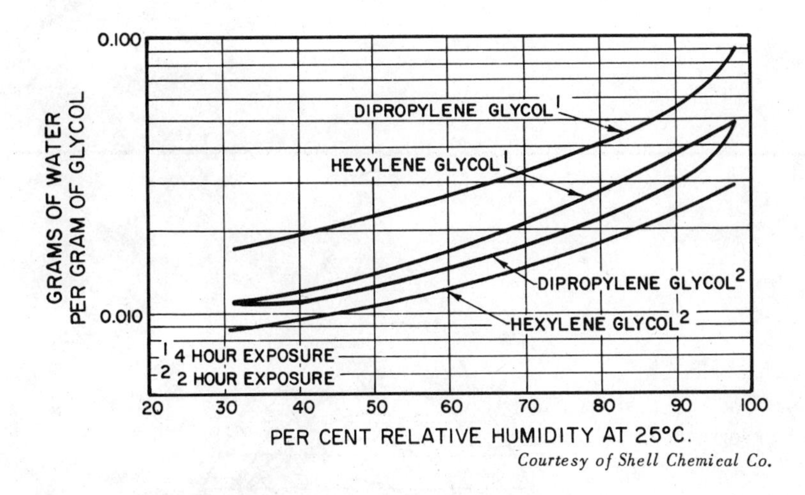

Courtesy of Shell Chemical Co.

Figure 73. Water Absorption by Glycols as a Function of Relative Humidity.

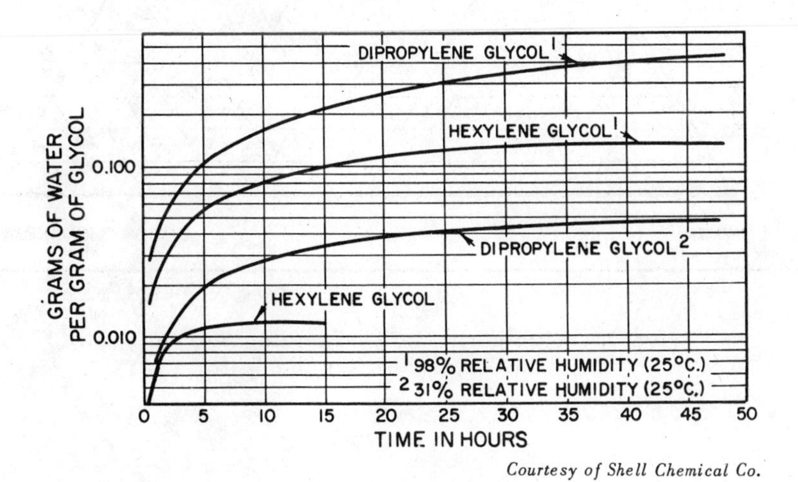

Courtesy of Shell Chemical Co.

Figure 74. Water Absorption by Glycols as a Function of Time.

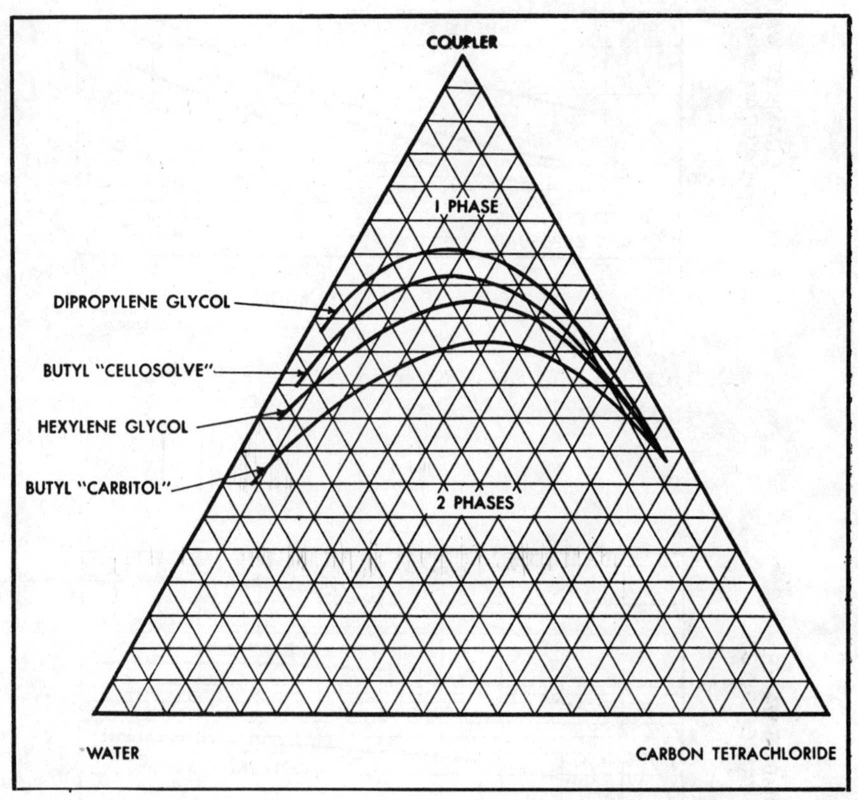

Courtesy of Shell Chemical Co.

Figure 75. Compatibility of Coupling Solvents with Carbon Tetrachloride and Water.

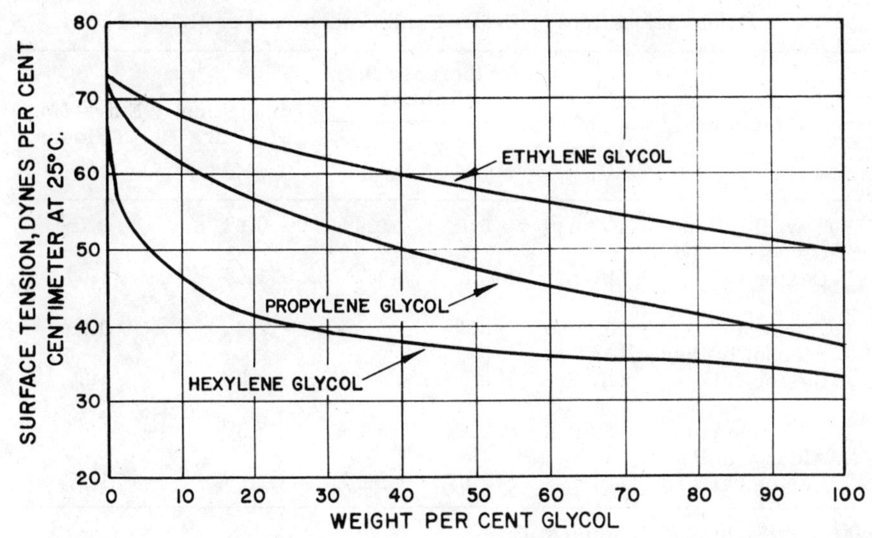

Courtesy of Shell Chemical Co.

Figure 76. Surface Tension of Glycol-Water Systems.

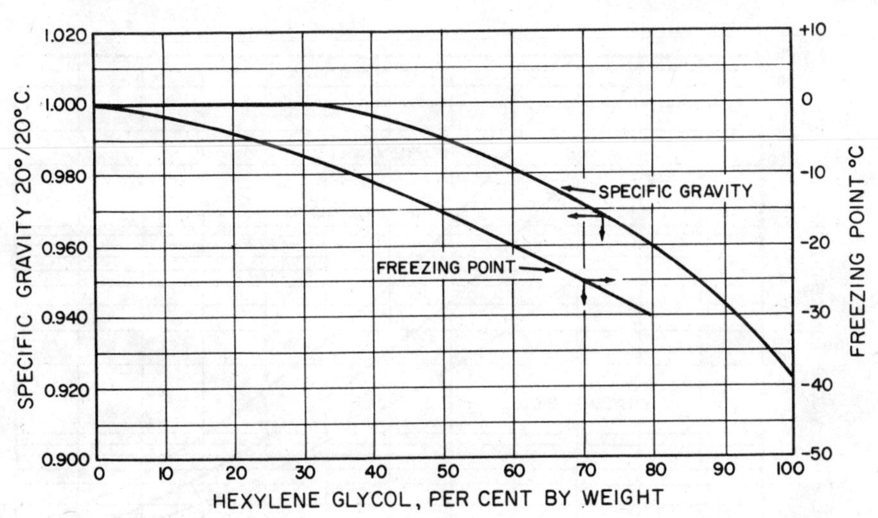

Courtesy of Shell Chemical Co.

Figure 77. Specific Gravity and Freezing Point of Hexylene Glycol-Water Mixtures.

Table 41. Effect of Brake Fluid Components on Rubber*

Solution	Type of Rubber	Increase in Volume		Absorption 24 Hours	Extraction 24 Hours
		24 Hours	1 Week		
50% w. Hexylene Glycol in Raw	Natural	0.1%	0.4%	0.9%	0.1%
Castor Oil	GR-S†	-0.6%	-1.7%	1.0%	1.0%
50% w. n-Butyl Alcohol in Raw	Natural	3.3%	4.5%	3.3%	0.9%
Castor Oil	GR-S	0.6%	1.4%	2.3%	1.3%
50% w. Diacetone Alcohol in Raw	Natural	2.4%	3.6%	3.3%	0.6%
Castor Oil	GR-S	2.0%	2.1%	2.5%	1.2%

*Courtesy of Shell Chemical Co.

†With this material the amount of extraction, although not as large as for the other materials examined, is large in comparison to the amount of absorption. This probably accounts for the negative solvent swelling.

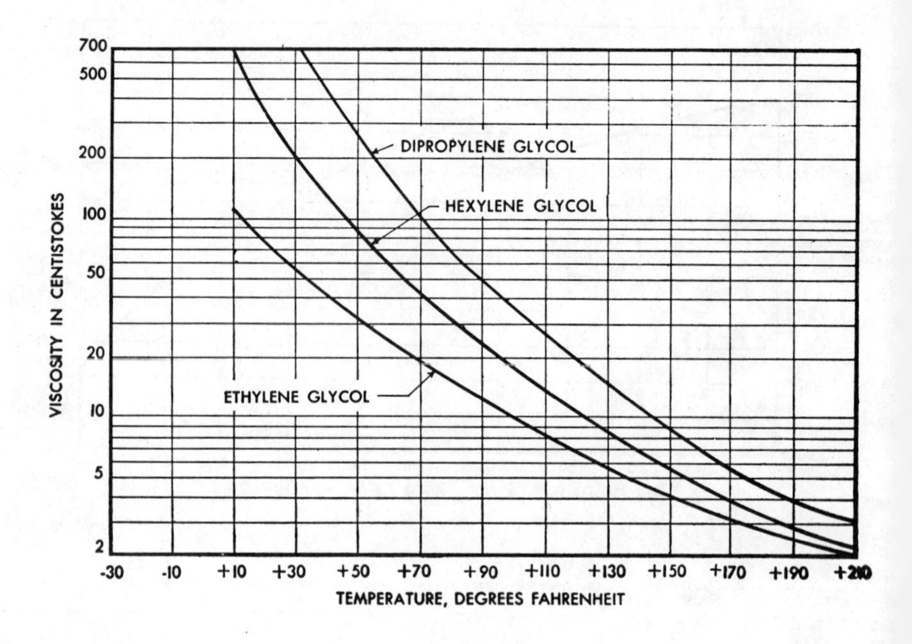

Figure 78. Viscosity of Glycols.

PINACOL

Pinacone
2,3-Dimethyl-2,3-butanediol $HOC(CH_3)_2 \cdot C(CH_3)_2OH$
Tetramethylethylene glycol

This glycol occurs in the anhydrous state as a crystalline solid, and as its hydrate (with 6 H_2O), as four-sided plates. Pinacol is formed in appreciable quantities when acetone is reduced with nascent hydrogen to form isopropyl alcohol.

This ditertiary glycol, containing six carbon atoms, is the first member of a series of such alcohols formed by the reduction of ketones. Like other alcohols, it oxidizes readily. It is freely soluble in hot water, ethyl alcohol, and ether, and slightly soluble in cold water, and carbon disulfide.

During World War I, Germany produced pinacol in large quantities by reducing acetone with aluminum. It was converted by heat and pressure into dimethyl butadiene, forming synthetic rubber when polymerized.

Physical Properties of Pinacol

Boiling point at 760 mm. Hg	174.4° C
Melting point	41.1° C
Molecular weight	118.17

The Hexahydrate

Melting point	45.4° C
Specific gravity, d^{15}	0.967 (supercooled liquid)

2,2-DIETHYL-1,3-PROPANEDIOL

$HOCH_2C(C_2H_5)_2CH_2OH$

This white crystalline solid glycol is a substituted propanediol. It is of interest because of its primary hydroxyl groups in the preparation of plasticizers, synthetic lubricants, and emulsifying agents.

Physical Properties of 2,2-Diethyl-1,3-Propanediol

Boiling point at 10 mm. Hg	125° C
Freezing point	61.3° C
Molecular weight	132.20
Solubility in water at 20° C	25% by wt.
Specific gravity (apparent) at 20° C	1.052

2-ETHYL-1,3-HEXANEDIOL

Ethohexadiol
Octanediol $HOCH_2CH(C_2H_5)CHOHC_3H_7$

2-Ethyl-1,3-hexanediol is a stable, colorless, high-boiling, slightly oily liquid, with a faint odor like witch hazel. It is prepared by the catalytic trimolecular condensation of butyraldehyde with magnesium aluminum ethoxide; the monobutyrate ester formed is hydrolyzed to 2-ethyl-1,3-hexamediol. [46] Union Carbide Chemicals prepares this product by the hydrogenation of butyraldol.

This glycol is relatively insoluble in water, mineral oils, and paraffin oils, and insoluble in cellulose nitrate and acetate, and unvulcanized rubber. It is soluble in ethyl alcohol, isopropyl alcohol, propylene glycol, ethers, castor oil, petroleum naphtha, toluene, carbon tetrachloride, trichloroethylene, and perchloroethylene. It is partly soluble in shellac, rosin, kauri, dewaxed dammar and ester gum. It may soften house paint, wood enamel, spar and floor varnish. When warm, it swells "Vinylite" resins AYAF and VYHH. It does not affect rayon, cellulose acetate, nylon, cellulose nitrate, vinyl resins, polystyrene, polymethyl methacrylate, phenolic resins, or natural rubber.

This glycol is found useful as a resin and dye solvent in certain specialty inks, and as a coupling agent in metal cleaners, dry-cleaning fluids, and industrial soaps. It is used in cosmetics for its coupling and blending properties, as well as its lubricating and emollient action, which resembles that of glycerol. It is therefore of value in hair dressings, shampoos, liquid cleansing creams, and lotions. It is also used as a plasticizer for nylon molding powders, and in the preparation of alkyd resins and polyurethane resins. 2-Ethyl-1,3-hexanediol is a notable insect repellent, effective against mosquitoes, black flies, gnats, chiggers, and so on. It has been included in the U.S. Pharmacopoeia.

Physical Properties of 2-Ethyl-1,3-Hexanediol

Acidity as acetic acid	0.01% by wt., max.
Boiling point at 760 mm. Hg	243.1° C
Color, Pt-Co	15, max.
Distillation range	241 to 249° C
Flash point, open cup	265° F
Freezing point	Sets to glass below -40° C
Molecular weight	146.22
Refractive index, 20° C, n_D	1.4511
Solubility in water, 20° C	4.2% by wt.
Solubility of water in, 20° C	11.7% by wt.
Specific gravity, 20/20° C	0.9422
Suspended matter	Substantially free
Vapor pressure, 20° C	Less than 0.01 mm. Hg
Viscosity, 20° C	323 cp.
Weight per gallon (average), 20° C	7.83 lb.

2,5-DIMETHYL-3-HEXYNE-2,5-DIOL

Dimethyl hexynediol

$$CH_3-\underset{\underset{OH}{|}}{\overset{\overset{CH_3}{|}}{C}}-C\equiv C-\underset{\underset{OH}{|}}{\overset{\overset{CH_3}{|}}{C}}-CH_3$$

This tertiary acetylenic glycol is a solid which has fair solubility in water and many organic solvents. It is nonhygroscopic, relatively stable thermally, somewhat surface-active, and it does not form hydrates. At 20° C, 27 per cent by weight is soluble in water. It is very soluble in acetone, "Cellosolve," cyclohexanone, ethyl acetate, ethyl alcohol, methylethyl ketone, and monethanolamine. It is slightly soluble in benzene, carbon tetrachloride, and petroleum ether (boiling point 60° C). It is insoluble in kerosene, mineral spirits, and soybean oil.

It is found to be useful as a coupling agent in spotting agent formulations for dry cleaning. It is also suggested as a coupling solvent in cutting oils, cosmetic preparations, special detergent compounds, textile finishes, and adhesives. As a dispersant, its use has been suggested in the synthesis of dyestuffs for reducing particle size. Other possible uses are as a heat and light stabilizer, in polymers, and as an intermediate in synthesis.

Physical Properties of 2,5-Dimethyl-3-Hexyne-2,5-Diol

Boiling point	205-6° C
Freezing point	94-5° C
Surface tension at 25° C	
5% in water	41.2 dynes/cm.
0.1% in water	60.9 dynes/cm.
0.01% in water	66.9 dynes/cm.

3,6-DIMETHYL-4-OCTYNE-3,6-DIOL

Dimethyl octynediol

$$CH_3-CH_2-\underset{\underset{OH}{|}}{\overset{\overset{CH_3}{|}}{C}}-C\equiv C-\underset{\underset{OH}{|}}{\overset{\overset{CH_3}{|}}{C}}-CH_2-CH_3$$

This ditertiary acetylenic glycol is a white, crystalline, nonhygroscopic solid. At 20° C, 8.8 per cent by weight is soluble in water. It is very soluble in acetone, benzene, carbon tetrachloride, "Cellosolve," cyclohexanone, ethyl acetate, ethyl alcohol, methylethyl ketone, and monoethanolamine. It is soluble in petroleum ether (boiling point 60° C) and insoluble in soybean oil. Dimethyl octynediol is liquid at normal temperatures when in the form of a solution with 20 per cent water. This solution will dissolve such resins as "Vinylite" AYAF, gum shellac, and oil-soluble phenolic types, but it is insoluble in cellulose acetate, polyisobutylene, and polyvinyl chloride (dispersion-formed). Suggested uses for this glycol are as a coupling agent, as a dispersant of solids in liquids, as heat and light stabilizers, in polymers, and as a chemical intermediate.

Physical Properties of 3,6-Dimethyl-4-Octyne-3,6-Diol

Boiling point at 20 mm. Hg	135° C
Freezing point	55.6° C
Surface tension at 25° C	
5% in water	30.7 dynes/cm.
0.1% in water	55.3 dynes/cm.
0.01% in water	63.9 dynes/cm.

p-XYLYLENE GLYCOL

ω, ω'-Dihydroxy-p-xylene $HOH_2C - \bigcirc - CH_2OH$

This glycol combines the characteristics of its p-hydroxymethyl groups with the aromaticity of the benzene ring. It is a white crystalline solid, with an aromatic odor. It is soluble at 25° C in the following substances, and in the percentages of: 1 to 10 per cent in water; 10 to 20 per cent in ethyl alcohol, acetone, ether, and toluene; and 1 per cent in carbon tetrachloride and chloroform. The uses suggested by its reactivity are as one of the components in the preparation of fibers, and in plasticizers, elastomers, surface coatings, cross-linking agents, potting compounds, and laminating compounds.

Physical Properties of p-Xylylene Glycol

Chlorine (total)	0.6% max.
Flash point (Cleveland open cup)	370° F
Molecular weight	138.16
Purity	95% min.
Set point	115-117.6° C
Specific gravity at 117° C	1.100
Toluene insolubles	0.5% max.

"KROMFAX" SOLVENT

Thiodiglycol
Thiodiethylene glycol $HOCH_2CH_2-S-CH_2CH_2OH$
β, β'-Dihydroxyethyl sulfide

This thiodiglycol, a product of Union Carbide Chemicals Company, is a nonvolatile, practically colorless liquid, with a mild odor, and is completely soluble in water. The hydroxyl groups in this solvent react similarly to other glycols by forming ethers and esters. It has hygroscopic and antioxidant properties. Because it is a powerful, chemically neutral solvent for vat, basic, and acid dyestuffs, it is used in preparing printing pastes from vat dyestuffs, where it is found to be superior to alcohol or glycerol in yielding a higher color intensity, finer dispersion of the dyestuff before reducing, and in improving the solubility of the sodium leuco form.

It is used as a solvent for pasting basic dyes, such as indulines and the nigrosines, used in combination with thiourea and ammonium sulfate as a single "universal assistant combination" in the printing of nylon with acid and direct colors. It acts by dissolving the dye, swelling the fiber, and fixing the dye in the fiber. "Kromfax" solvent is also employed as a cleaner for printing rolls, where dye pastes have become laked.

Physical Properties of "Kromfax" Solvent

Acidity	1.0 mg. KOH/g. sample, max.
Boiling point at 760 mm. Hg	283° C
50 mm. Hg	194° C
Δ Boiling point/Δ p	0.055° C/mm. Hg
Color (Pt-Co)	200 max.
Coefficient of expansion at 55° C	0.00061/° C
Flash point (open cup)	320° F
Freezing point	-10° C
Heat of vaporization at 1 atm.	235 Btu/lb.
Molecular weight	122.19
Refractive index at 20° C n_D	1.5217
Specific gravity	1.1847
Δ Sp. Gr./Δ t	0.00072
Vapor pressure at 20° C	Less than 0.01 mm. Hg
Viscosity at 20° C	65.2 cp.
Weight per gallin at 20° C	9.85 lb.
at 15.56° C	9.88 lb.

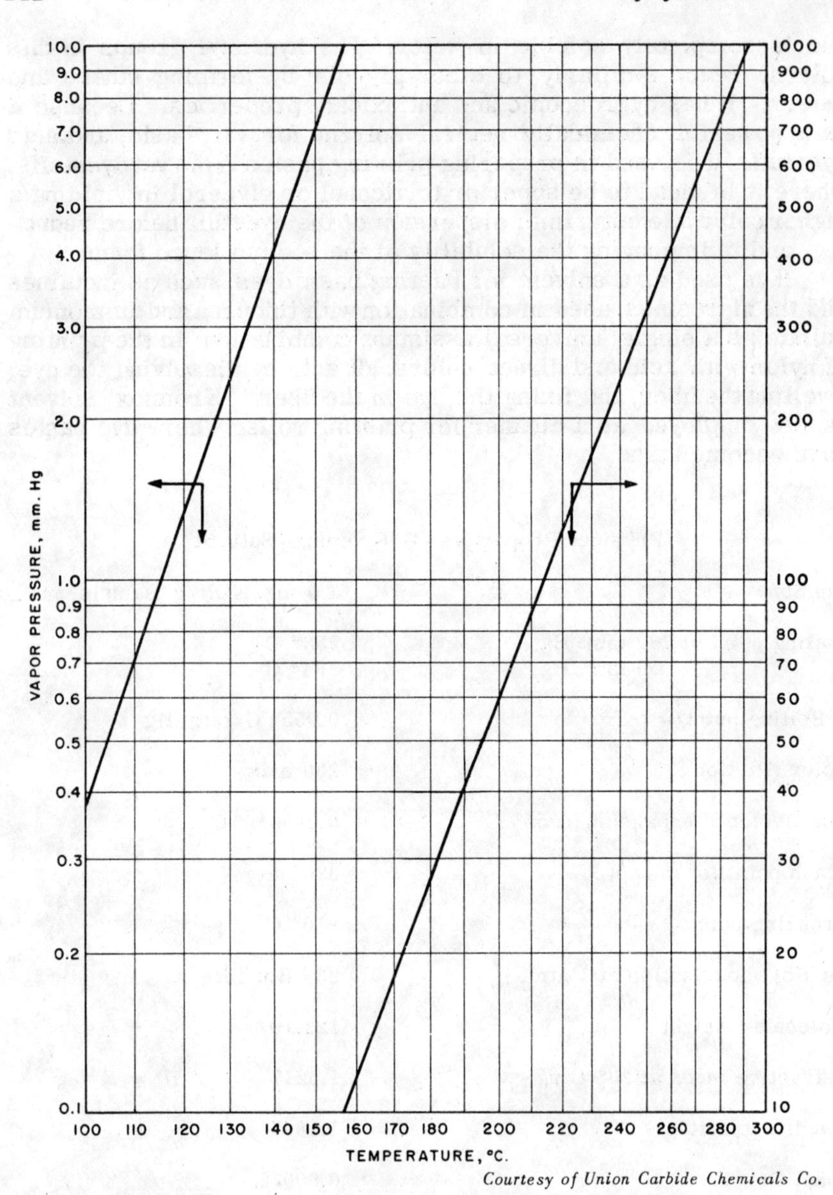

Courtesy of Union Carbide Chemicals Co.

Figure 79. Vapor Pressure of "Kromfax" Solvent (Thiodiglycol) at Various Temperatures.

2-ETHYL-2-BUTYL-1,3-PROPANEDIOL

$HOCH_2C(C_2H_5)(C_4H_9)CH_2OH$

This nine-carbon glycol is a substituted propanediol in the form of a white crystalline solid. It has been found to be an effective insect repellent for impregnating clothing and fabrics. It is also of interest in the preparation of plasticizers, synthetic lubricants, and emulsifying agents.

Physical Properties of 2-Ethyl-2-Butyl-1,3-Propanediol

Boiling point at 100 mm. Hg	195° C
Melting point	41.4° C
Molecular weight	160.25
Solubility in water at 20° C	0.8% by wt.
Specific gravity (apparent) at 50/20° C	0.931

2,2,4-TRIMETHYL-1,3-PENTANEDIOL

$$CH_3-CH(CH_3)-CH(OH)-C(CH_3)_2-CH_2-OH$$

This diol is a white solid, its solubility being less than 1 per cent in water. Water is soluble in it in the same percentage. It has been suggested as an ingredient in insect-repellent formulations, to be used against mosquitoes and chiggers. It is used in the synthesis of hydraulic fluids and lubricant additives, and in the production of alkyd resins.

Physical Properties of 2,2,4-Trimethyl-1,3-Pentanediol

Boiling point at 4 mm. Hg	109-111° C
Melting point	49-51° C
Purity	95% min.

3. TRIHYDRIC ALCOHOLS

Glycerol, as a major compound of world-wide industrial significance, is the outstanding member of the trihydric alcohols. The need for it is apparent, not only during normal times, but even more urgently, during national emergencies when the demand exceeds the supply. Therefore, there is a continuing demand for reliable sources of supply. It was not until economical methods of production and purification were developed that the extensive possibilities of glycerol were exploited, and it reached its present commercial value.

Other industrially important trihydric alcohols to be considered here include 1,2,4-butanetriol, 1,2,6-hexanetriol, and trimethylolpropane.

GLYCEROL

1,2,3-Propanetriol $CH_2OH.CHOH.CH_2OH$
Glycerin

Glycerol was discovered by accident when, in 1779, Karl Scheele, a Swedish chemist, heated olive oil with lead oxide and then unintentionally spilled water on the mixture. This resulted in the formation of a clear, sweetish syrup on the surface, which was recognized by Scheele to be a "discorery of a peculiar sweet and volatile matter," and a new substance which he distinguished as the "sweet principle of fat."

Development and Production

About forty years after Scheele's discovery, the French chemist Michel Chevreul, studying the composition of fats and fixed oils, showed them to be compounds of glycerin, with various fatty acid esters, which could be decomposed with alkalies into glycerin and the salt of the fatty acid—a process we know as "saponification." A patent was issued to him in 1823, in which this process of producing the fatty acid and the recovery of glycerin was described. He also gave glycerin its name, taking it from the Greek word *glykeros* meaning "sweet."

The empirical formula of glycerin was established through the work of Pelouze in 1836, and its chemical constitution was further investigated by Berthelot in 1856. Wurtz during this same time also became interested in the chemistry of glycerin, which eventually led him to the discovery of glycol in 1859.

R. A. Tilghman of Philadelphia originated a process, in 1854, known as "fat-splitting," in which fats and oils were subjected to the action of water at high temperature and pressure, and hydrolyzed to fatty acids and glycerin. Following closely on the development of this method was the discovery, [47] in 1856, of a process of distilling glycerol with the use of steam. As the interest in glycerol progressed, other methods of preparation were investigated using a variety of materials, such as fermentation of sugars, hydrogenolysis of carbohydrates, and as a by-product of the manufacture of higher alcohols. [78-83] However, none of these succeeded commercially, since they could not be carried out economically. Of these methods, the first two have had short periods of production, but were discontinued as unprofitable. Consequently, the two processes in which glycerol is a by-product, namely, saponification and fat-splitting, remained the principal sources of commercial supply until the successful synthesis of glycerol in 1948. Synthesis then became a major and seriously competitive means of supply.

One of the earliest and largest industrial applications of glycerol was as a humectant and spinning lubricant in French textile mills about 100 years ago. This situation changed when, following the discovery of nitroglycerin by the Italian chemist Sobrero in 1846, it was made safe to handle through the work of Alfred Nobel in 1867, who incorporated it in *kieselguhr*. The demand for glycerol reached a degree seldom paralleled in chemical history. Its use in dynamite helped uncover the world's natural resources of fuels, metals, and chemicals, presaging the chemical and technical development of the twentieth century.

Saponification and Fat-Splitting

The soap and fat-splitting industries represented the chief sources for glycerol as a by-product until 1948, when synthetic glycerol first became available in commercial quantities. Although about one-third of available glycerol in the United States today is synthetic, there is nevertheless no expectation of supplanting the glycerol derived from the fat in soap-making and from the manufacture of fatty acids and their derivatives.

In the kettle method of soap-making, the fat is combined with an alkali metal and the resulting spent soap lye contains up to about 10 per cent of the dissolved glycerol. This is evaporated to what is known commercially as an 80 per cent soap-lye crude glycerol. In the more modern method of soap-making—a continuous process—the fat is first subjected to high pressure hydrolysis, by which a good supply of glycerol is dissolved in the resulting "sweetwater." The glycerol is then concentrated by evaporation to the commercial product known as "88 per cent saponification crude."

Modern distillation processes have achieved an efficiency by which chemically pure glycerol of up to 98.7 per cent can be obtained. Distillation is carried out under vacuum with the aid of superheated steam. Where greater purity is desired, glycerol is distilled twice, and is then known as "double-distilled glycerol."

Synthetic Glycerol

Interest in the synthesis of glycerol was evident long before it became a reality in 1948. For the past 100 years investigators proposed methods that failed to attract commercial attention because the basic materials used were uneconomical. Such syntheses started with acetylene, trichloropropane, or allyl alcohol. The Shell Chemical Company, after ten years of research, found in propylene an economical starting point for the synthesis of glycerol. The process begins with the high-temperature (500° C) chlorination of propylene to allyl chloride. The next step may be either (1) the hydrolysis of allyl chloride to allyl alcohol, which is treated with hypochlorous acid to form glycerol monochlorohydrin, or (2) the direct addition of hypochlorous acid to the allyl chloride, to form glycerol dichlorohydrin. Glycerol is then obtained by the hydrolysis of these chlorohydrins with a dilute solution of sodium hydroxide. Glycerol in a dilute solution is purified and concentrated, and is found to compare with the natural "high-gravity" glycerol. The allyl chloride process is valued not only as a source of synthetic glycerol, but also for a number of useful intermediate products.

More recently, Shell Chemical Company has made known that a new process for the synthesis of glycerol is to be put into operation. In this process, hydrogen peroxide is added to acrolein in the presence of osmium tetroxide to form glyceraldehyde. This is then hydrogenated to glycerol. The acrolein is produced by the oxidation of propylene.

Fermentation Glycerol

The production of glycerol by the yeast fermentation of sugars and starches has been known since Pasteur recognized its occurrence during alcoholic fermentation. He estimated the quantity present as 2.5 to 3 per cent by weight of glycerol. Interest in raising the yield of glycerol was stimulated by the work of Neuberg *et al.* conducted during the early years of this century and before World War I. They were the first to explain the mechanism of glycerol formation during alcoholic fermentation, and the reactions of the acetaldehyde formed. Greater yields of glycerol could be produced by fixing the acetaldehyde with such compounds as sulfites or bisulfites, or those of the carbazide or hydrazine type. In this case, acetaldehyde combines with the sulfite, and the reduction of acetaldehyde to alcohol is prevented. Thus, for each molecule of acetaldehyde bound, a molecule of glycerol is formed.

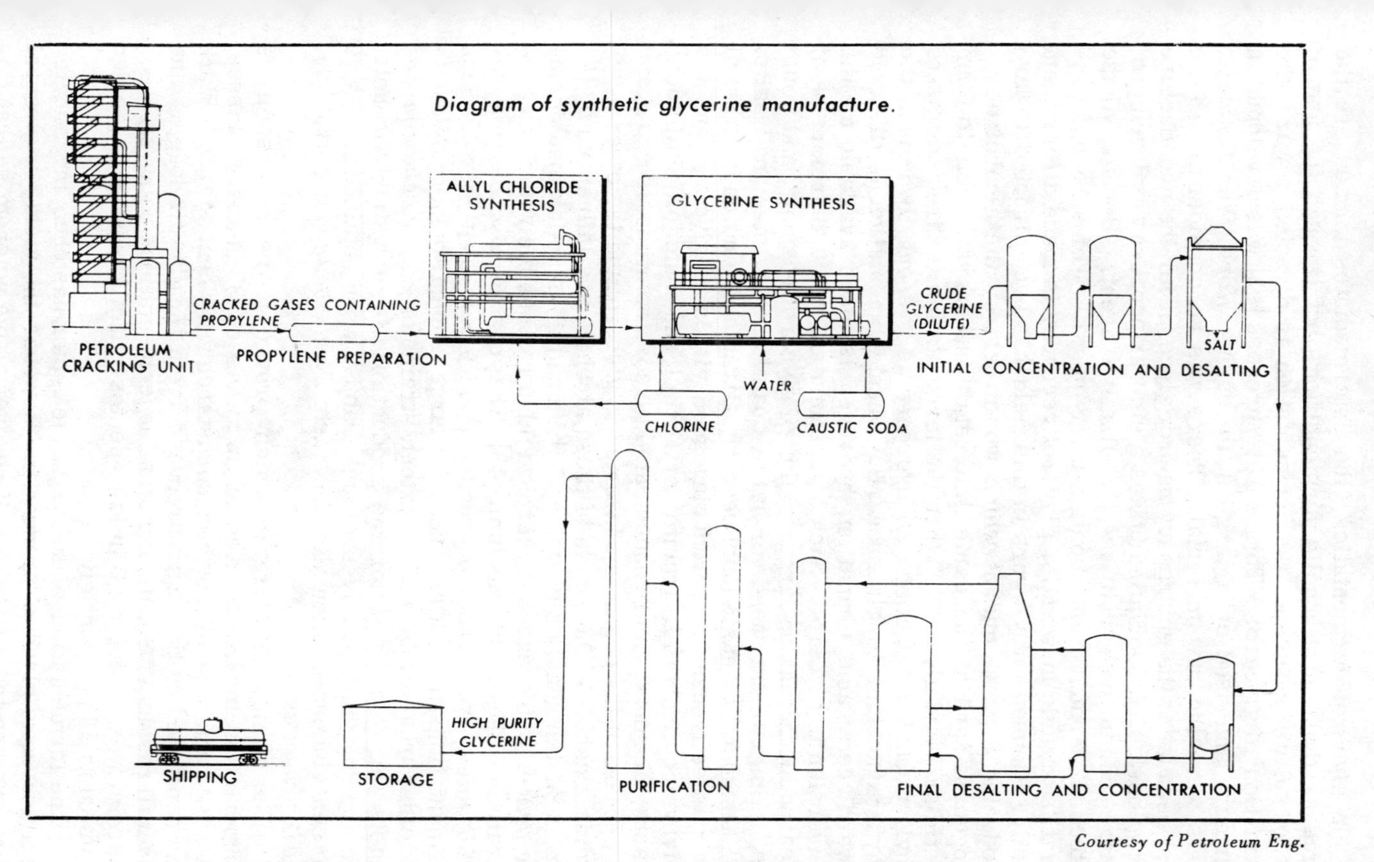

Courtesy of Petroleum Eng.

Figure 80. A Close-Up of Equipment in Operation at New Synthetic Glycerine Plant.

In glycerol fermentation, the intermediates formed are the same as those in alcoholic fermentation, but through the use of these sulfite reagents, the fermentation is directed toward the formation of glycerol. This sulfite process [93] was developed in Germany and used on a large scale during World War I. Sugar beets were the raw material. There was no consideration as to cost because of the emergency need of glycerol for the manufacture of explosives. In the United States a similar process was developed, using sodium carbonate as the fixative agent. Because these "steered" fermentations contain large quantities of salts and non-volatile organic materials, glycerol recovery is made difficult and costly. Consequently, work in this field has been directed toward producing a yeast mutant which would destroy the alcohol dehydrogenase, and at the same time retain the enzymes able to form acetic acid and glycerol. When the fermentation is directed toward ethyl alcohol production, no hydrogen is present to reduce the dihydroxyacetone to glycerol. But when fermentation is directed toward acetic acid formation, hydrogen is made available for the conversion to glycerol. Such a yeast mutant would therefore be of great value in making larger yields of glycerol possible, and would also eliminate the need for large quantities of "steering" salts.

Osmophilic yeasts have recently attracted attention because of their effectiveness in producing good yields of glycerol and the polyhydric alcohols D-arabitol, erythritol, and mannitol. With these yeasts, fermentation of concentrated glucose solutions is rapid, and 60 per cent of the sugar is converted to glycerol and the other polyhydric alcohols. The yields of these alcohols are influenced by the strain of the yeast employed and the conditions maintained during the process. Increased glycerol yields are possible with increased aeration of the culture medium. [48] The yeast *Zygosaccharomyces acidifaciens* was found to produce good yields of glycerol. Such fermentations eliminate the need for large amounts of inorganic salts and other organic materials. Sixteen strains of *Zygosaccharomyces* yeasts were screened for the production of polyhydric alcohols. Outstanding yields of glycerol and arabitol were obtained from a 10 per cent glucose solution with the yeasts *Z. nussbaumeri*, *Z. richteri*, and *Z. rugosus*.

The various substrates which proved to be successful as fermentation media are blackstrap molasses, high-test molasses, sucrose, and acid-hydrolyzed cornstarch or wheat starch. Work was conducted on the sugar produced from Douglas fir logging and sawmill residues. Sulfite and alkaline fermentations using softwood hydrolyzates, which contain less pentose than hardwoods, yielded from 30 to 35 per cent glycerol.

The fermentation of sulfite waste liquor has been investigated as a source of glycerol production. However, the yields of glycerol were low, and the difficulties of recovery gave no promise that this material could be a possible source of glycerol manufacture.

Hydrogenolysis of Sugars

Glycerol can also be produced by the hydrogenolysis of sugars. Stengel *et al.* [39] have patented a process for producing glycerol by catalytic hydrogenation of sugars. Two stages are involved. In the first, the conversion to hexitols takes place, and in the second, the hexitols are converted to glycerol and glycols. Nickel catalysts and water improved the yields of glycerol, and the best temperature was found to be below 220° C. Glycerol was also obtained by the hydrogenolysis of wood sugars. [18, 84-89] Waste wood sugar solutions underwent hydrogenolysis using a nickel catalyst. Purification was accomplished by an ion-exchange method. About 30 to 40 per cent of glycerol was formed, the rest of the product containing glycols.

In the United States, production of glycerol by means of fermentation or hydrogenolysis of sugars has not progressed beyond the laboratory or pilot-plant stage, because of high recovery costs. Nevertheless, work on various materials which can produce glycerol continues, because it is felt that every means should be explored that can assure an adequate supply of this important commodity during fluctuations of existing sources of production and during national emergencies.

Purification and Grades

Affecting the economy of glycerol production are the conditions of its recovery. In the modern method of distilling it, the use of high vacuum and lower temperatures reduces steam consumption and loss of the chemical. An important development in glycerol recovery was made with ion-exchange resins. Early application of this deionizing treatment of crude glycerol obtained from soap lye or sweet waters required final distillation before a chemically pure glycerol could be obtained. With the development of high-capacity synthetic resins, it is now possible to prepare a chemically pure glycerol by ion-exchange or ion-exclusion, or a combination of both methods, and final evaporation. [95-97]

In the deionizing treatment, the crude glycerol is diluted to about 25 per cent, and passed through beds of cation and anion exchange resins, which completely remove the salts. It is more difficult to purify synthetic crude glycerol by ion-exchange. This is due to the presence of certain nonionized impurities, such as polyglycerides and allyl chloride, which are not removed by ion-exchange. The ion-exclusion method has been found of value when used together with ion-exchange.

The former involves loading a volume of crude glycerol on an ion-exchange resin and eluting with water. The ionic and nonionic materials in the feed solution appear in successive fractions of the effluent and are separated from each other.

The grades of glycerol are usually manufactured in accordance with the specifications of a particular application, and the glycerol content is determined by its specific gravity. Thus U.S.P. glycerol, also known as C.P. or chemically pure glycerol, is a water-white product, of 95 per cent minimum strength, suitable for the requirements of pharmaceutical and food preparations. Its minimum specific gravity is 1.249 at 25° C. A 99 per cent C.P. glycerol, equal in quality to U.S.P. glycerol, is of a higher specific gravity, 1.2595 at 25° C minimum. High-gravity glycerol, which is close to white in color, is designated as a B grade in federal specifications. It also meets the standards of AST for high-gravity glycerol for alkyd resins having a minimum content of 98.7 per cent and a minimum specific gravity of 1.2587 at 25° C.

Dynamite glycerol is a high-gravity grade, with a color no darker than specified by grade B of the federal color standard.

Yellow distilled glycerol—minimum 96 per cent—is of grade C quality according to federal specifications. It serves those needs which require less critical standards of color and concentration.

Characteristics and Uses

Glycerol is a clear, colorless, syrupy liquid with a slight, characteristic odor and a sweetish taste, and is oily and warm to the touch. Because of its exceptional hydroscopicity, it can absorb water from the air up to 50 per cent of its weight. It also absorbs such gases as hydrogen sulfide, sulfur dioxide, and hydrogen cyanide. It forms hydrates by suppressing the vapor pressure of water. The one secondary and two terminal primary hydroxyl groups in its structure will react to form ethers and esters. Having weak acidic properties, it forms salts with alkali and heavy metals.

Glycerol is stable up to its boiling point. It is difficult to crystallize, having a tendency to supercool. However, once crystalline nuclei have formed, glycerol will solidify and melt at 18° C.

Herron [49] has worked out a nomograph to be used for estimating viscosity of aqueous glycerol solutions from 0 to 95 per cent glycerol by weight, and covering the temperature range from 20 to 50° C. The construction of this nomograph is based on the equation:

$$\log \mu = \frac{\underline{A}}{\underline{t} - 230} \quad \underline{B}$$

where $\underline{t}$ = temperature, °C, and $\underline{A}$ and $\underline{B}$ are empirical constants based on glycerol concentration in water.

Physical Properties and Specifications of Glycerol

Acidity	Neutral to litmus
Ash	0.01% by wt., max.
Auto ignition point (on glass)	804° F†
Boiling point at 760 mm. Hg	290° C*
Boiling points at low pressures:	
at 1 mm.	125.0° C
5 mm.	153.8° C
10 mm.	167.2° C
20 mm.	182.2° C
40 mm.	198.0° C
Chlorine	0.0005% by wt., max.
Color, Pt-Co (Hazen) standards	20 max.
Fatty acids, mez/100 g.	1 max.
Fire point	400° F†
Flash point, tag open cup	350° F†
tag closed cup	320° F†
Freezing point	17.9° C*
Glycerol	99.5% by wt., min. (sp. gr. at 20° C, in air 1.2626)*
Heat of fusion	47.5 cal./g.
Latent heat of vaporization at 55° C	228.7 g.-cal./g.
at 195° C	197.3 g.-cal./g.
Melting point	17.9° C*
Molecular weight	92.094
Refractive index at 25° F	1.4722†
Specific gravity at 25/25° C	1.262†
Specific heat at 25° C	0.577 cal./g. °C†
Surface tension at 20° C	63.3 dynes/cm.
90° C	58.6 dynes/cm.
150° C	51.9 dynes/cm.
Vapor pressure at 20° C	0.0016 mm. Hg
200° C	42 mm. Hg
Viscosity at 25° C	945 cp.†
Weight per gallon at 25° C	10.50 lb.

*D. R. Stull, Ind. Engl. Chem., 39, 517 (1947).
†ACS Monograph, No. 117.

Table 42. Solubility of Various Compounds in Glycerol*

Substance	Glycerol Concentration % Weight	Temperature °C	Solubility in Parts per 100 Parts of Solvent
Alum	†	15	40
Ammonium carbonate	†	15	20
Ammonium chloride	†	15	20.06
Atropine	†	15	3
Benzoic acid	98.5	--	2
Boric acid	98.5	20	24.80
Calcium hydroxide	35	25	1.3
Calcium hypophosphite	99.04	20	2.5
Calcium sulfate	†	15	5.17
Codeine hydrochloride	99.04	20	11.1
Ethyl ether	99.04	20	0.65
Ferrous sulfate	†	15	25
Guaiacol	99.04	20	13.1
Iodine	†	15	2
Iodoform	95	15	0.12
Iron and potassium tartrate	†	15	8
Iron lactate	†	15	16
Morphine acetate	†	15	20
Novocaine	99.04	20	11.2
Phenacetin	99.04	20	0.47
Phenol	99.04	20	276.4
Potassium iodide	†	15	39.72
Quinine sulfate	98.5	--	1.32
Salicin	†	15	12.5
Sodium bicarbonate	†	15	8.06
Sodium carbonate (crystals)	†	15	98.3
Sodium tetraborate (borax)	†	15	60
Tannic acid	†	15	48.8
Tartar emetic	†	15	5.5
Urea	†	15	50
Zinc chloride	†	15	49.87
Zinc iodide	†	15	39.78

*Courtesy of Glycerine Producers' Assoc.

†Glycerol concentration not specified, probably 95 to 100 per cent.

Table 43. Effects of Temperature and Initial Glucose Concentration on Polyhydric Alcohol Production*

Initial Glucose Concentration, Mg./Ml.	Temperature, °C	Rate of Glucose Utilization G./Liter/Day	Total Polyols as Glycerol, Mg./Ml.	Fraction 1 as Glycerol, Mg./Ml.‡	Glycerol, Mg./Ml.	D-Arabitol, Mg./Ml.	Polyol/Glucose Ratio
			Experiment I				
200	25	11§	29	--	--	--	--
200	30	24	76	--	39	61	0.45
200	33.5	29	96	--	57	65	0.55
200	37	42	102	--	64	70	0.60
			Experiment II				
200	30	20	91	--	--	--	--
230	30	23	97	--	73	55	0.50
260	30	26	117	--	85	55	0.48
290	30	29	127	--	103	51	0.48
			Experiment III				
200	30	29	80	17	40	56	0.48
200	37	40	92	13	36	63	0.50
200	40	0	--	--	--	--	--
200	43	0	--	--	--	--	--
			Experiment IV				
300	30	47	119	30	63	49	0.37
300	37	50	130	21	60	85	0.48
300	40	28§	70#	--	--	--	--
			Experiment V				
350	30	49	128	42	60	64	0.36
350	37	64	144	47	59	65	0.36
350	40	30§	80#	40	24	34	0.29

*Courtesy of Agr. Food Chem.

†Ratio of glucose to corn steep liquor and urea 2000:75:35. Sulfite oxidation rate, 62 mmoles O_2/liter/hour.

‡First fraction from Celite-water column used in separating glycerol and D-arabitol. Composition unknown.

§Glucose utilization stopped after glucose concentration fell to 120 to 150 g./liter.

#Determined after active glucose utilization ceased.

Table 44. Glycerol and Ethanol Production and Sugar Consumption by Commercial Yeast Grown on a 5% Sugar-Beet Molasses Medium with Varying Amounts of Magnesium Sulphite (yields expressed as g. per 100 ml. of medium; initial sugar = 2.34%)*

Time	17 Hr.				41 Hr.				65 Hr.			
$MgSO_3$, %	Glycerol, %	Ethanol, %	Residual Sugar, %	Yield Glycerol on Sugar Used, %	Glycerol, %	Ethanol, %	Residual Sugar, %	Yield Glycerol on Sugar Used, %	Glycerol, %	Ethanol, %	Residual Sugar, %	Yield Glycerol on Sugar Used, %
Control	0.08	0.77	0.0	3.25	--	--	--	--	--	--	--	--
1	0.11	0.11	1.64	15.65	0.30	0.65	Trace	12.65†	--	--	--	--
2	0.14	0.13	1.63	19.4	0.35	0.58	Trace	14.96†	0.36	0.54	Not determined	15.34†
3	0.17	0.14	1.45	18.6	0.38	0.50	0.07	17.00	0.36	0.43	Not determined	15.34†
4	0.14	0.13	1.56	17.8	0.35	0.39	0.40	17.34	0.43	0.36	0.13	19.5
5	0.14	0.11	1.58	18.6	0.29	0.36	0.65	16.77	0.44	0.39	0.10	19.42
6	0.12	0.07	1.62	16.8	0.30	0.35	0.74	18.44	0.43	0.41	0.13	19.28

*Courtesy of Can. J. Technol.
†Calculated on the assumption that all the sugar was used.

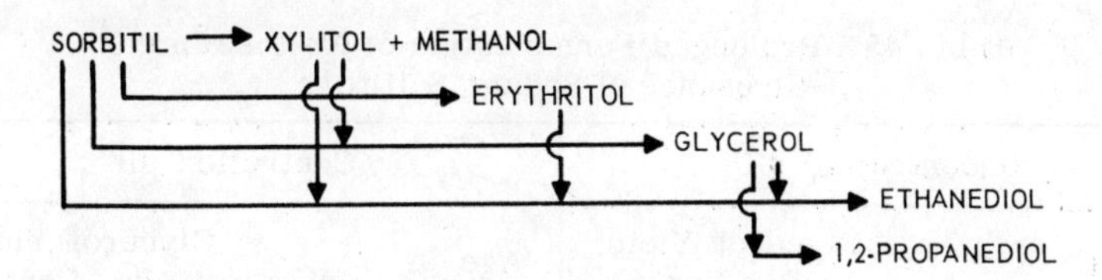

Figure 81. The Principal Reactions in Sorbitol Hydrogenolysis.

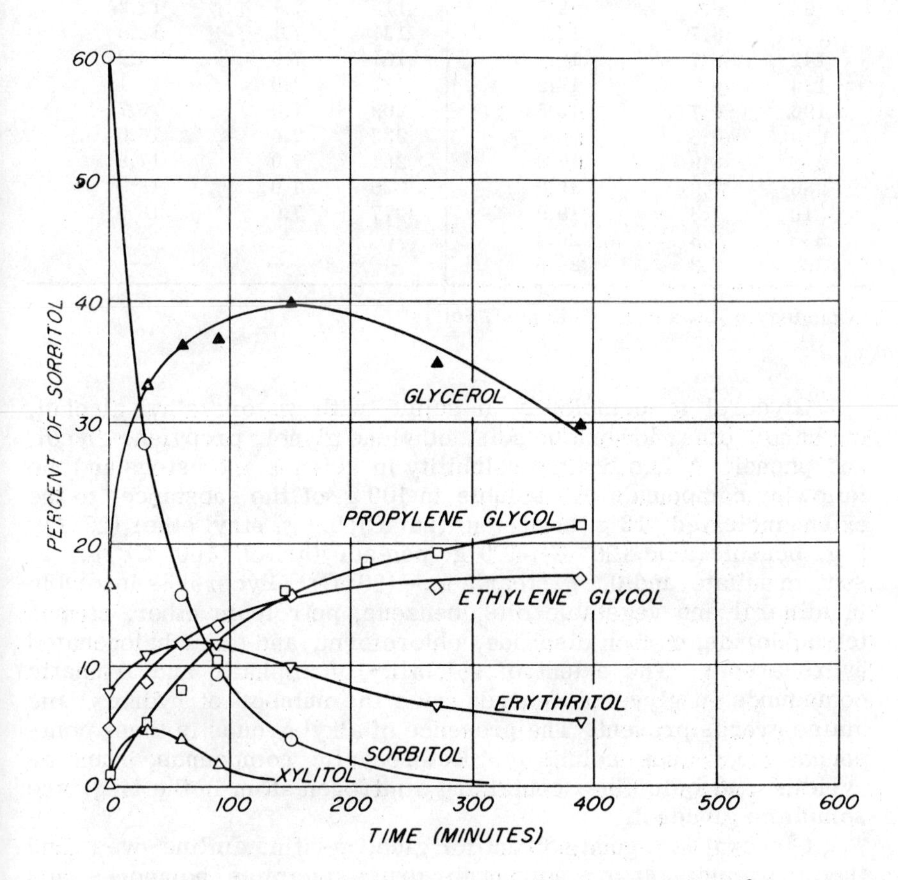

Figure 82. The Hydrogenolysis of Sorbitol at 215° C and a Hydrogen Pressure of 2,000 Psi.

Table 45. Prolonged Fermentation of Maltose in the Presence of Sodium Sulfite*

Uncontrolled pH			Controlled pH		
Age in Hrs.	pH	Glycerol Yield, Per Cent of Sugar	Age in Hrs.	pH	Glycerol Yield, Per Cent of Sugar
5	7.1	0.5	17	7.1	1.3
23	7.0	1.4	41	6.9	4.9
46	6.8	5.1	65	6.9	8.6
70	6.7	7.5	90	7.0	10.1
94	6.7	9.7	113	7.1	12.2
118	6.7	11.1	137	7.1	12.9
142	6.7	12.8	161	7.0	14.2
166	6.7	14.2	185	7.0	15.1
190	6.7	15.5	209	7.0	15.7
214	6.8	16.4	233	7.0	16.6
238	6.9	17.9	281	7.0	17.8
286	7.0	19.2	329	7.0	18.3
310	7.3	19.9	377	7.0	18.5
338	7.3	20.4	--	--	--
362	7.3	20.8	--	--	--

*Courtesy of Iowa State College J. Sci.

Glycerol is completely miscible with water, ethyl alcohol, methanol, other lower alcohols, ethylene glycol, propylene glycol, and phenol. It has limited solubility in ketones and esters and the following compounds are soluble in 100 g. of the substance, to the extent indicated: 13 g. of acetone (25° C); 0.7 g. ethyl ether (20° C); 2 g. benzoic acid (20° C); 9.3 g. pentaerythritol (100° C); 8.1 g. sodium sulfate; and 0.1 g. stearic acid (20° C). Glycerol is insoluble in mineral and vegetable oils, benzene, petroleum ether, carbon tetrachloride, carbon disulfide, chloroform, and other halogenated hydrocarbons. The extent of solubility of aliphatic and aromatic compounds in glycerol depends upon the number of hydroxyl and amine groups present. The presence of alkyl groups in these compounds decreases solubility. Heterocyclic compounds, such as pyridine and quinoline, containing a nitrogen atom in the ring, are soluble in glycerol.

Glycerol is a good solvent for glue, gelatin, aniline dyes, and flavor extracts. It is a solvent for drugs, vitamins, hormones, and is used in the extraction of pepsin, antibiotics, perfumes from flowers, and so forth. It is a solvent for such medicinal substances as iodine, bromine, tannin, alkaloids, thymol, phenol, mercuric chloride, boric acid, fixed alkalies, and the like. Glycerol forms azeotropes with turpentine, cyclohexane, chloroform, and other compounds.

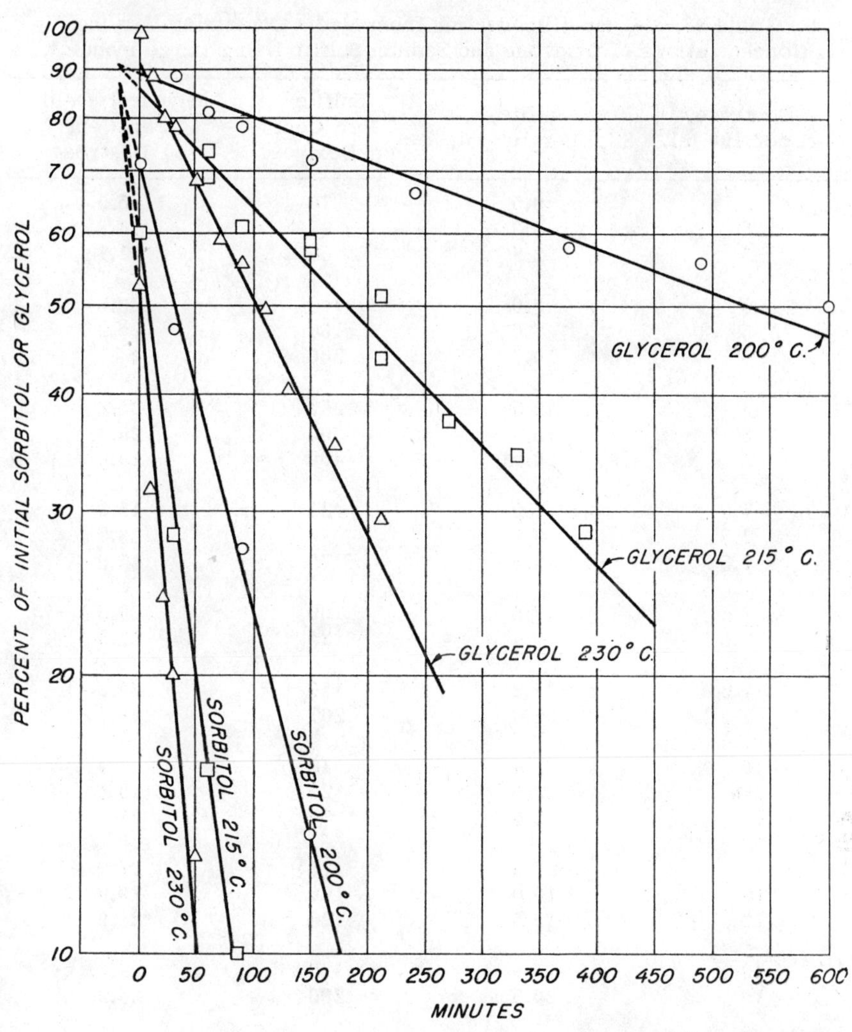

Courtesy of Dept. of Agriculture.

Figure 83. The Hydrogenolysis of Sorbitol and of Glycerol at a Hydrogen Pressure of 2,000 Psi.

Table 46. Glycerol Production from Media Containing Varying Concentrations of Dextrose and Sodium Sulfite Using Large Inocula*

Dextrose, g. per 100 ml.	Sulfite, g. per 100 ml.	Sulfite Per Cent on Dextrose	Glycerol Yield, Per Cent on Dextrose
5	0.5	10	5.9
5	1.3	25	14.8
5	2.5	50	21.1
5	5.0	100	23.8
5	7.5	150	25.2
5	10.0	200	24.7
5	12.5	250	25.8
5	15.0	300	26.3
5	20.0†	400	28.8
7.5	1.9	25	15.1
7.5	3.8	50	23.7
7.5	5.6	75	25.8
7.5	7.5	100	26.9
7.5	9.4	125	27.9
7.5	11.3	150	28.2
7.5	20.0†	267	28.5
10	1.0	10	6.4
10	2.5	25	15.6
10	5.0	50	25.8
10	7.5	75	27.9
10	10.0	100	29.0
10	12.5	125	28.9
10	15.0	150	27.0
10	20.0	200	26.2
12.5	3.1	25	14.6
12.5	6.3	50	23.9
12.5	9.4	75	27.1
12.5	12.5	100	28.2
12.5	15.6	125	28.7
12.5	18.8	150	27.6

*Courtesy of Iowa State College J. Sci.
†Analyzed after fermentation for 8 days.

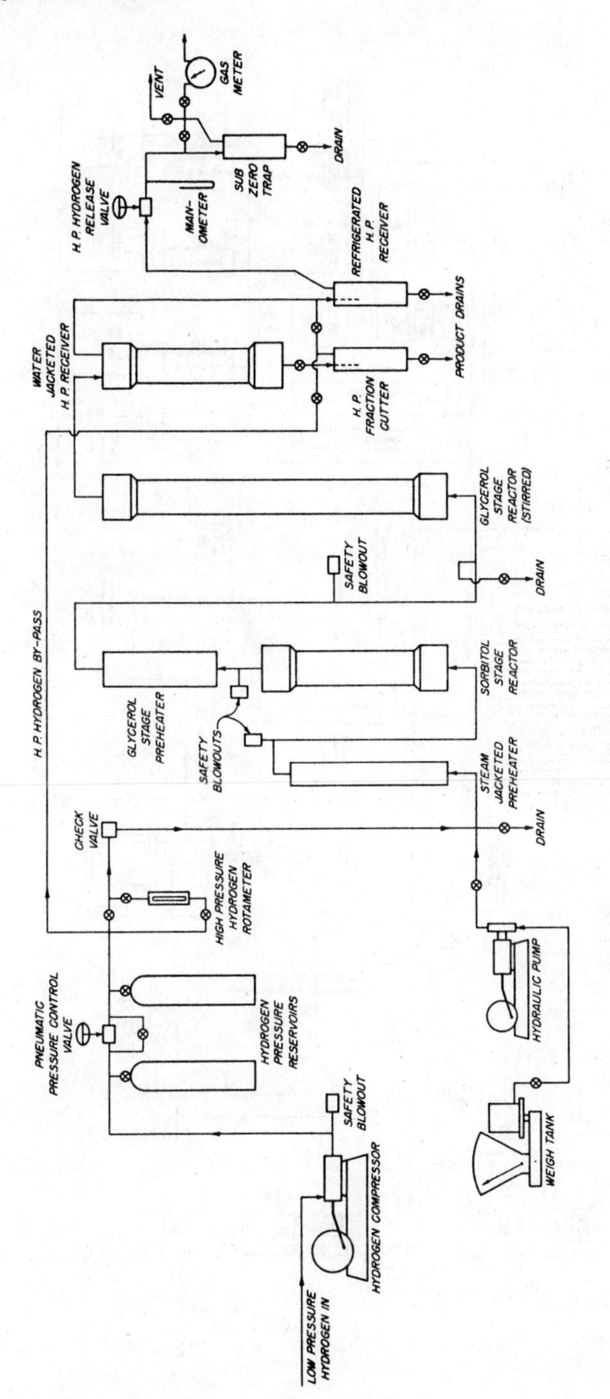

Figure 84. Flow Diagram for Continuous Hydrogenolysis System.

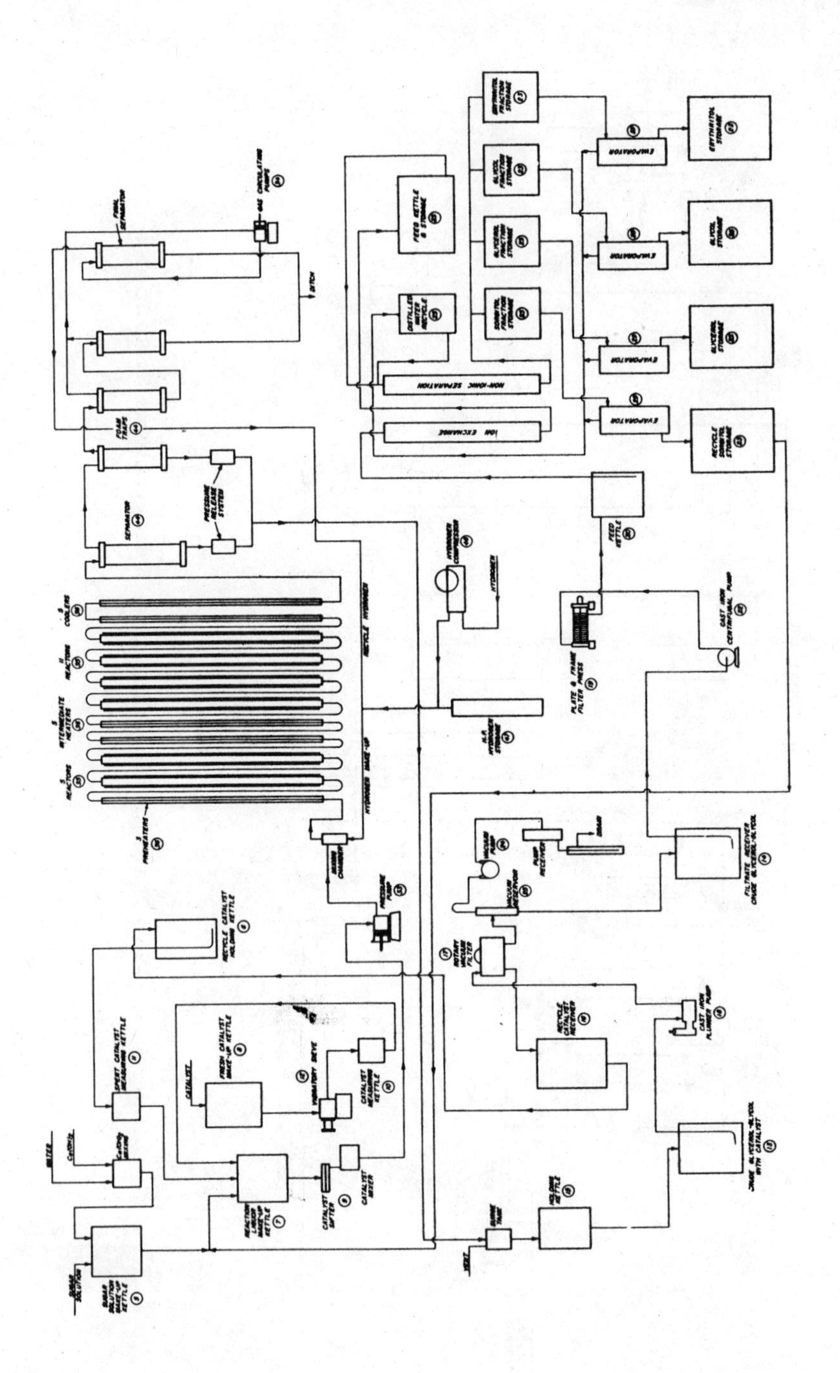

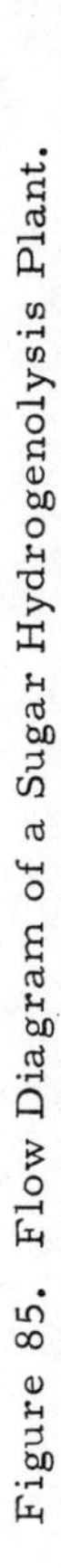

Figure 85. Flow Diagram of a Sugar Hydrogenolysis Plant.

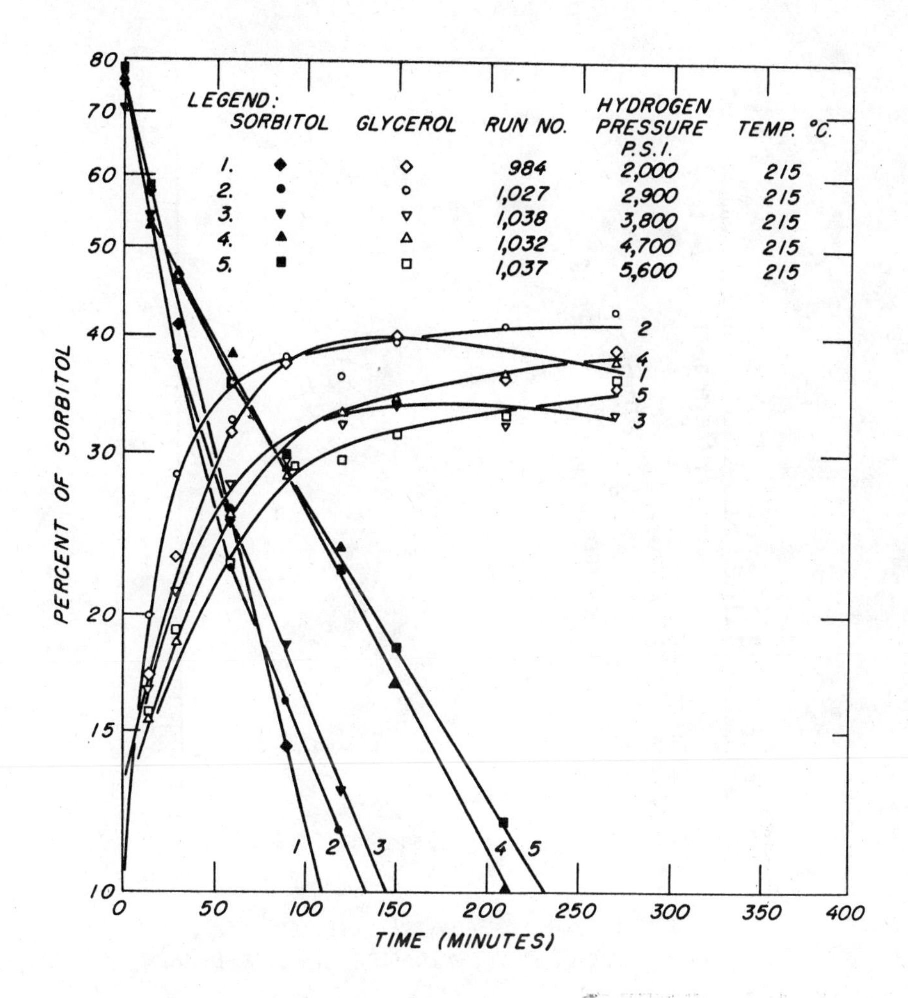

Figure 86. The Hydrogenolysis of Sorbitol at 215° C.

Among the many and varied uses of glycerol, the largest consumption of this alcohol is in the manufacture of alkyd resins for varnishes and enamels; this consumes about 30 per cent of the annual supply. Second in importance is its use in the manufacture of explosives. It is also used to a large extent in food processing, confections, beverages; as a solvent for natural and artificial flavors and food colors; and as a humectant, sweetener, and preservative. Glycerol is a major ingredient in pharmaceuticals and cosmetics, serving as a solvent, humectant, plasticizer, penetrant, sweetener, and antifreeze.

It is used as a plasticizer for cellophane and many types of paper, as a humectant for tobacco, and as an aid to dyeing and

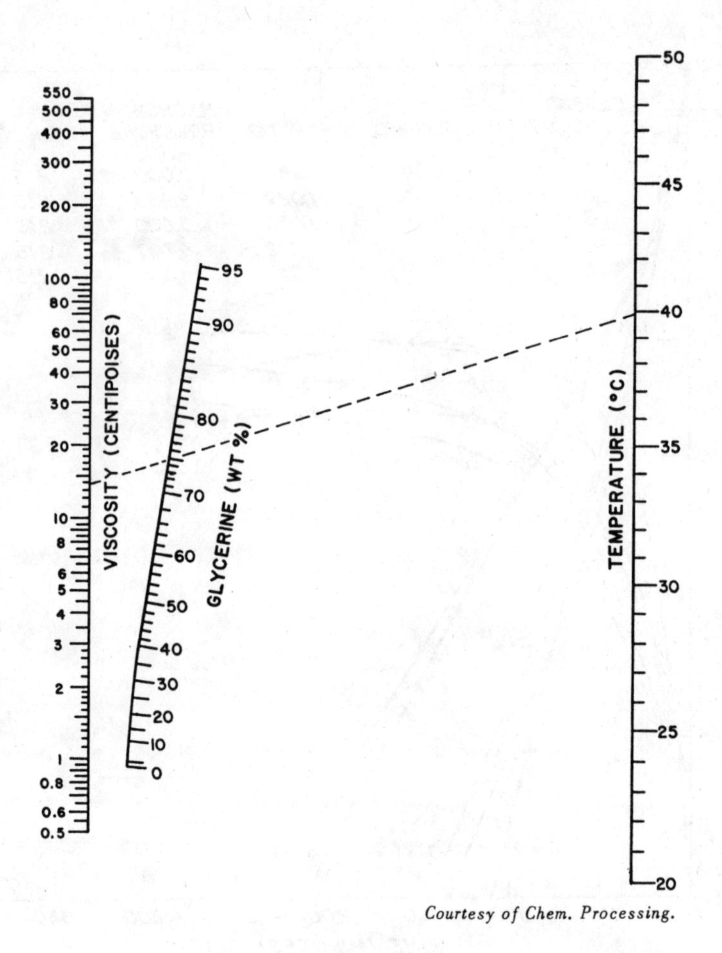

Courtesy of Chem. Processing.

Figure 87. Viscosity of Water-Glycerine Solutions.

printing, and a softener, sizing aid, and plasticizer in the textile industry. It is a suspending agent and humectant in cleaning compounds, and in photography is used to increase solvent and penetrating power of solutions for color film. It is a softener in cork compositions, adhesives, printers' rollers, and leather, rubber, and molded goods. It is an additive in shaving creams. It increases the effectiveness of antibiotic sprays. It has found increasing application in pressure-packaged foods because of its ability to dissolve gases, to increase emulsion stability, to dissolve flavors and colors, and to increase the body of the product. It is also used as a humectant in pressure-packaged toothpaste.

Glycerol also finds use in hydraulic fluids. By adding small amounts of formaldehyde to glycerol, the swelling of rubber pistons is prevented. [92]

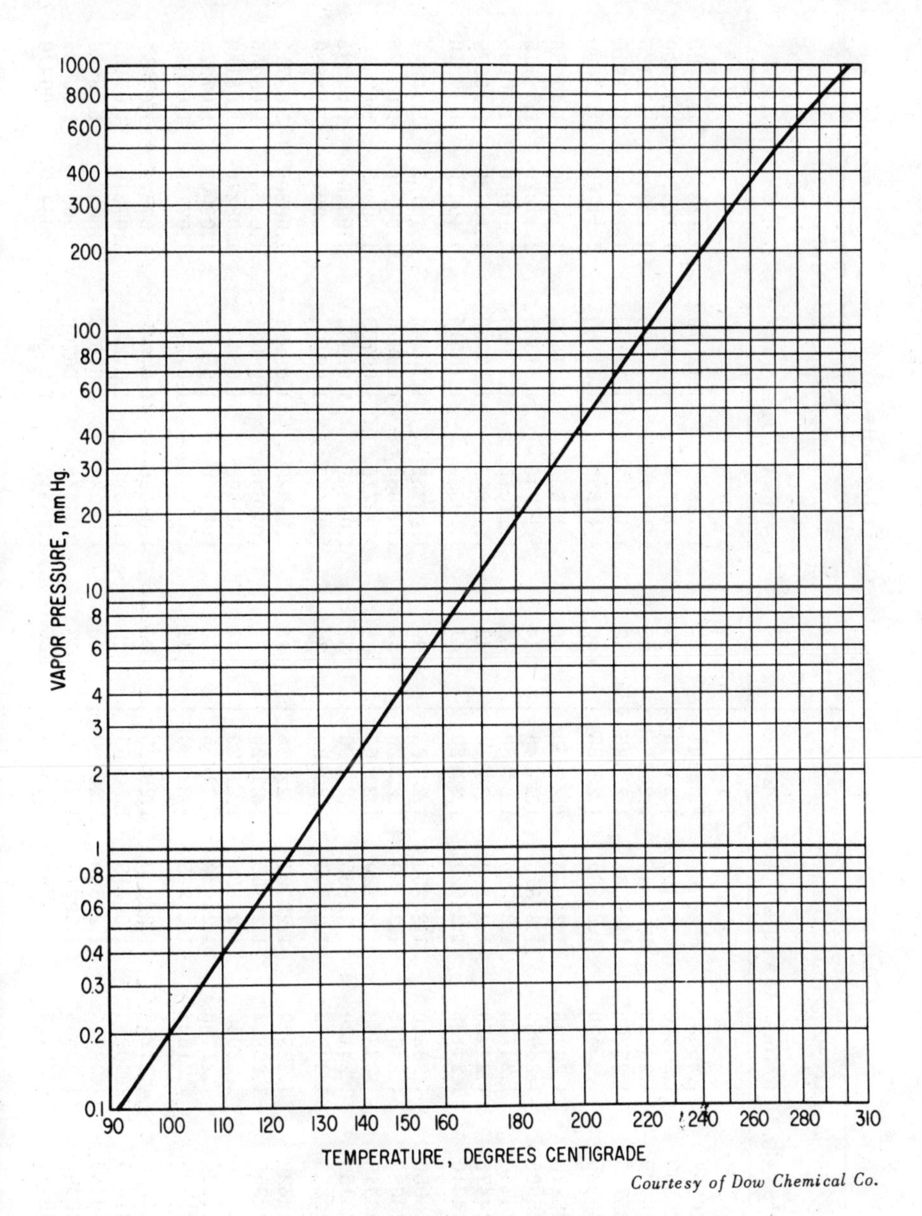

Courtesy of Dow Chemical Co.

Figure 88. Vapor Pressure of Glycerol.

Table 47. Specific Gravity and Per Cent Glycerol*

Glycerol	Apparent Specific Gravity				Glycerol	Apparent Specific Gravity			
	15/15° C	15.5/15.5° C	20/20° C	25/25° C		15/15° C	15.5/15.5° C	20/20° C	25/25° C
Per Cent					Per Cent				
100	1.26557	1.26532	1.26362	1.26201	50	1.12985	1.12970	1.12845	1.12720
99	1.26300	1.26275	1.26105	1.25945	49	1.12710	1.12695	1.12570	1.12450
98	1.26045	1.26020	1.25845	1.25685	48	1.12440	1.12425	1.12300	1.12185
97	1.25785	1.25760	1.25585	1.25425	47	1.12165	1.12150	1.12030	1.11915
96	1.25525	1.25500	1.25330	1.25165	46	1.11890	1.11880	1.11760	1.11650
95	1.25270	1.25245	1.25075	1.24910	45	1.11620	1.11605	1.11490	1.11380
94	1.25005	1.24980	1.24810	1.24645	44	1.11345	1.11335	1.11220	1.11115
93	1.24740	1.24715	1.24545	1.24380	43	1.11075	1.11060	1.10950	1.10845
92	1.24475	1.24450	1.24280	1.24115	42	1.10800	1.10790	1.10680	1.10575
91	1.24210	1.24185	1.24020	1.23850	41	1.10525	1.10515	1.10410	1.10310
90	1.23950	1.23920	1.23755	1.23585	40	1.10255	1.10245	1.10135	1.10040
89	1.23680	1.23655	1.23490	1.23320	39	1.09985	1.09975	1.09870	1.09775
88	1.23415	1.23390	1.23220	1.23055	38	1.09715	1.09705	1.09605	1.09510
87	1.23150	1.23120	1.22955	1.22790	37	1.09445	1.09435	1.09335	1.09245
86	1.22885	1.22855	1.22690	1.22520	36	1.09175	1.09165	1.09070	1.08980
85	1.22620	1.22590	1.22420	1.22255	35	1.08905	1.08895	1.08805	1.08715
84	1.22355	1.22325	1.22155	1.21990	34	1.08635	1.08625	1.08535	1.08455
83	1.22090	1.22055	1.21890	1.21720	33	1.08365	1.08355	1.08270	1.08190
82	1.21820	1.21790	1.21620	1.21455	32	1.08100	1.08085	1.08005	1.07925
81	1.21555	1.21525	1.21355	1.21190	31	1.07830	1.07815	1.07735	1.07660
80	1.21290	1.21260	1.21090	1.20925	30	1.07560	1.07545	1.07470	1.07395
79	1.21015	1.20985	1.20815	1.20655	29	1.07295	1.07285	1.07210	1.07135
78	1.20740	1.20710	1.20540	1.20380	28	1.07035	1.07025	1.06950	1.06880
77	1.20465	1.20440	1.20270	1.20110	27	1.06770	1.06760	1.06690	1.06625
76	1.20190	1.20165	1.19995	1.19840	26	1.06510	1.06500	1.06435	1.06370

75	1.19915	1.19890	1.19720	1.19565	25	1.06250	1.06240	1.06175	1.06115
74	1.19640	1.19615	1.19450	1.19295	24	1.05985	1.05980	1,05915	1.05860
73	1.19365	1.19340	1.19175	1.19025	23	1.05725	1.05715	1.05655	1.05605
72	1.19090	1.19070	1.18900	1.18755	22	1.05460	1.05455	1.05400	1.05350
71	1.18815	1.18795	1.18630	1.18480	21	1.05200	1.05195	1.05140	1.05095
70	1.18540	1.18520	1.18355	1.18210	20	1.04935	1.04935	1.04880	1.04840
69	1.18260	1.18240	1.18080	1.17935	19	1.04685	1.04680	1.04630	1.04590
68	1.17985	1.17965	1.17805	1.17660	18	1.04435	1.04430	1.04380	1.04345
67	1.17705	1.17685	1.17530	1.17385	17	1.04180	1.04180	1.04135	1.04100
66	1.17430	1.17410	1.17255	1.17110	16	1.03930	1.03925	1.03885	1.03850
65	1.17155	1.17130	1.16980	1.16835	15	1.03675	1.03675	1.03635	1.03605
64	1.16875	1.16855	1.16705	1.16560	14	1.03425	1.03420	1.03390	1.03360
63	1.16600	1.16575	1.16430	1.16285	13	1.03175	1.03170	1.03140	1.03110
62	1.16320	1.16300	1.16155	1.16010	12	1.02920	1.02920	1.02890	1.02865
61	1.16045	1.16020	1.15875	1.15735	11	1.02670	1.02665	1.02640	1.02620
60	1.15770	1.15745	1.15605	1.15460	10	1.02415	1.02415	1.02395	1.02370
59	1.15490	1.15465	1.15325	1.15185	9	1.02175	1.02175	1.02155	1.02135
58	1.15210	1.15190	1.15050	1.14915	8	1.01935	1.01930	1.01915	1.01900
57	1.14935	1.14910	1.14775	1.14640	7	1.01690	1.01690	1.01675	1.01660
56	1.14655	1.14635	1.14500	1.14365	6	1.01450	1.01450	1.01435	1.01425
55	1.14375	1.14355	1.14220	1.14090	5	1.01210	1.01205	1.01195	1.01185
54	1.14100	1.14080	1.13945	1.13815	4	1.00965	1.00965	1.00955	1.00950
53	1.13820	1.13800	1.13670	1.13540	3	1.00725	1.00725	1.00720	1.00710
52	1.13540	1.13525	1.13395	1.13265	2	1.00485	1.00485	1.00480	1.00475
51	1.13265	1.13245	1.13120	1.12995	1	1.00240	1.00240	1.00240	1.00235

*Courtesy of Ind. & Eng. Chem. and Glycerine Producers' Assoc.

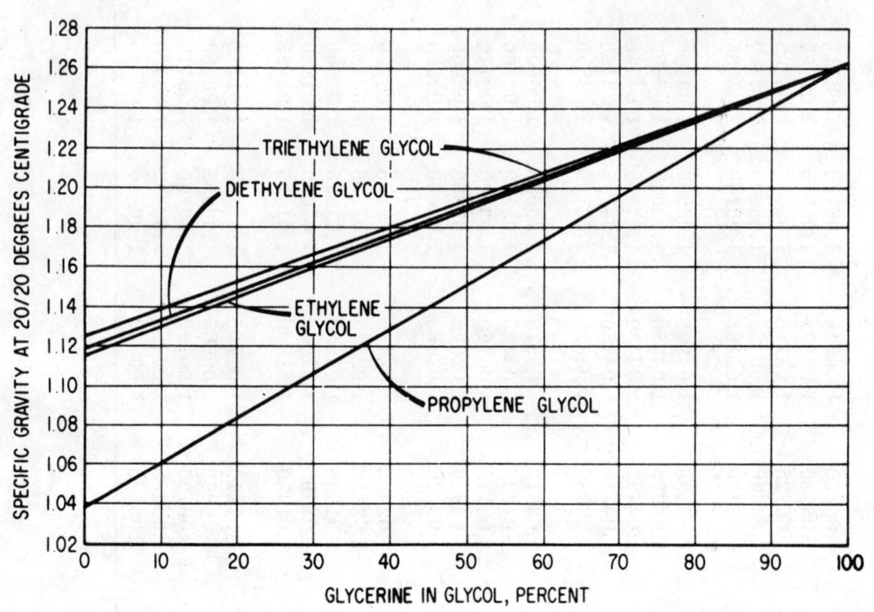

Courtesy of Dow Chemical Co.

Figure 89. Specific Gravities of Glycerine-Glycol Mixtures.

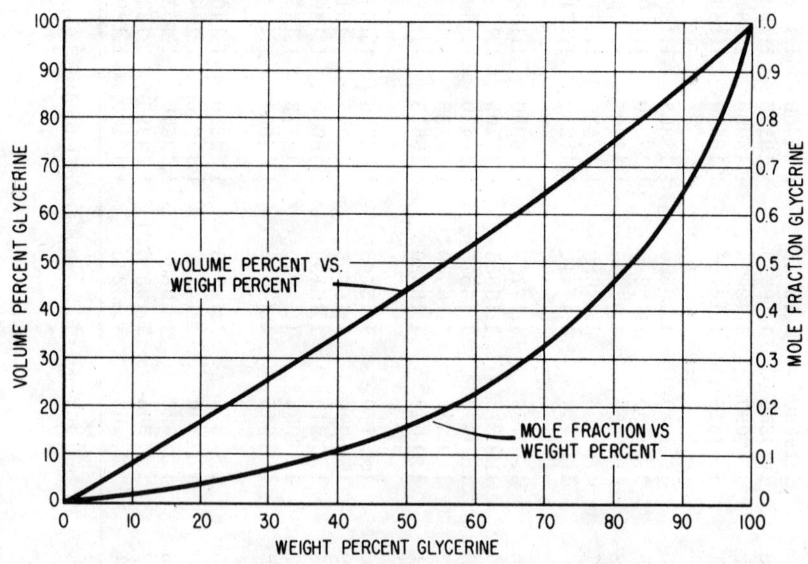

Courtesy of Dow Chemical Co.

Figure 90. Conversion Chart for Aqueous Glycerine Solutions (25° C).

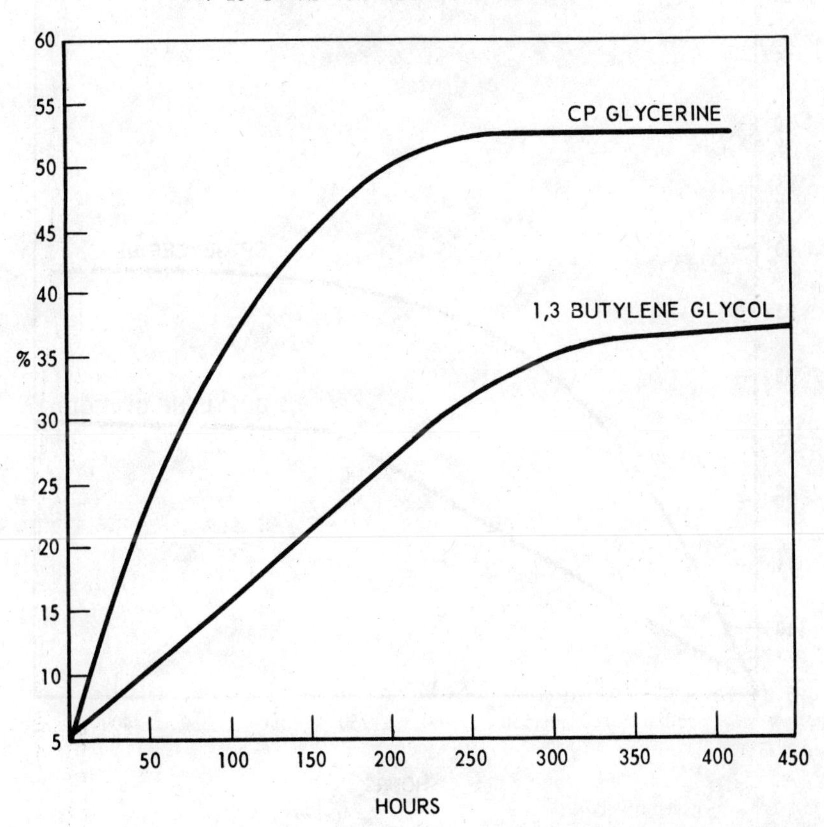

Courtesy of Celanese Corp. of America.

Figure 91. Hygroscopicity.

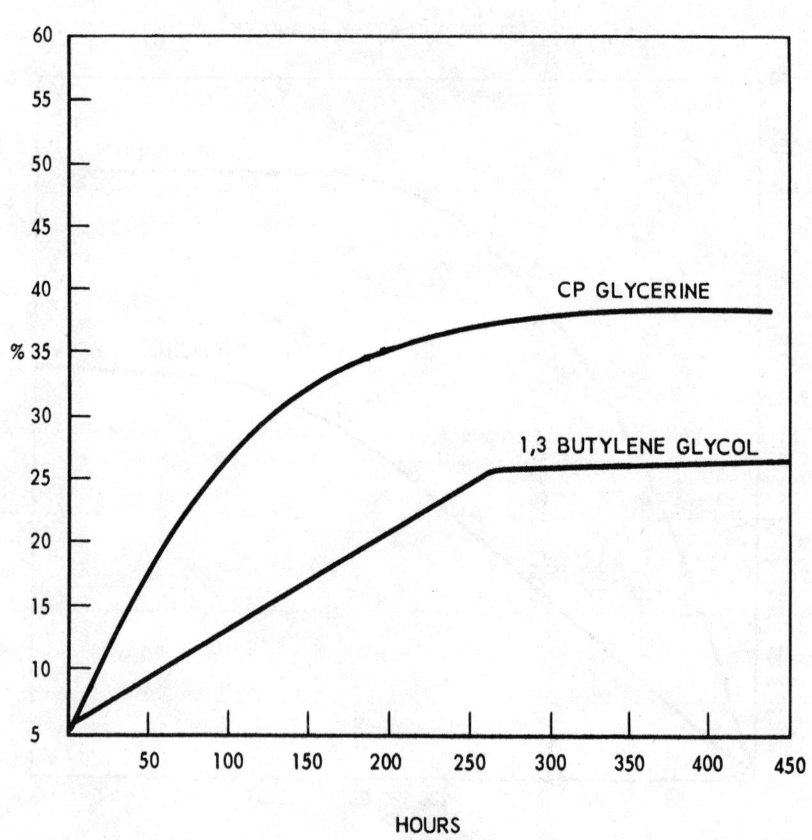

Courtesy of Celanese Corp. of America.

Figure 92. Hygroscopicity.

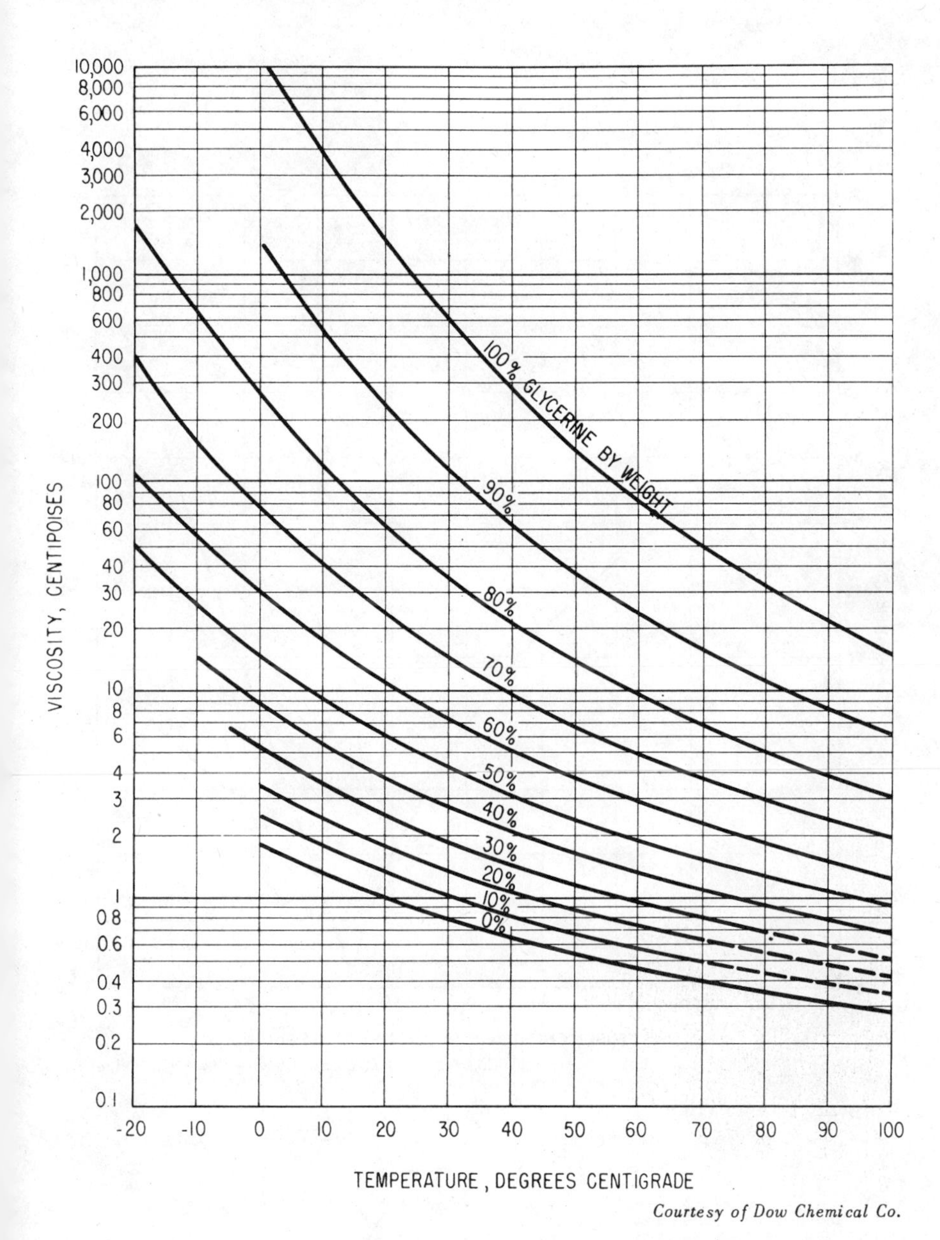

Courtesy of Dow Chemical Co.

Figure 93. Viscosities of Aqueous Solutions of Glycerine.

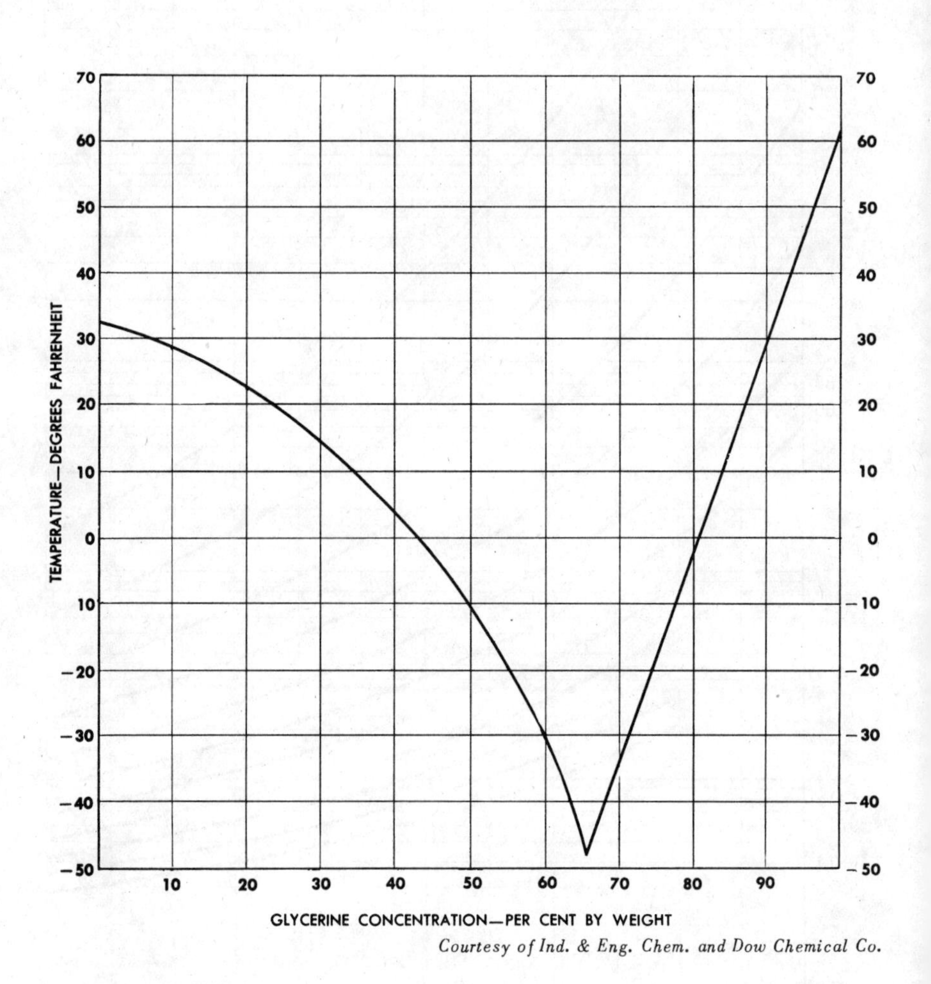

Courtesy of Ind. & Eng. Chem. and Dow Chemical Co.

Figure 94. Freezing Points of Glycerol-Water Solutions.

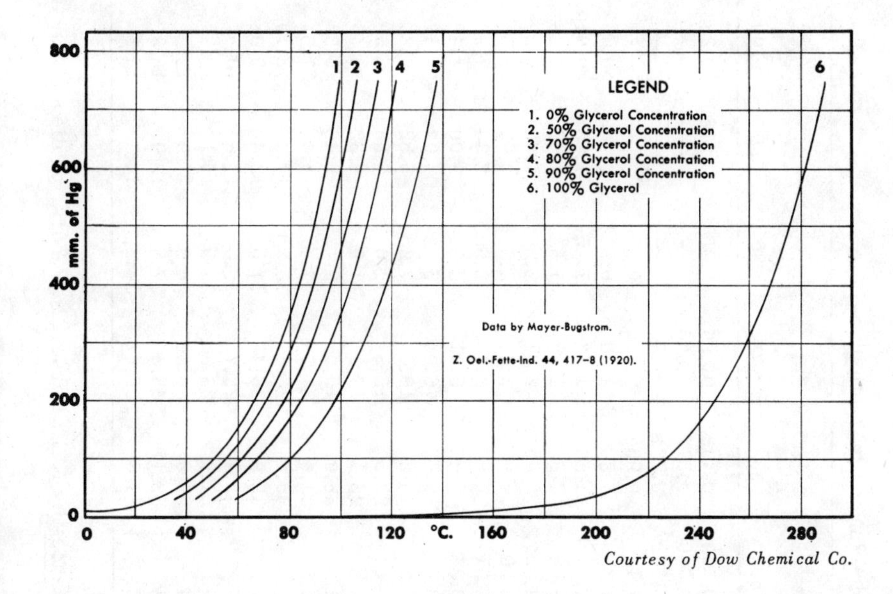

Courtesy of Dow Chemical Co.

Figure 95. Vapor Pressure of Glycerol-Water Solutions.

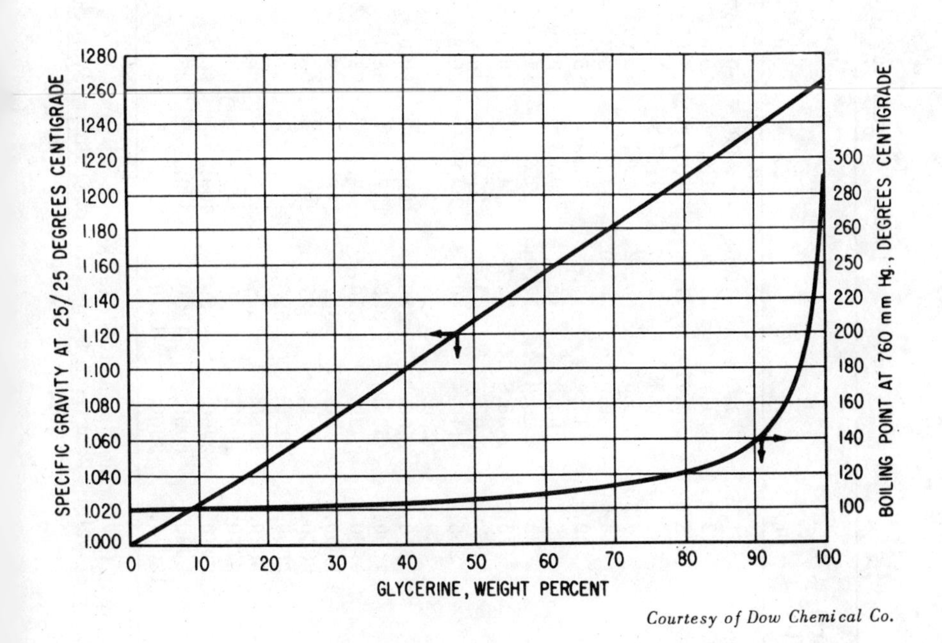

Courtesy of Dow Chemical Co.

Figure 96. Boiling Points and Specific Gravities of Aqueous Solutions.

Table 48. Viscosity of Aqueous Glycerol Solutions in Centipoises*

Glycerol % Wt.	Temperature °C.										
	0	10	20	30	40	50	60	70	80	90	100
0†	1.792	1.308	1.005	0.8007	0.6560	0.5494	0.4688	0.4061	0.3565	0.3165	0.2838
10	2.44	1.74	1.31	1.03	0.826	0.680	0.575	0.500	---	---	---
20	3.44	2.41	1.76	1.35	1.07	0.879	0.731	0.635	---	---	---
30	5.14	3.49	2.50	1.87	1.46	1.16	0.956	0.816	0.690	---	---
40	8.25	5.37	3.72	2.72	2.07	1.62	1.30	1.09	0.918	0.763	0.668
50	14.6	9.01	6.00	4.21	3.10	2.37	1.86	1.53	1.25	1.05	0.910
60	29.9	17.4	10.8	7.19	5.08	3.76	2.85	2.29	1.84	1.52	1.28
65	45.7	25.3	15.2	9.85	6.80	4.89	3.66	2.91	2.28	1.86	1.55
67	55.5	29.9	17.7	11.3	7.73	5.50	4.09	3.23	2.50	2.03	1.68
70	76.0	38.8	22.5	14.1	9.40	6.61	4.86	3.78	2.90	2.34	1.93
75	132.	65.2	35.5	21.2	13.6	9.25	6.61	5.01	3.80	3.00	2.43
80	255.	116.	60.1	33.9	20.8	13.6	9.42	6.94	5.13	4.03	3.18
85	540.	223.	109.	58.0	33.5	21.2	14.2	10.0	7.28	5.52	4.24
90	1310.	498.	219.	109.	60.0	35.5	22.5	15.5	11.0	7.93	6.00
91	1590.	592.	259.	127.	68.1	39.8	25.1	17.1	11.9	8.62	6.40
92	1950.	729.	310.	147.	78.3	44.8	28.0	19.0	13.1	9.46	6.82
93	2400.	860.	367.	172.	89.0	51.5	31.6	21.2	14.4	10.3	7.54
94	2930.	1040.	437.	202.	105.	58.4	35.4	23.6	15.8	11.2	8.19
95	3690.	1270.	523.	237.	121.	67.0	39.9	26.4	17.5	12.4	9.08
96	4600.	1580.	624.	281.	142.	77.8	45.4	29.7	19.6	13.6	10.1
97	5770.	1950.	765.	340.	166.	88.9	51.9	33.6	21.9	15.1	10.9
98	7370.	2460.	939.	409.	196.	104.	59.8	38.5	24.8	17.0	12.2
99	9420.	3090.	1150.	500.	235.	122.	69.1	43.6	27.8	19.0	13.3
100	12070.	3900.	1410.	612.	284.	142.	81.3	50.6	31.9	21.3	14.8

*Courtesy of Glycerine Producers' Assoc.
†Viscosity of water taken from Properties of Ordinary Water-Substances by N. E. Dorsey, New York, publisher ? 1940, p. 184.

Table 49. Density of Glycerol Solutions*

Glycerol %	Temperature F.p.	-5°	-10°	-20°	-30°	-40°
10	-1.6°	---	---	---	---	---
20	-4.8°	---	---	---	---	---
30	-9.5°	1.0810	---	---	---	---
40	-15.4°	1.1096	1.1109	---	---	---
50	-23.0°	1.1387	1.1407	1.1450	---	---
60	-34.7°	1.1663	1.1685	1.1732	1.1787	---
66.7	-46.5°	1.1860	1.1889	1.1945	1.1985	1.2034
70	-38.5°	1.1954	1.1993	1.2038	1.2079	---
80	-20.3°	1.2210	1.2255	1.2305	---	---
90	-1.6°	---	---	---	---	---

*Courtesy of Dow Chemical Co.

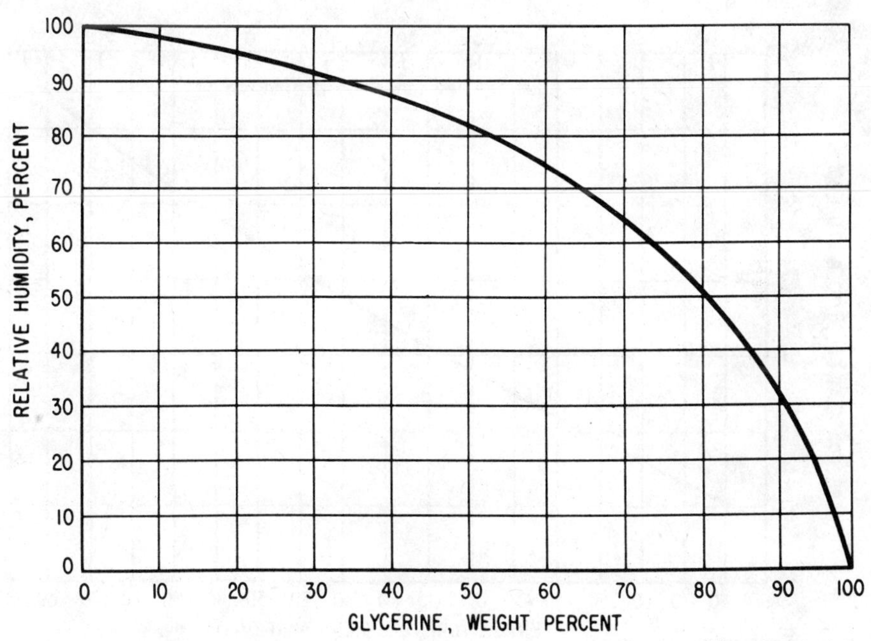

Courtesy of Dow Chemical Co.

Figure 97. Relative Humidities over Aqueous Glycerine Solutions (20-100° C).

Table 50. Viscosity of Glycerol Solutions
(all viscosities expressed in centipoises)*

Temperature Glycerol %	F.p.	-5°	-10°	-20°	-30°	-40°
10	-1.6°	---	---	---	---	---
20	-4.8°	---	---	---	---	---
30	-9.5°	6.5	---	---	---	---
40	-15.4°	10.3	14.4	---	---	---
50	-23.0°	18.8	24.4	48.1	---	---
60	-34.7°	41.6	59.1	108.0	244.0	---
66.7	-46.5°	74.7	113.0	289.0	631.0	1398.0
70	-38.5°	110.0	151.0	394.0	1046.0	---
80	-20.3°	419.0	683.0	1600.0	---	---
90	-1.6°	---	---	---	---	---

*Courtesy of Dow Chemical Co.

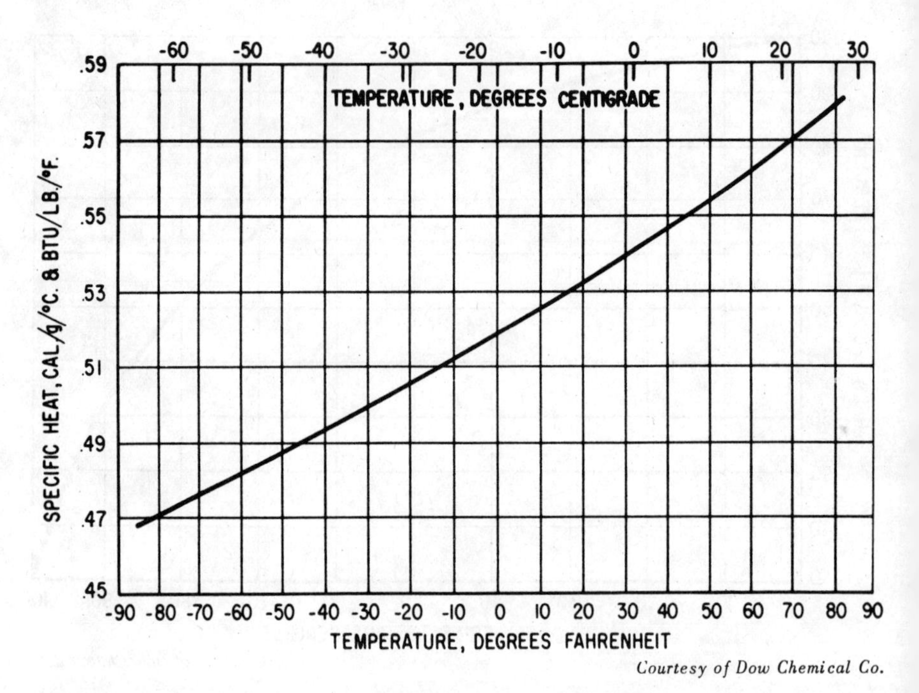

Figure 98. Specific Heat of Glycerine.

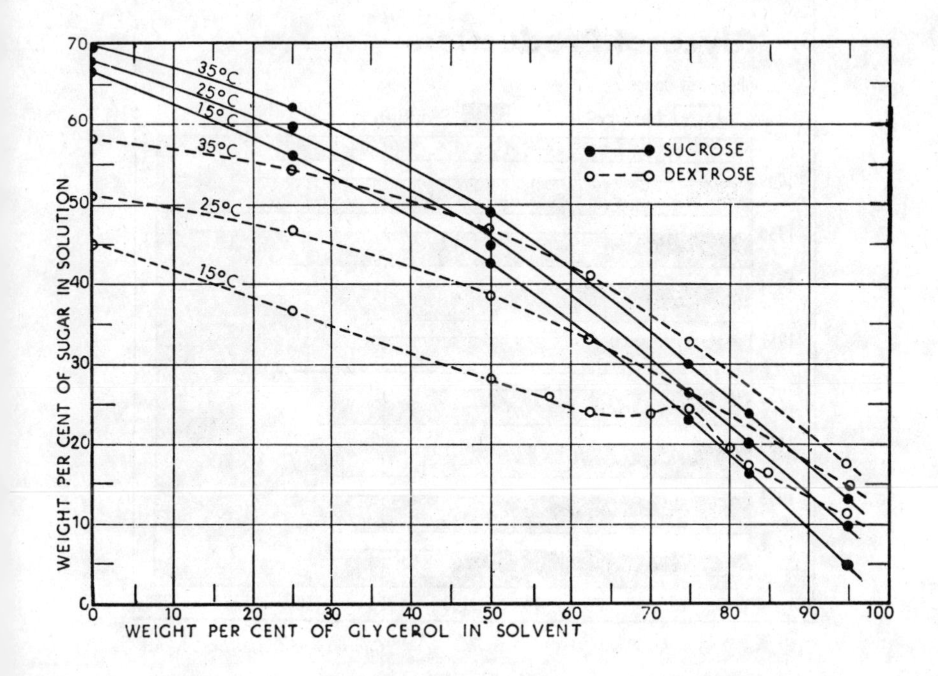

Figure 99. Solubility of Sucrose and Dextrose in Aqueous Glycerol at 15°, 24°, and 35° C.

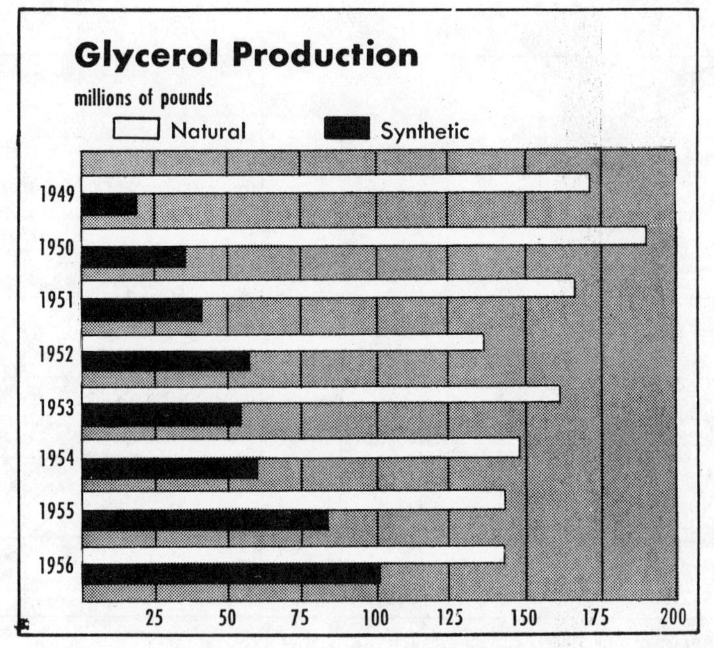

Courtesy of Chem. Eng. News.

Figure 100. Glycerol Production.
The production of both natural and synthetic glycerol has increased in 1959, to over 260 million pounds.

Table 51. Freezing Points of Glycerol-Water Mixtures*

Glycerol by Weight Per Cent	Water Per Cent	Freezing Points °C	Glycerol by Weight Per Cent	Water Per Cent	Freezing Points °C
0.0	100.0	0	65.0	35.0	-43.0
5.0	95.0	-0.6	65.6	34.4	-44.5
10.0	90.0	-1.6	66.0	34.0	-44.7
11.5	88.5	-2.0	66.7	33.3	-46.5
15.0	85.0	-3.1	66.1	32.9	-45.5
20.0	80.0	-4.8	67.3	32.7	-44.5
22.6	77.4	-6.0	68.0	32.0	-44.0
25.0	75.0	-7.0	70.0	30.0	-38.9
30.0	70.0	-9.5	70.9	29.1	-37.5
33.3	67.0	-11.0	75.0	25.0	-29.8
35.0	65.0	-12.2	75.4	24.6	-28.5
40.0	60.0	-15.4	79.0	21.0	-22.0
44.5	55.5	-18.5	80.0	20.0	-20.3
45.0	55.0	-18.8	84.8	15.2	-10.5
50.0	50.0	-23.0	85.0	15.0	-10.9
53.0	47.0	-26.0	90.0	10.0	-1.6
55.0	45.0	-28.2	90.3	9.7	-1.0
60.0	40.0	-34.7	95.0	5.0	7.7
60.4	39.6	-35.0	95.3	4.7	7.5
64.0	36.0	-41.5	98.2	1.8	13.5
64.7	35.3	-42.5	100.0	0.0	17.0

*Courtesy of Ind. & Eng. Chem. and Glycerine Producers' Assoc.

Table 52. Vapor Pressure of Glycerol*

Temperature, °C	V. P. mm. Hg.	Temperature, °C	V. P. mm. Hg.
120	--	210	63.8
130	1.47	220	91.9
140	2.61	230	130
150	4.48	240	181
160	7.44	250	248
170	12.0	260	334
180	18.9	270	445
190	29.0	280	586
200	43.4	290	760

*Courtesy of Dow Chemical Co.

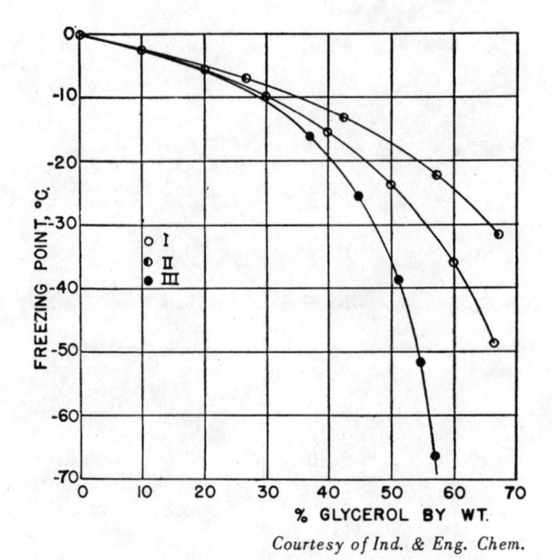

Courtesy of Ind. & Eng. Chem.

Figure 101. Freezing Points of Glycerol-Water Mixtures. (I) Observed; (II) Theoretical, without hydration; (III) Theoretical, with complete hydration.

1,2,4-Butanetriol

$HOCH_2CHOHCH_2CH_2OH$

This triol is an almost colorless and odorless liquid, completely miscible with water and ethyl alcohol. The purified grade is colorless and odorless.

Physical Properties of Commercial 1,2,4-Butanetriol

Boiling point at 760 mm. Hg	312° C*
0.17 mm. Hg	116° C
Fire point, Cleveland open cup	393° F
Flash point	343° F
Freezing point	Supercools (resistance to crystallization)
Refractive index at 25° C, n_D	1.473
Specific gravity, d/4	1.82
Viscosity at 25° C	1038 cs. (kinematic) 1227 cp.
Weight per gallon at 25° C	9.86 lb.

Purified 1,2,4-Butanetriol

Fire point, Cleveland open	387° F
Flash point, Cleveland open cup	332° F
Heat of combustion	555 kcal./mole
Heat of formation	165.1 kcal./mole (liquid) 157 kcal./mole (gas)
Heat of vaporization	14.0 kcal./mole
Specific gravity, d/4	1.184

*Decomposes before reaching boiling point at atmospheric pressure. This is an extrapolated value.

1,2,6-Hexanetriol

$HOCH_2CHOH(CH_2)_3CH_2OH$

This acrolein derivative contains three hydroxyl groups and has a chemical behavior similar to glycerol. 1,2,6-Hexanetriol is a stable, high-boiling liquid, and its hygroscopicity is about 40 per cent of that of glycerol. It is completely miscible with water, and soluble in the proportion of 1 cc. of 1,2,6-hexanetriol to 4 cc. of the following solvents: acetone, butanol, butyl "Cellosolve," "Cellosolve" solvent, diacetone alcohol, absolute ethyl alcohol, isophorone, and pine oil. It is insoluble in the same proportion in benzene, butyl acetate, castor oil, "Cellosolve" acetate, dibutyl phthalate, dichlorethyl ether, ethyl acetate, ethyl ether, heptane, methyl isobutyl ketone, mineral oil, toluene, and trichloroethylene.

This triol is compatible with animal glue, casein, and zein; partly compatible with gelatin and shellac; and incompatible with beeswax, carnauba wax No. 3, ester gum C, ethyl "Cellosolve," nitrocellulose, paraffin wax, and rosin.

Uses suggested by its properties are as a coupling agent and solvent for special hydraulic fluids, duplicating fluids, textile dyes, adhesives and metal cleaners. It is a plasticizer for animal glues, water-soluble resins, and for dextrin adhesives, in which it functions as an anticurling agent. It is used in pharmaceuticals and cosmetics as a hygroscopic agent and plasticizers, reducing low-temperature graininess in ointments. It is also employed in the preparation of alkyd-type resins, polyurethane resins, and plasticizers.

Physical Properties of 1,2,6-Hexanetriol

Boiling point at 5 mm. Hg	178° C
Coefficient of expansion at 20° C	0.00054/° C
Flash point, open cup	375° F
Freezing point	-32.8° C (freezes under controlled conditions; usually sets to glass at below -20° C)
Molecular weight	134.17
Refractive index	1.4771
Specific gravity at 20/20° C	1.1063
Δ Sp. Gr./Δ t at 10 to 40° C	0.00059/°C
Vapor pressure at 20° C	Less than 0.01 mm. Hg
Viscosity at 20° C	2584 cp.
Weight per gallon at 20° C	9.19 lb.
Δ lb./gal./Δ t	0.00499° C

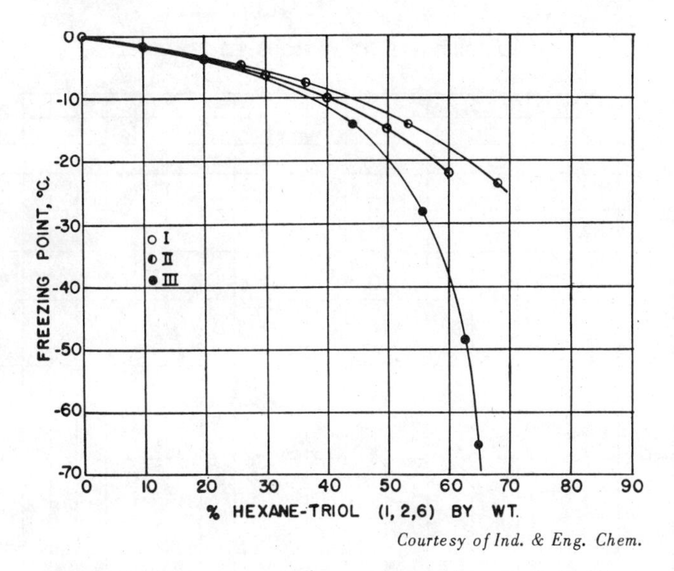

Courtesy of Ind. & Eng. Chem.

Figure 102. Freezing Points of Hexanetriol-Water Mixtures. (I) Observed; (II) Theoretical, without hydration; (III) Theoretical, with complete hydration.

Trimethylolpropane

2,2-Dihydroxymethyl-1-butanol
Ethyl trimethylolmethane $C_2H_5C(CH_2OH)_3$
TMP

Trimethylolpropane is a white, crystalline flaked solid, about one-half as hygroscopic as glycerol. It is made synthetically by the aldol condensation of formaldehyde and butyraldehyde. This trihydric alcohol is freely soluble in water, ethyl alcohol, and other lower alcohols, glycerol, and dimethylformamide. Forty grams of this triol are soluble in 100 ml. of acetone; 8 g., in 100 ml. of ethyl acetate; and 0.02 g., in 100 g. of benzene. It is slightly soluble in carbon tetrachloride, ethyl ether, and chloroform, but it is insoluble in aliphatic, aromatic, and chlorinated hydrocarbons.

This alcohol is used in the production of alkyd resins, polyurethane resins, rosin esters, synthetic drying oils, elastomers, adhesives, heat-convertible polyesters, explosives, surface-active agents, and plasticizers. It offers such advantages over other triols as higher resistance to thermal degradation and compatibility with organic solvents.

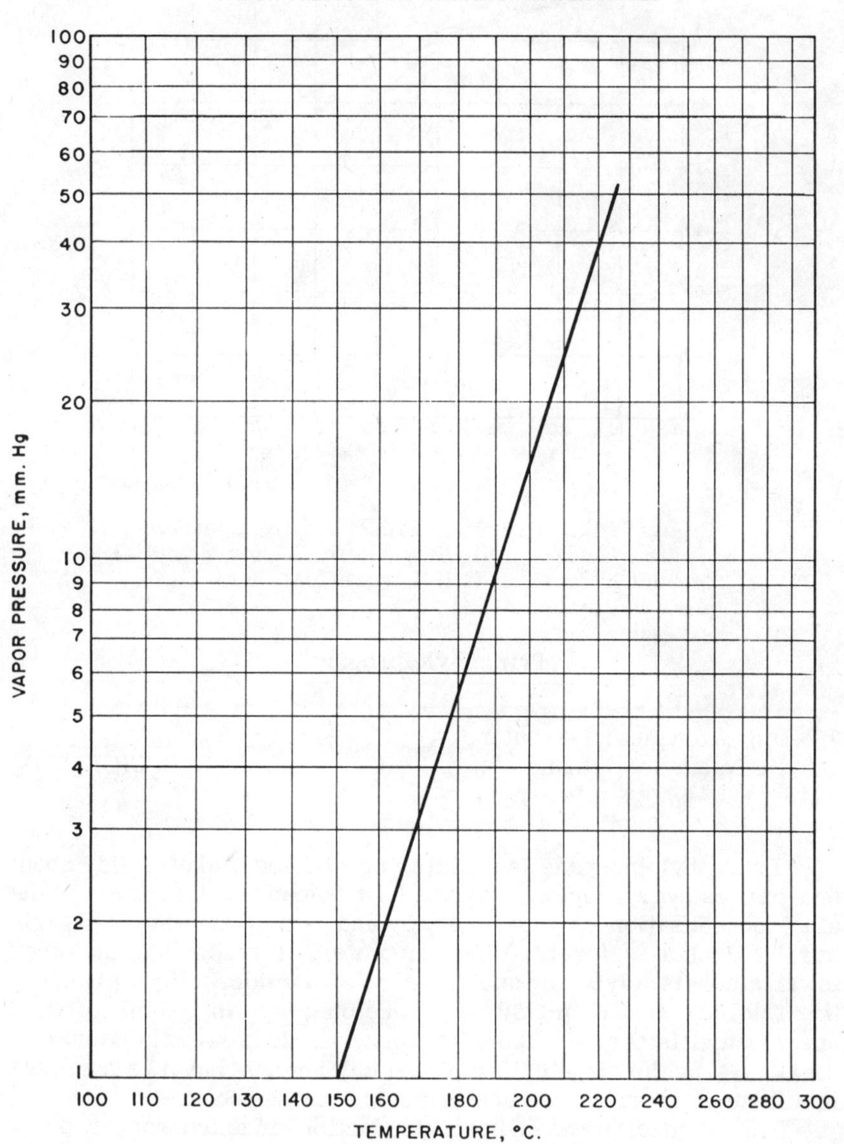

Courtesy of Union Carbide Chemicals Co.

Figure 103. 1,2,6-Hexanetriol.

Physical Properties of Trimethylolpropane

Acidity as formic acid	0.002% by wt., max.
Ash	0.01% by wt., min.
Boiling point at 5 mm. Hg abs.	160° C
50 mm. Hg abs.	210° C
760 mm. Hg (extrapolated)	295° C
Bulk density (free-flowing)	35.5 lb/ft^3
Color of 10% aqueous solution	5 Pt-Co units, max.
Combining weight	44.72
Fire point, Cleveland open cup	380° F
Flash point, Cleveland open cup	355° F
Freezing point	59° C
Hydroxyl content	37.5% by wt., min.
Hygroscopicity (water absorbed in 68 hrs.):	
at 27° C and 18 to 26% RH	0.00% by wt.
at 25° C and 29 to 44% RH	0.06% by wt.
at 27° C and 70 to 80% RH	0.23% by wt.
Melting point range	57 to 59° C
Molecular weight	134.18
Phthalic color, Gardner	1 max.
Water content as packaged	0.05% by wt., max.

4. OTHER POLYHYDRIC ALCOHOLS

The higher polyhydric alcohols containing four, five, and six hydroxyl groups have long been known, since many of them are found in nature. Yet they failed to attract commercial interest due to the limited demand for their use and the high cost of producing them. However, this situation changed rapidly with the development of petroleum chemistry and the discovery that these polyhydric alcohols were by-products in processes based on petroleum. As a consequence, it became practical to search for markets in which these products could be absorbed. At the present time sorbitol is the only polyhydric alcohol of commercial importance.

Erythritol and d-Arabitol

Both erythritol [40] and d-arabitol are produced by the fermentation of osmophilic yeasts. Influencing the yields of these polyhydric alcohols are the external conditions of fermentation and the inherent enzymatic composition of the yeasts. Some of these organisms will produce larger quantities of erythritol, with little d-arabitol, and the reverse will take place with other osmophilic yeasts; some produce both compounds in more equal quantities.

A recovery method [50] has been developed for these polyhydric alcohols produced by fermentation. Hot alcohol is added to remove the gums present, and erythritol and d-arabitol are readily crystallized from this alcoholic solution. They are then removed by filtration.

Pentaerythritol

Tetramethylolmethane
PE

$$
\begin{array}{c}
CH_2OH \\
| \\
HOH_2C - C - CH_2OH \\
| \\
CH_2OH
\end{array}
$$

This tetrahydric alcohol, containing four primary hydroxyl groups, is a white, crystalline, nonhygroscopic solid, available in granular and pellet forms. Its introduction on a commercial scale in the United States occurred in 1938. Technical pentaerythritol is a mixture of monopentaerythritol and from 10 to 20 per cent dipentaerythritol, prepared from acetaldehyde and formaldehyde in the presence of an alkaline condensing agent.

Its solubility is as follows, for 100 g. of solvent: In water, 7 g. are soluble at 25° C; 19 g., at 55° C; and 76 g., at 97° C. At 100° C, 12 g. are soluble in ethylene glycol; 10 g., in glycerol; 21 g., in formamide; and less than 1 g., in pyridine. At 78° C, 16 g. are soluble in n-butylamine, and less than 1 g. is soluble in carbon tetrachloride. At 76° C less than 1 g. is soluble in ehtyl acetate; at 56° C less than 1 g., in acetone; at 80° C less than 1 g., in benzene; and at 35° C less than 1 g., in ethyl ether. At 25° C it is very slightly soluble in ethyl alcohol, and insoluble in fats and oils.

Pentaerythritol is largely used in the paint and varnish industry and in related industries, where it enters into the production of alkyd and other resins, rosin esters, synthetic drying oils, plasticizers, emulsifiers, waxes, and wetting agents. It is also used as a glycerol substitute. It contributes hardness and toughness to coatings, as well as improved water and alkali resistance and longer pigment life and gloss.

Physical Properties of Pentaerythritol

Ash	0.01% by wt., max.
Bulk density	40 lb./ft.^{3}
Dipentaerythritol (combined)	0.3%
Hydroxyl content	47.0% min. (technical) 49.5% (pure)
Melting point (capillary final)	240° C 250° C initial (pure)
Melting point range	185-245° C (technical)
Moisture	0.40% by wt. (technical) 0.10% by wt. (pure)
Molecular weight	136.1
Monopentaerythritol	88.0% by wt. (technical) 97.0% by wt. (pure)
Nonvolatile	99.50% min.
Specific gravity at 25/4° C	1.38

Sorbitol

d-Sorbitol
Sorbit
Sorbol
d-Glucitol

$CH_2OH(CHOH)_4CH_2OH$

This hexahydric alcohol, also classified as a sugar alcohol, has been known to exist since the nineteenth century, and attempts have been made to isolate it from its natural sources in fruits and berries. The first announcement of its isolation from the mountain ash

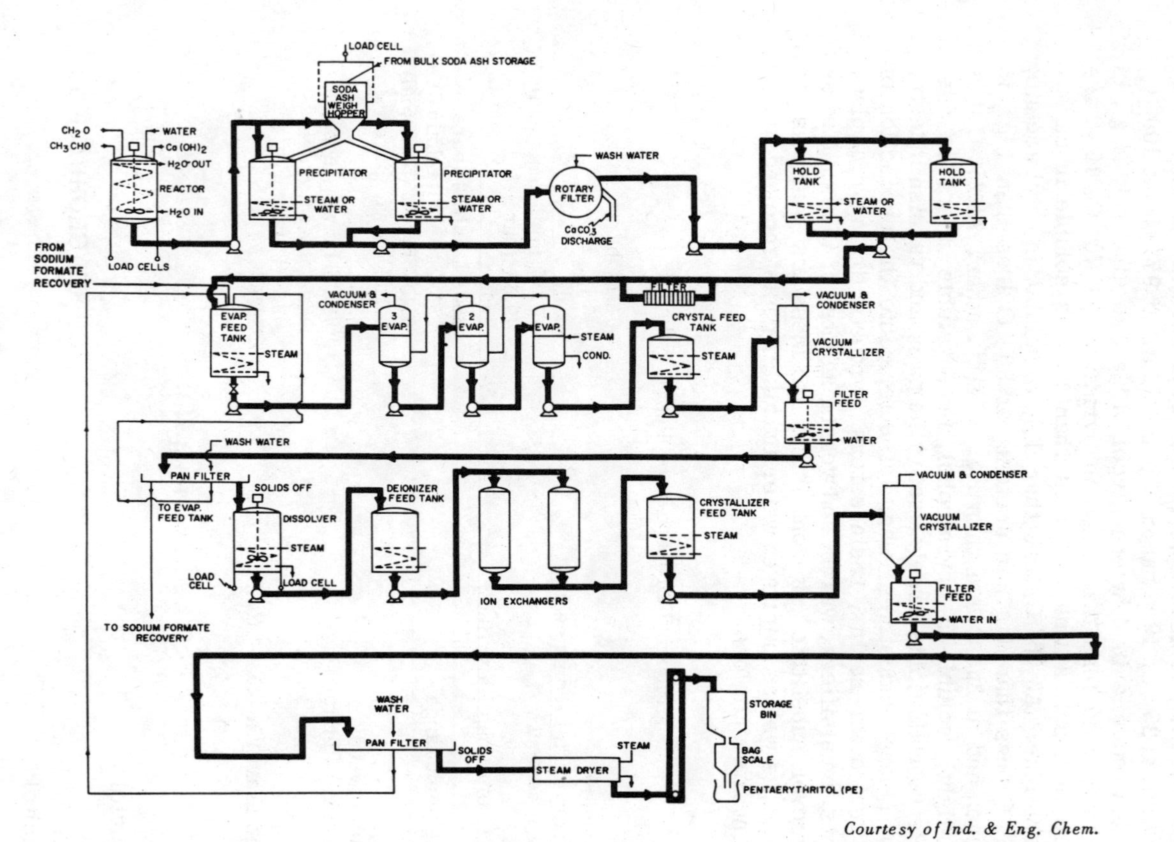

Courtesy of Ind. & Eng. Chem.

Figure 104. Flowsheet for the Manufacture of Pentaerythritol, Hercules Powder Co., Louisiana, Mo.

berry was made by Joseph Boussingault, a French Chemist, in 1872. Since none of its natural sources are important commercially, it remained a rare substance until its synthesis and production on a pilot scale, early in the 1930's by the Atlas Powder Company. By 1937, it was brought into full production. Sorbitol is prepared by the copper-chromium hydrogenation of glycose derived from corn, beet, and cane. [52-55]

Pure sorbitol is a white, odorless, crystalline powder with a taste that is faint, sweet, cooling, and pleasant. There are two crystalline forms, stable or metastable, depending on the method used in its crystallization. It is stable when either in a dry state or in a sterile aqueous solution. Sorbitol appears commercially in a 70 per cent solution under the trade name "Sorbo"; a 76 per cent solution, in which its anhydrides are also present, known as "Sorbitol Special"; a solution in which isomers and anhydrides of sorbitol are present, known as "Arlex"; and crystalline d-sorbitol. The presence of small amounts of other substances affects the supersaturation tendency of sorbitol, its crystallizability, and its melting point.

Sorbitol is very soluble in water and hot ethyl alcohol; slightly soluble in methanol, cold ethyl alcohol, acetic acid, phenol, and acetamide; and almost insoluble in most common organic solvents.

It is often used as a vehicle in syrups and elixirs containing antihistamines, phenobarbital, vitamin B_{12}, and other drugs. [51, 56, 57, 60] To preserve solutions of sorbitol containing alcohol and water, 0.15 per cent sorbic acid can be used. [58, 59]

Sorbitol is useful in increasing the solubility of casein in milk powder. [70] It is used in the manufacture of alkyd and other synthetic resins, plasticizers, surface-active agents, varnishes, and vitamin C. It is a moisture conditioner on printing rolls, in glues, and in textile finishes, leather, tobacco, cosmetics, and pharmaceuticals. It is a sugar substitute for diabetics under the name of "Sionon." The presence of sorbitol in mixtures with other polyhydric alcohols imparts valuable properties.

Physical Properties of Sorbitol

Density at -5° C	1.472
Heat of combustion	3994 cal./gm.
Negative heat of solution	-26.5 cal./gm.
Molecular weight	182.17
Melting point, metastable form	93° C
stable form	97.7° C
Refractive index at 25° C, in 10% aqueous solution	1.3477
Rotation, $^{25}_{D}$	-0.985° C

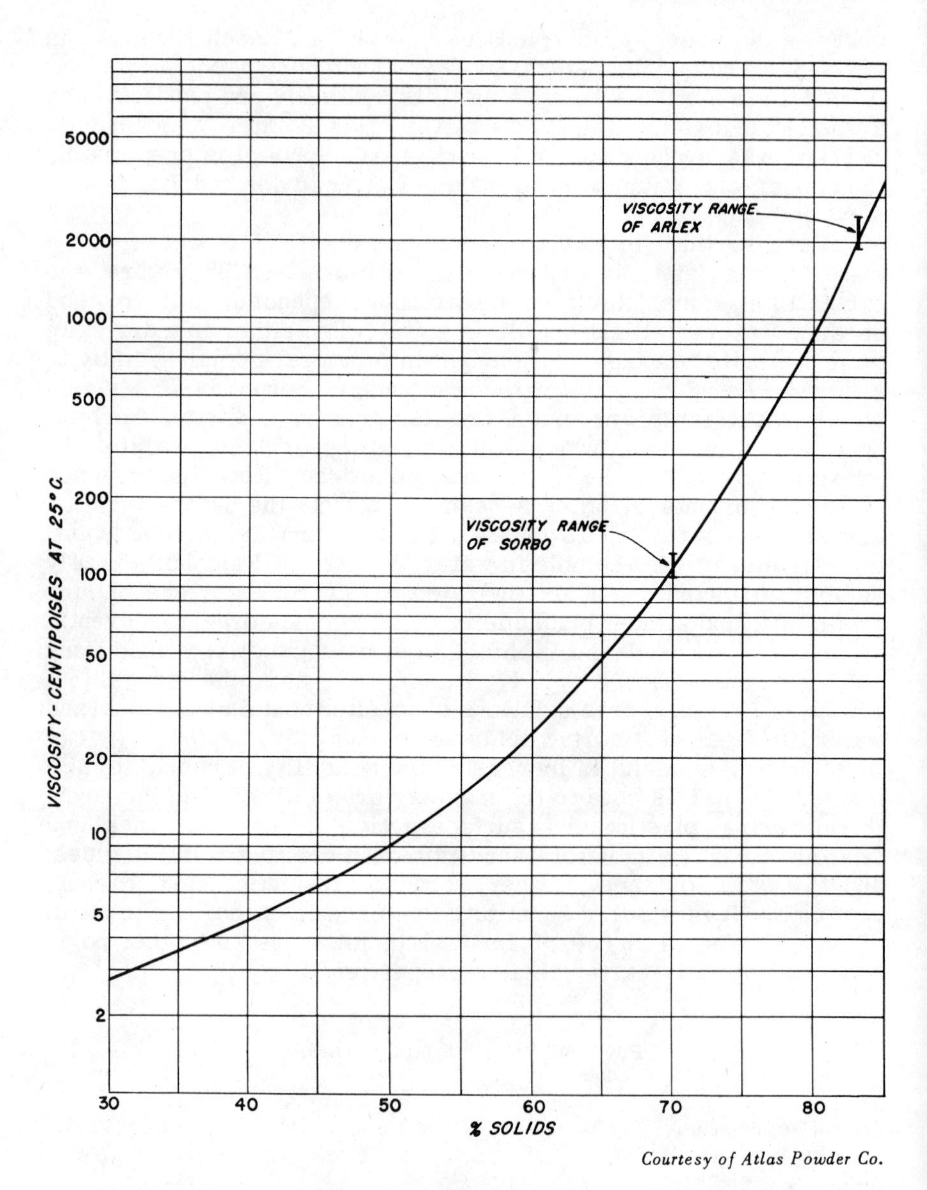

Courtesy of Atlas Powder Co.

Figure 105. Viscosity Curve for Pure d-Sorbitol Solutions of Various Concentrations.

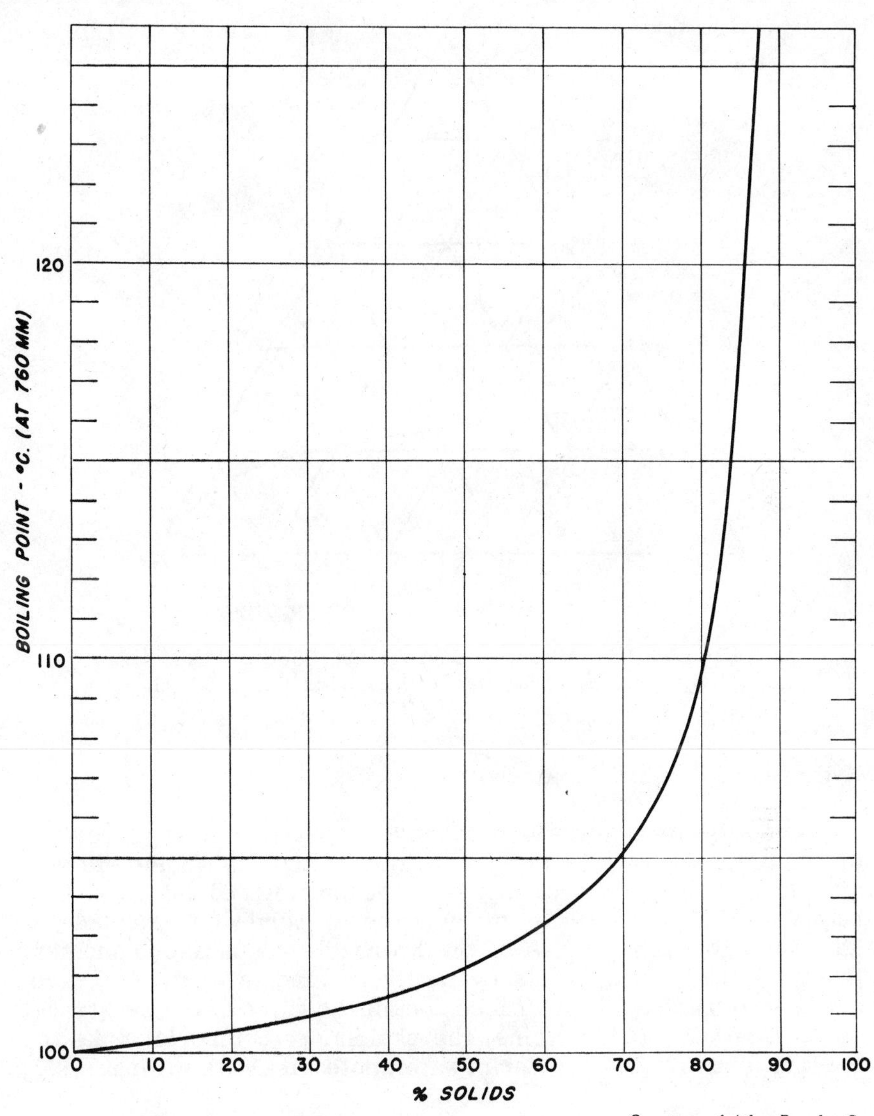

Courtesy of Atlas Powder Co.

Figure 106. Boiling Point of Sorbitol Solutions (approximately the same for Sorbo, Sorbitol Special and Arlex).

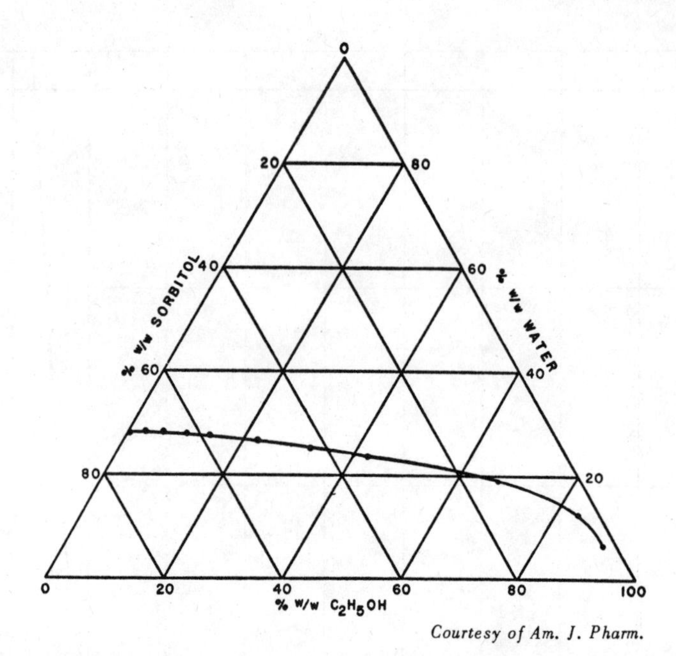

Courtesy of Am. J. Pharm.

Figure 107. Phase Diagram of Sorbitol Solubility in Hydroalcoholic Liquids at 25° C.

Hydrates of Polyhydric Alcohols

The aliphatic glycols form hydrates and have a striking resemblance to the hydrate-forming monohydric alcohols. Some of these glycols are ethylene glycol, meso-2,3-butanediol, and 2-methyl-2,3-butanediol. The formation of hydrates by polyhydric alcohols is attributed to the nearness of the hydroxyl groups to one another. Hydrates of aliphatic glycols, cyclic glycols, and polyhydric alcohols are given in Tables 53-55. These contain the name of the substance, the number of carbon atoms, the skeletal structure formula, the melting point, and the number of water molecules in the hydrate. [99]

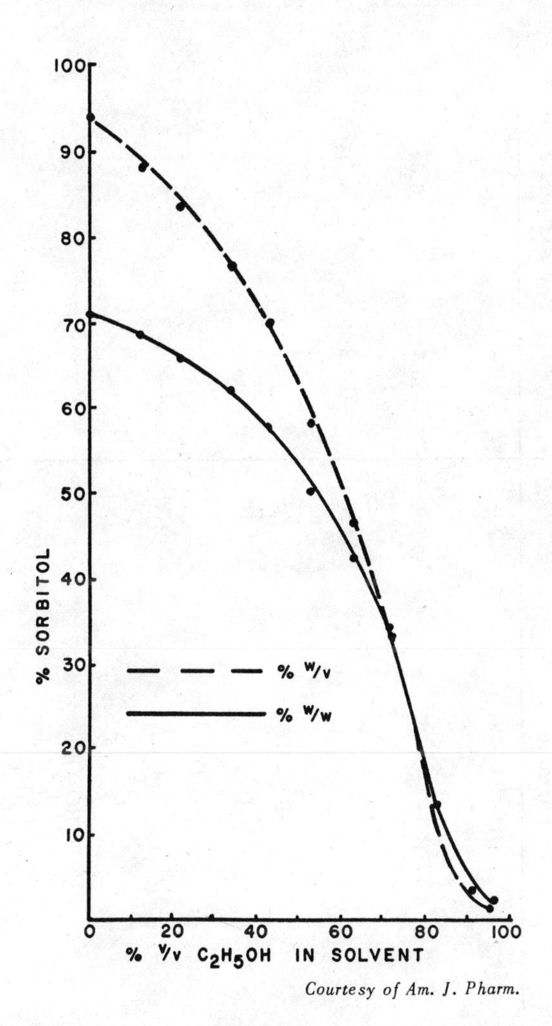

Courtesy of Am. J. Pharm.

Figure 108. Solubility of Sorbitol in Hydroalcoholic Liquids at 25° C.

Table 53. Hydrates of Aliphatic Glycols*

Glycol				Hydrate	
Number of C Atoms	Name	Skeletal Structural Formula	M.p. (°C)	M.p. (°C)	n in $R(OH)_2 \times nH_2O$
2	Ethylene glycol	HO-C-C-OH	-12.9	-49.6 (cong.)	2
2	Ethylene glycol	HO-C-C-OH	-12.9	-40.7	0.67
4	meso-2,3-Butanediol	HO OH C-C-C-C	34.4	16.8	6(5)†
4	±2,3-Butanediol	HO OH C-C-C-C	7.6	---	0
5	2-Methyl-2,3-butanediol	HO OH C-C-C-C C	liq.	23.5-4	6
6	Pinacol	HO OH C-C-C-C C C	41.4	41.25	1
6	Pinacol	HO OH C-C-C-C C C	41.4	46.5	6

8	2,5-Dimethyl-2,5-hexanediol	HO OH C-C-C-C-C-C C C	92	41-2	6
9	2,6-Dimethyl-2,6-heptanediol	HO OH C-C-C-C-C-C-C C C	76-77	60-61	1
10	2,7-Dimethyl-2,7-octanediol	HO OH C-C-C-C-C-C-C-C C C	92	59	2
13	2,10-Dimethyl-2,10-undecanediol	HO OH C-C-CCCCCCC-C-C C C	61	---	?
14	2,11-Dimethyl-2,11-dodecanediol	HO OH C-C-CCCCCCCC-C-C C C	67.5	---	?

*Courtesy of Rev. Pure & Appl. Chem.

†$5H_2O$ (50% H_2O) has been assigned. The maximum of the very flat freezing point curve has been found at 55% H_2O, no formula being assigned. This composition agrees excellently with $6H_2O$ which requires 54.5% H_2O.

Table 54. Hydrates of Cyclic Glycols*

Glycol				Hydrate	
Number of C Atoms	Name	Skeletal Structural Formula	M.p. (°C)	M.p. (° C)	n in $R(OH)_2 \times nH_2O$
9	trans-Octa-hydroindan-8,9-diol		73-4	---	0.5 to 1.0
10	trans-Decahydro-naphthalene-9,10-diol		96	80-5	1.0 ?
10	cis-Decahydro-naphthalene-9,10-ciol		89.5	---	Unknown
10	trans-p-Menth-8 (9) -ene-1,2-diol		73	60	3
10	cis-p-Menth-8 (9) -ene-1,2-diol		71-2	---	0
10	cis(?)-p-Menth-1 (2) -ene-3,6-diol		53-4	27	3 ?

10	cis-Terpin†	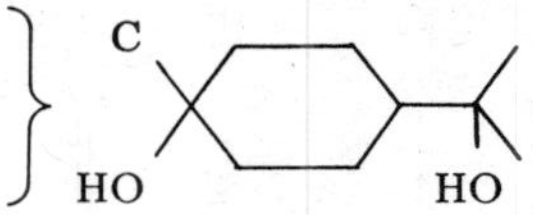 [structure]	105	121	1
10	trans-Terpin‡	[structure]	156-8	---	0
10	p-Menthane-2,5-diol	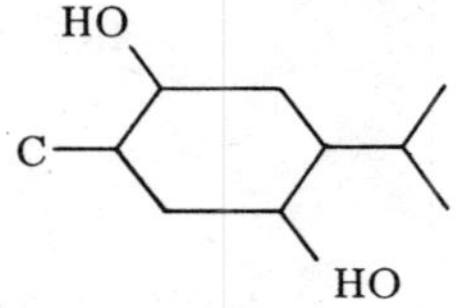 [structure]	88-9	58-9	3
10	p-Menthane-1,2-diol	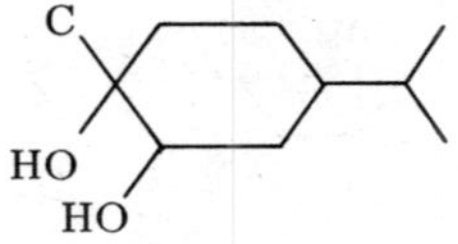 [structure]	89	52	3 & 1
10	p-Menthane-2,8-diol (neoiso-dihydrocarveol hydrate)	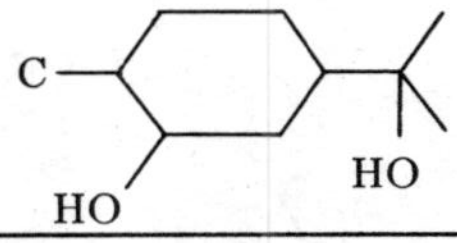 [structure]	93-4	65-75	Unknown

*Courtesy of Rev. Pure & Appl. Chem.
†Subject of crystallographic studies.
‡Stelzner's Literatur Register 1919-21 reports the formation of a hydrate and cites O. Aschan, "Bidrag till kännedon af Finlands natur ochfolk," 77, No. 1 (1918). The report appears to be without foundation.

Table 54—Continued

	Glycol			Hydrate	
Number of C Atoms	Name	Skeletal Structural Formula	M.p. (°C)	M.p. (°C)	n in $R(OH)_2 \times nH_2O$
10	(+)-Carene-β-glycol or 3,4-Carane-diol (*trans*-2,3-dihydroxy-3,7,7-trimethyl-*bicyclo*-0,1,4-heptane)	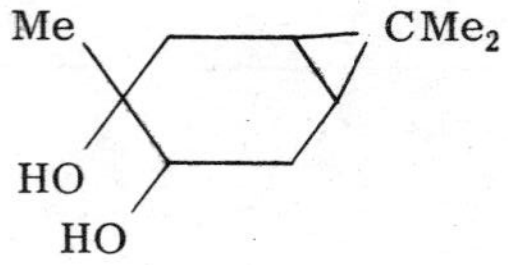 Me, CMe_2, HO, HO	90-91	75	1
11	Homoterpin	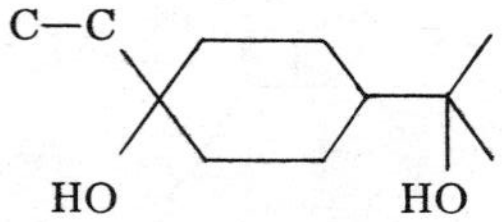 C—C, HO, HO	75-6	---	1
14	*iso* (±)-Hydrobenzoin	PhCHOHCHOHPh	121	96	Unknown
20	Dihydrodicarveol	$C_{20}H_{26}O_2$	166	100	2
29	3,3'-Dihydroxy-3,3'-diphenyl-2,2'-*spiro*-biindan	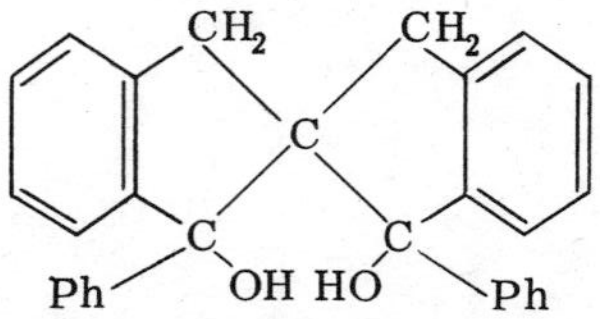 CH_2, CH_2, C, C, C, Ph, OH, HO, Ph	164	125-30	1 & 3

31	3,3'-Dihydroxy-3,3'-dibenzyl-2,2'-spiro-biindan	CH_2, CH_2, C, C, C, PhH_2C, OH, HO, CH_2Ph	169	134	3
38	α-s-2,2'-Diphenylbenzopinacol	Ph Ph, C—C, HO HO, Ph, Ph	175	---	1
38	β-s-2,2'-Diphenyl-benzopinacol	(same structure as above)	152-8	---	1

Table 55. Hydrates of Polyhydric Alcohols*

Alcohol				Hydrate	
Number of C Atoms	Name	Skeletal Structural Formula	M. p. (°C)	M. p. (°C)	n in $R(OH)_m \cdot nH_2O$
A. Trihydric Alcohols					
6	α (or cis)-Phloroglucitol	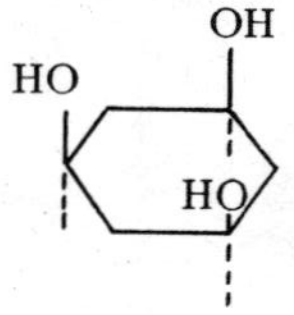	185	115	2
9	4(1,2-Dihydroxy-n-propyl)-cyclohexanol	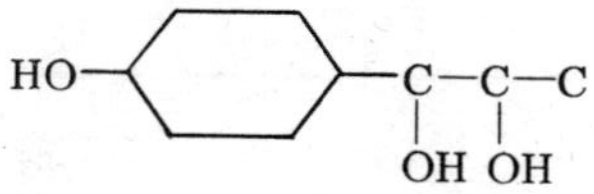	63	31	3
10	p-Menthane-1,4,8-triol	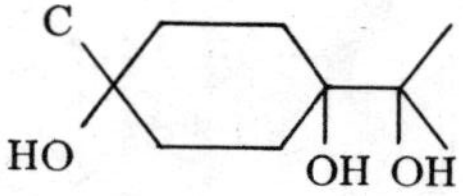	110-112	96	1
10	p-Menthane-1,2,4-triol	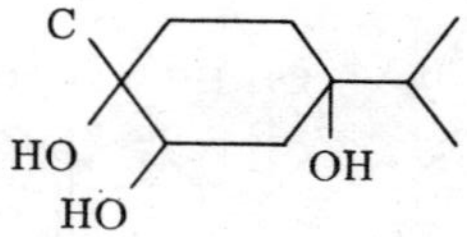	129	115	---
10	Glycol (a dihydroxyether?)	$C_{10}H_{18}O_3$	103-105	---	1

13	2(2,3-Dihydroxy-n-propyl)-2-hydroxy camphane		---	---	---
B. Tetrahydric Alcohols					
6	cycloHexane-1,2,4,5-tetrol		---	195	1
6	cycloHexane-1,2,4,5-tetrol	?	242	---	2
8	A dimethylether of an inositol	$C_6H_6(OH)_4(OCH_3)_2$	230	---	3
10	trans(?)-p-Menthane-1,2,6,8-tetrol		156	100-105	2

*Courtesy of Rev. Pure & Appl. Chem.

Table 55—Continued

Alcohol				Hydrate	
Number of C Atoms	Name	Skeletal Structural Formula	M. p. (°C)	M. p. (°C)	n in $R(OH)_m \cdot nH_2O$
10	p-Menthane-1,2,4,8-tetrol	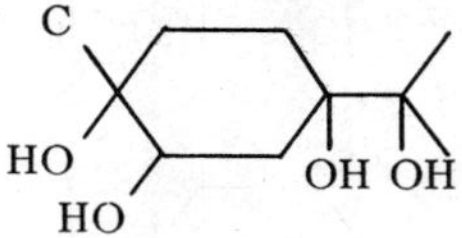 C; HO; HO; OH OH	149	100	1
10	p-Menthane-1,2,3,4-tetrol	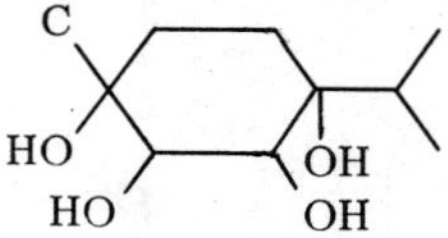 C; HO; HO; OH; OH	130	---	1
38	2,2'-Dihydroxy-6,6'-bis (α-hydroxybenzhydryl)-diphenyl	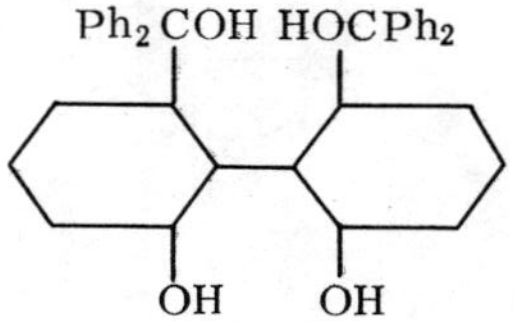 Ph_2COH $HOCPh_2$; OH OH	308	141-145	2
C. Pentahydric Alcohols					
6	Viburnitol (cyclohexane-2,3,5/4,6-pentol)	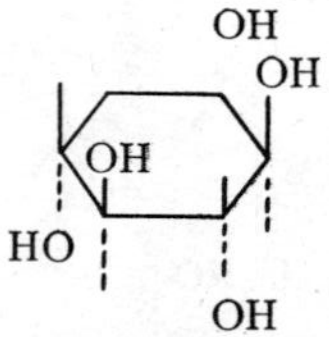 OH; OH; OH; HO; OH	181	---	1

6	Inositol bromohydrin	$C_6H_6(OH)_5Br$	170-5	---	1
6	Inositol chlorohydrin	$C_6H_6(OH)_5Cl$	180-5	---	2
6	Scyllitol chlorohydrin	$C_6H_6(OH)_5Cl$	---	---	2
7	1-Methylene-cyclohexane-2,4,6/3,5-pentol	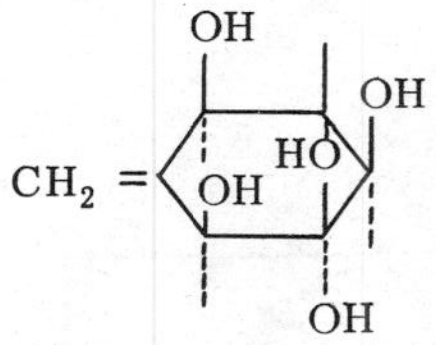 $CH_2 =$ OH OH HO OH OH	205	---	2

D. Hexahydric Alcohols

6	(+)-Sorbitol	$HOH_2C(CHOH)_4CH_2OH$	111	55 75	1 0.5
6	meso-Inositol (1,2,3,5/4,6-cyclohexanehexol)	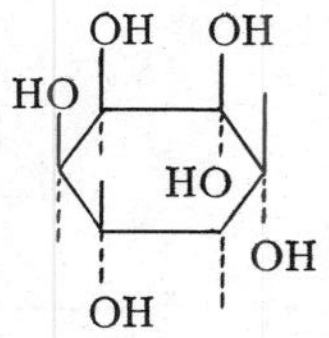 OH OH HO HO OH OH	225	---	2
6	d- and l-Inositols (active) (1,3,4/2,5,6-cyclohexanehexol)	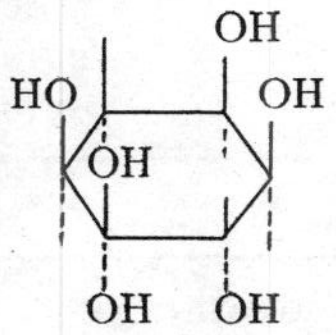 OH HO OH OH OH OH	248	---	2

Table 55—Continued

Alcohol				Hydrate	
Number of C Atoms	Name	Skeletal Structural Formula	M. p. (°C)	M. p. (°C)	n in $R(OH)_m \cdot nH_2O$
7	Mytilitol	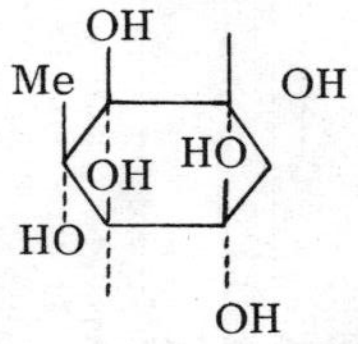 Me, OH, OH, OH, HO, HO, OH	259	---	2
18	1,1-Diphenyl-hexane-1,2,3,4,5,6-hexol	$Ph_2C\ (CHOH)_4\ CH_2OH$	157-160	---	1

References

1. K. A. Clendenning, F. J. Macdonald, and D. E. Wright, *Can. J. Research*, B 28, 608 (1950).
2. H. K. Ross, *Ind. Eng. Chem.*, 46, 601 (1954).
3. H. J. Bernstein, *J Am. Chem. Soc.*, 74, 2674 (1952).
4. W. T. Diefenbach, *Am. Ink Maker* (Jan. 1954).
5. F. Ullmann, *Enzyklopadie*, 6, 290 (1919).
6. U.S. Patent 1,422, 184.
7. J. R. Scott, *J. Rubber Research*, 16, 219 (1947).
8. M. A. Seidenfeld, P. J. Hanzlik, *J. Pharmacol. Exptl. Therap.*, 44, 109 (1932).
9. P. J. Hanzlik, *Ind. & Eng. Chem.*, 24, 836 (1932).
10. R. Hunt, *Ind. & Eng. Chem.*, 24, 361, 836 (1932).
11. C. W. Hoopen, U.S. Patent 2,030,792 (1936).
12. M. W. Green, K. L. Kelly, and C. A. Steinmetz, *Bull. Natl. Formulary Comm.*, 1191 (1943).
13. S. W. Goldstein, and U. Burnacher, *Drug Standards*, 20, Nos. 1-2, 14,(Jan.-Feb. 1952).
14. H. Adkins, and W. H. Zartman, *J. Am. Chem. Soc.*, 55, 4559 (1933).
15. G. Natta, R. Rigamouti, and E. Beati, *Ber.*, 76B, 641 (1943).
16. C. W. Lenth, and R. N. Du Puis, *Ind. & Eng. Chem.*, 37, 152 (1945).
17. U.S. Dept. of Commerce FIAT, Final Report No. 872, June 1947.
18. Ira T. Clark, Richard J. Farnum, and Roger D. Lloyd, *The Production of Glycerol by the Hydrogenolysis of Wood Sugars*, U.S. Dept. of Agriculture, Forest Products Lab., Project No. TAI-3603 (*n*), Final Technical Report, June 30, 1957.
19. Wyandotte Chemicals Corp., Wyandotte, Michigan.
20. J. Levene, and R. Walti, *Org. Syntheses Coll.*, 11, 545 (1943).
21. O. H. Robertson, *et al.*, *Science*, 93, 213 (1941).
22. K. F. Lampe, and O. D. Easterday, *J. Am. Pharm. Assoc.*, 42, No. 7, 455 (1953).
23. E. I. Fulmer, L. M. Christensen, and A. R. Kendall, *Ind. & Eng. Chem.*, 25, 798 (1933).
24. A. C. Blackwood, J. A. Wheat, J. D. Leslie, G. A. Ledingham and F. L. Simpson, *Can. J. Research*, F 27, 199-210 (1949).
25. S. B. Fratkin, and G. A. Adams, *Can. J. Research*, F 24, 29-38 (1946).
26. R. V. Tomkins, D. S. Scott, and F. J. Simpson, *Can. J. Research*, F 26, 497-502 (1948).
27. R. W. Watson, J. A. R. Cooper, and J. L. Barnwell, *Can. J. Chem.*, 29, 885-894 (1951).
28. D. Murphy, and D. W. Stranks, *Can. J. Tech.*, 29, 413-420 (1951).

29. D. Murphy, R. W. Watson, D. R. Muirhead, and J. L. Barnwell, *Can. J. Tech.*, 29, 375-381 (1951).
30. D. Perlman, *Ind. & Eng. Chem.*, 36, 803 (1944).
31. J. A. Hall, Forest Products Laboratory, Forest Service, U.S. Dept. of Agriculture, No. 1984 (1954).
32. E. Clandon, and C. Morin, *Compt. rend.*, 104, 1109 (1887).
33. A. Henninger, *Compt. rend.*, 95, 94 (1882).
34. A. Henninger, and B. Sanson, *Compt. rend.*, 106, 208 (1888).
35. A. C. Neish, *Can J. Research,* B 28, 660-661 (1950).
36. L. A. Mikeska, and E. Arundale, U.S. Patent 2,449,001 (1948).
37. K. A. Clendenning, and D. E. Wright, *Can J. Research,* F 24, 287-299 (1946).
38. K. A. Clendenning, *Can. J. Research,* F 24, 249-71 (1946).
39. L. A. Stengel, *et al.*, U.S. Patent 2,381,316 (1945).
40. J. F. T. Spencer, A. C. Neish, A. C. Blackwood, and H. R. Sallans, *Can J. Biochem. Physiol.,* 34, 495-501 (1956).
41. K. A. Clendenning, *Can. J. Research,* B 24, 269-79 (1946).
42. J. A. Wheat, *Can. J. Tech.*, 31, 73-84 (1953).
43. A. C. Blackwood, and F. J. Simpson, *Can. J. Research,* C 28, 613-22 (1950).
44. W. G. Crewther, *Australian J. Appl. Sci.*, 1, No. 4, 437-79 (1950).
45. A. C. Neish, and G. A. Ledingham, *Can. J. Research,* B 27, 694-07 (1949).
46. M. S. Kulpinski, and F. F. Nord, *J. Org. Chem.*, 8, 256-70 (1943).
47. C. F. Wilson, *J Soc. Arts*, Jan. 5, 1956.
48. J. F. T. Spencer, and H. R. Sallans, *Can. J. Microbiol.*, 2, 72 (1956).
49. R. E. Herron, *Chem. Processing* (ed., D. S. Davis) June, 1953, p. 47.
50. J. M. Ronburgh, J. F. T. Spencer, and H. R. Sallans, *Can. J. Technol.*, 34, 248 (1956).
51. Atlas Powder Company, Wilmington, Del.
52. G. Natta, and E. Beati, *Ber.*, 892, 590 (1956).
53. L. Kasehagen, and M. M. Luskin, U.S. Patent 2,759,024 (1956).
54. C. M. H. Kool, *et al.*, U.S. Patent 2,759,023 (1956).
55. Atlas Powder Company, British Patent 740,560.
56. M. Barr, and L. E. Tice, *Am. J. Pharm.*, 129, 358 (1957).
57. M. Barr, S. R. Kohn, and L. E. Tice, *J. Am. Pharm. Assoc.*, 46, No. 11, 650 (1957).
58. E. D. Fogg, *et al.*, *Anal. Chem.*, 27, 1609 (1955).
59. M. Barr, R. S. Kohn, and L. E. Tice, *Am. J. Pharm.*, 129, 102 (1957).
60. M. Barr, and L. E. Tice, *J. Am. Pharm. Assoc., Sci. Ed.*, 46, 221, (1957).
61. C. Crisan, *Ann. chim.* (Paris), (13) 1, 436 (1956).
62. J. Wiemann, *Compt. rend.*, 238, 585 (1954).

63. B. T. Brook, *The Science of Petroleum*, New York, Oxford University Press, 1953, V, Pt. 11, Sec. 1, p. 56.
64. P. Ferrero, *et al.*, *Industrie chim. belge*, 19, 113 (1954).
65. W. Chodkiewicz, *Compt. rend.*, 240, 1903 (1955).
66. A. Guyer, et al., *Helv. Chim. Acta*, 38, 976 (1955).
67. Societe Industrielle de derives de l'Acetylene, British Patent 758,788 (1959).
68. P. I. Smith, *Am. Perfumer Aromat.*, 67, No. 5, 54 (1956).
69. E. H. Freung, and K. Domous, U.S. Patent 2,745,775 (1956).
70. S. Y. Gerlsma, *Neth. Milk Dairy J.*, 11, 83 (1957).
71. A. J. Rajner, *J. Soc. Chem. Ind.*, 45, 265; 287 (1956).
72. N. C. Robertson, U.S. Patent 2,780,634 (1957).
73. J. H. Gardner, and N. C. Robertson, U.S. Patent 2,780,635.
74. L. A. Underkofler, and R. J. Hickey, *Industrial Fermentation*, New York, Chemical Publishing Co., Inc., 1954.
75. M. I. Farberov, *Doklady Acad. Nauk SSSR*, 110, 1005 (1956).
76. J. P. Copes, and C. McKinley, U.S. Patent 2,686,817.
77. J. Wolinski, *Roczniki Chem.*, 27, 366 (1953) (French summary).
78. P. G. Segeev, *et al.*, *Khim. Nauk. i. Prom.*, 1, 281 (1951).
79. N. V. de Bataafsche, British Patent 725,375 (1955).
80. A. E. Corey, and J. N. Cosby, U.S. Patent 2,739,173 (1956).
81. Spanish Patent 218,941 (1954).
82. J. Ploquin, *Bull. soc. pharm. Bordeaux*, 96, 53 (1957).
83. W. Langenbeck, and W. Bollow, *Naturwissenschaften*, 42, 389 (1955).
84. H. W. Kellar, *et al.*, *J. Am. Oil Chemists' Soc.*, 33, 435 (1956).
85. D. R. Asher, and D. W. Simpson, *J. Phys. Chem.*, 60, 519 (1956).
86. G. E. Prielipp, and H. W. Keller, *J. Am. Oil Chemists' Soc.*, 33, 103 (1956).
87. K. J. C. Luckhurst, British Patent 717,939 (1956).
88. J. Blair, British Patent 723,230 (1956).
89. J. Miroluboff, Belgian Patent 517,358 (1956).
90. K. A. Clendenning, *Can. J. Research*, F 26, 209 (1948).
91. H. L. Cox, U.S. Patent 2,003,429 (1935).
92. N. Natorff, *Chem. Abs.*, 54, 784 (1960).
93. L. Raphael, *Mfg. Chemist*, 35, No. 6, 245, 260 (1959).
94. *Dow Diamond*, 6, No. 1, 4 (1943).
95. D. R. Asher, and D. W. Simpson, *J. Phys. Chem.*, 60, 518 (1956).
96. D. W. Simpson, and W. C. Bauman, *Ind. & Eng. Chem.*, 46, 1958 (1954).
97. D. W. Simpson, and R. M. Wheaton, *Chem. Eng. Progress*, 50, 45 (1954).
98. H. R. Mehta, and F. G. Drommond, *J. Am. Pharm. Assoc.*, *Practical Pharm. Ed.*, 15, No. 2 (Feb., 1954).
99. H. H. Hatt, *Rev. Pure & Appl. Chem.*, 6, No. 3, 153 (1956).

General References

Curme, G. O., *Glycols*, New York, Reinhold Publishing Corp., 1952.
Kirk, R. E., and D. F. Othmer, *Encyclopedia of Chemical Technology* New York, Interscience Publishers, Inc., 1951.
Lawrie, J. W., *Glycerol and the Glycols*, New York, Chemical Catalog Co., Inc., 1928.
Lesser, M. A., *Modern Chemical Specialties*, New York, MacNair-Dorland Co., 1950.
Martin, G., and H. J. Strausz, *The Manufacture of Glycerol*, Great Britain, Technical Press, Ltd., 1956.
Miner, C. S., and N. N. Dalton, *Glycerol*, New York, Reinhold Publishing Corp., 1953.

INDEX

Arabitol, 184
Berstein, 12
Boiling points, 16, 17
1,2-Butanediol, 79
  Physical properties, 85
  Refractive index, 85
  specific gravity, 79
  Viscosity, 79, 85
1,3-Butanediol, 80-83
  Freezing point, 82
  properties of, 81
  refractive index, 82
  specific gravity, 83
  synthesis, 80
  viscosity, 83, 84
1,4-Butanediol, 119-121
  physical properties, 120
  specific gravity, 121
  viscosity, 121
2,3-Butanediol, 86-119
  boiling points, 97, 99, 112
  characteristics, 95
  formation, 86-95
  freezing points, 98, 100-103, 109
  hygroscopicity, 104-6
  optical rotation, 115-6
  physical properties, 96-7
  refractive index, 117, 119
  specific gravity, 113-4
  surface tension, 112
  viscosity, 99, 101-3, 107, 110-1
Butanediols, 76-124
1,2,4-Butanetriol, 179
2-Butene-1,4-diol, 123
2-Butyne-1,4-diol, 122
Clendenning, et al., 6
Diefenbach, 19-23
2,2-Diethyl-1,3-propanediol, 137
Dihydric alcohols, 18-46
2,2-Dimethyl-2,3-butanediol, 137
2,5-Dimethyl-3-hexyne-2,5-diol, 139
3,6-Dimethyl-4-octyne-3,6-diol, 139
2,2-Dimethyl-1,3-propanediol, 126
Erythritol, 184
2-Ethyl-2-butyl-1,3-propanediol, 143
2-Ethyl-1,3-hexanediol, 138
Ethylene glycol, 24-40
  boiling points, 34
  characteristics, 27, 28
  constant boiling mixtures, 32, 33
  conductivity, 36
  density, 40, 41
  dew point, 42
  freezing points, 35
  method of production, 26, 27
  physical properties, 28, 29, 30, 31
  relative humectant, 44
  specific gravity, 31
  specific heat, 38, 39
  synthesis, 24, 25, 26
  vapor-liquid composition, 43
  vapor pressure, 37
  viscosity, 45
Freezing points, 14, 15
Glycerol, 144-178
  aqueous solution, 166
  boiling points, 171

Glycerol—Continued
characteristics, 150
freezing points, 170, 177, 178
hygroscopicity, 167, 168
physical properties, 151
production, 144-150, 153-161, 176
relative humidity, 173
specific gravity, 164-6
specific heat, 174
solubility, 152, 175
vapor pressure, 163, 171, 178
viscosity, 150, 162, 169, 172
Glycols, 1, 18-46
1,6-Hexanediol, 127
1,2,6-Hexanetriol, 180, 181
Hexylene glycol, 127-136
compatibility, 134
formation, 127, 128
freezing points, 131
physical properties, 129-30
specific gravity, 135
solubility, 128, 129
surface tension, 135
vapor pressure, 132
water absorption, 133
Hydrates of glycols, 192, 202
Hydroscopicity, 19-23
Hydroxyl group, 2
"Kromfax" solvent, 140
2-Methyl-2,4-pentanediol, 127-136
Neopentyl glycol, 126
Pentaerythritol, 184-5
1,5-Pentanediol, 124-5
2,4-Pentanediol, 126
Pinacol, 137
Pentanediols, 124-6
Polyhydric alcohols, 1
formation, 2-6
nomenclature, 2, 7, 8
physical characteristics, 2-6
production, 12
structure, 2-6
1,2-Propanediol, 46-71
aqueous solutions, 60
boiling point, 59
constant boiling mixture, 53
conductivity, 58
density, 55
development, 46-7
freezing points, 56-7, 67
heat of vaporization, 62
preparation, 57
properties, 47-9
relative humidities, 71
solubility, 50-2, 68-70
specific gravity, 57, 66
specific heat, 59
vapor-liquid composition, 64
vapor pressure, 63, 66
viscosity, 61
1,3-Propanediol, 71-9
Freezing points, 73
properties, 71, 72
viscosity, 74
specific gravity, 75
1,2,3-Propanetriol, 144
Propylene glycol, 46-79
References, 203-6
Refractive index, 7, 10, 11, 12
Ross, 10, 11, 12
Sorbitol, 185
boiling point, 189
formation, 186
hydrates, 190
physical properties, 187
viscosity, 188
solubility, 191
Thiodiglycol, 140-2
Trihydric alcohols, 144, 183
Trimethylolpropane, 181-3
2,2,4-Trimethyl-1,3-pentanediol, 143
Viscosity, 13, 14, 21
Wurtz, C., 18, 24
p-Xylylene glycol, 140

TP 594 .M4
3135476
Mellan, Ibert.

Polyhydric alcohols